P9-CFN-639

Practicing Physics

CONCEPTUAL

Physics

tenth edition

Paul G. Hewitt

City College of San Francisco

PEARSON

Addison Wesley

San Francisco   Boston   New York
Cape Town   Hong Kong   London   Madrid   Mexico City
Montreal   Munich   Paris   Singapore   Sydney   Tokyo   Toronto

Editor-in-Chief: Adam Black
Project Editor: Liana Allday
Senior Production Supervisor: Corinne Benson
Main Text Cover Designer: Yvo Riezebos Design
Supplement Cover Manager: Paul Gourhan
Supplement Cover Designer: Joanne Alexandris
Senior Manufacturing Buyer: Michael Early
Cover Printer: Phoenix Color
Text Printer: Bind-Rite Graphics
Cover Credits: **Wave and surfer** Photolibrary.com/AMANA AMERICA INC. IMA USA INC.;
particle tracks Lawrence Berkeley National Laboratory, University of California.

ISBN   0-8053-9198-3

Copyright © 2006 Paul G. Hewitt. All rights reserved. Manufactured in the United States of
America. This publication is protected by Copyright and permission should be obtained from the
publisher prior to any prohibited reproduction, storage in a retrieval system, or transmission in any
form or by any means, electronic, mechanical, photocopying, recording, or likewise. To obtain
permission(s) to use material from this work, please submit a written request to Pearson Education,
Inc., Permission Department, 1900 E. Lake Ave., Glenview, IL 60025. For information regarding
permissions, call (847) 486-2635.

PEARSON

Addison
Wesley

2 3 4 5 6 7 8 9 10 —BRG— 08 07 06 05
www.aw-bc.com/physics

Welcome
to the CONCEPTUAL PHYSICS PRACTICE BOOK

These practice pages supplement *Conceptual Physics, Tenth Edition*. Their purpose is as the name implies—practice—not testing. You'll find it is easier to learn physics by *doing* it—by practicing. AFTER you've worked through a page, check your responses with the reduced pages with answers beginning on page 131.

Pages 193 to 290 show answers to the odd-numbered exercises and solutions to the problems in the textbook.

Enjoy your physics!

Table of Contents

CONCEPTUAL **Physics** PRACTICE PAGE

Chapter 1 About Science
Making Hypotheses

The word science comes from Latin, meaning "to know."
The word *hypothesis* comes from Greek, "under an idea."
A hypothesis (an educated guess) often leads to new
knowledge and may help to establish a theory.

*WHICH IS AN EDUCATED GUESS···
A HYPOTHESIS OR A THEORY?*

WHICH RESULTS FROM A LARGE BODY OF KNOWLEDGE?

Examples:
1. It is well known that objects generally expand when
   heated. An iron plate gets slightly bigger, for example,
   when placed in an oven. But what of a hole in the middle
   of the plate? One friend may say the size of the hole will
   increase, and another may say it will decrease.

I CUT A DISK FROM THIS IRON PLATE. WHEN I HEAT THE PLATE, WILL THE HOLE GET BIGGER, OR SMALLER?

   a. What is your hypothesis about hole size, and if you
      are wrong, is there a test for finding out?

_____

WHAT HAPPENS IF HE PLUGS THE DISK BACK INTO THE HOLE BEFORE HEATING EVERYTHING?

   b. There are often several ways to test a hypothesis. For example, you can perform
      a physical experiment and witness the results yourself, or you can use the library
      or internet to find the reported results of other investigators. Which of these two
      methods do you favor, and why?

_____

_____

2. Before the time of the printing press, books were hand-copied by scribes,
   many of whom were monks in monasteries. There is the story of the scribe
   who was frustrated to find a smudge on an important page he was copying.
   The smudge blotted out part of the sentence that reported the number of
   teeth in the head of a donkey. The scribe was very upset and didn't know
   what to do. He consulted with other scribes to see if any of their books
   stated the number of teeth in the head of a donkey. After many hours of
   fruitless searching through the library, it was agreed that the best thing to
   do was to send a messenger by donkey to the next monastery and continue
   the search there. What would be your advice?

_____

Making Distinctions
Many people don't seem to see the difference between a thing and
the abuse of the thing. For example, a city council that bans skateboarding may not distinguish between skateboarding and reckless
skateboarding. A person who advocates that a particular technology
be banned may not distinguish between that technology and the
abuses of that technology. There's a difference between a thing and
the abuse of the thing.

On a separate sheet of paper, list other examples where use and abuse are often not distinguished.
Compare your list with others in your class.

Chapter 1 About Science
Pinhole Formation

Look carefully on the round spots of light on the shady ground beneath trees. These are *sunballs*, which are images of the sun. They are cast by openings between leaves in the trees that act as pinholes. (Did you make a pinhole "camera" back in middle school?) Large sunballs, several centimeters in diameter or so, are cast by openings that are relatively high above the ground,

while small ones are produced by closer "pinholes." The interesting point is that the ratio of the diameter of the sunball to its distance from the pinhole is the same ratio of the Sun's diameter to its distance from the pinhole. We know the Sun is approximately 150,000,000 km from the pin-hole, so careful measurements of of the ratio of diameter/distance for a sunball leads you to the diameter of the Sun. That's what this page is about. Instead of measuring sunballs under the shade of trees on a sunny day, make your own easier-to-measure sunball.

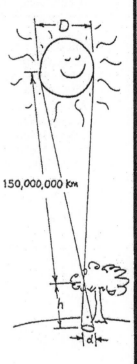

150,000,000 km

1. Poke a small hole in a piece of card. Perhaps an index card will do, and poke the hole with a sharp pencil or pen. Hold the card in the sunlight and note the circular image that is cast. This is an image of the Sun. Note that its size doesn't depend on the size of the hole in the card, but only on its distance. The image is a circle when cast on a surface perpendicular to the rays—otherwise it's "stretched out" as an ellipse.

2. Try holes of various shapes; say a square hole, or a triangular hole. What is the shape of the image when its distance from the card is large compared with the size of the hole? Does the shape of the pinhole make a difference?

_____

_____

3. Measure the diameter of a small coin. Then place the coin on a viewing area that is perpendicular to the Sun's rays. Position the card so the image of the sunball exactly covers the coin. Carefully measure the distance between the coin and the small hole in the card. Complete the following:

$$\frac{\text{Diameter of sunball}}{\text{Distance of pinhole}} = \underline{\hspace{3cm}}$$

With this ratio, estimate the diameter of the Sun. Show your work on a separate piece of paper.

WHAT SHAPE Do SUNBALLS HAVE DURING A PARTIAL ECLIPSE OF THE SUN ?

4. If you did this on a day when the Sun is partially eclipsed, what shape of image would you expect to see?

_____

Hewitt Drew it!

Name _____ Date _____

Chapter 2 Newton's First Law of Motion—Inertia
Static Equilibrium

1. Little Nellie Newton wishes to be a gymnast and hangs from a variety of positions as shown. Since she is not accelerating, the net force on her is zero. That is, $\Sigma F = 0$. This means the upward pull of the rope(s) equals the downward pull of gravity. She weighs 300 N. Show the scale reading(s) for each case.

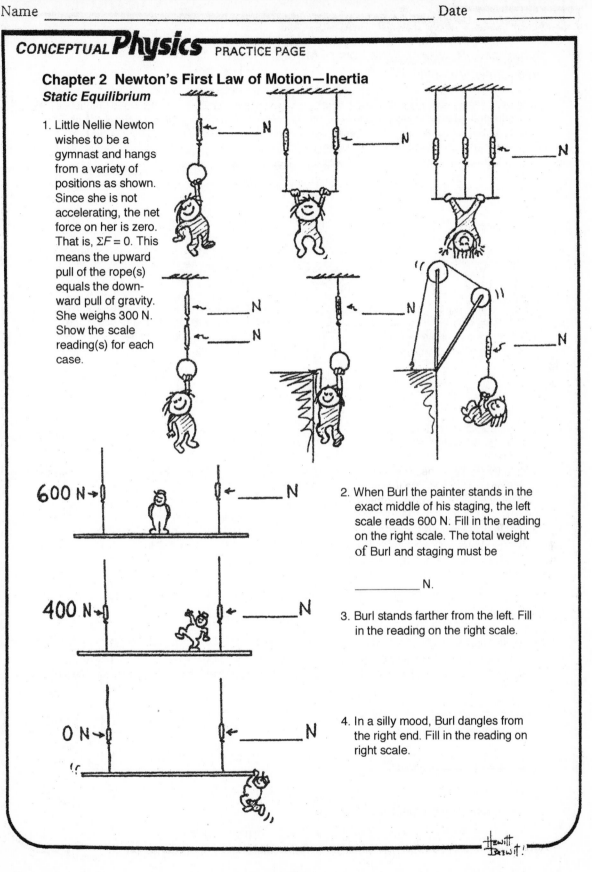

600 N→ _____ N

400 N→ _____ N

0 N→ _____ N

2. When Burl the painter stands in the exact middle of his staging, the left scale reads 600 N. Fill in the reading on the right scale. The total weight of Burl and staging must be

_____ N.

3. Burl stands farther from the left. Fill in the reading on the right scale.

4. In a silly mood, Burl dangles from the right end. Fill in the reading on right scale.

Chapter 2 Newton's First Law of Motion—Inertia
The Equilibrium Rule: ΣF = 0

1. Manuel weighs 1000 N and stands in the middle of a board that weighs 200 N. The ends of the board rest on bathroom scales. (We can assume the weight of the board acts at its center.) Fill in the correct weight reading on each scale.

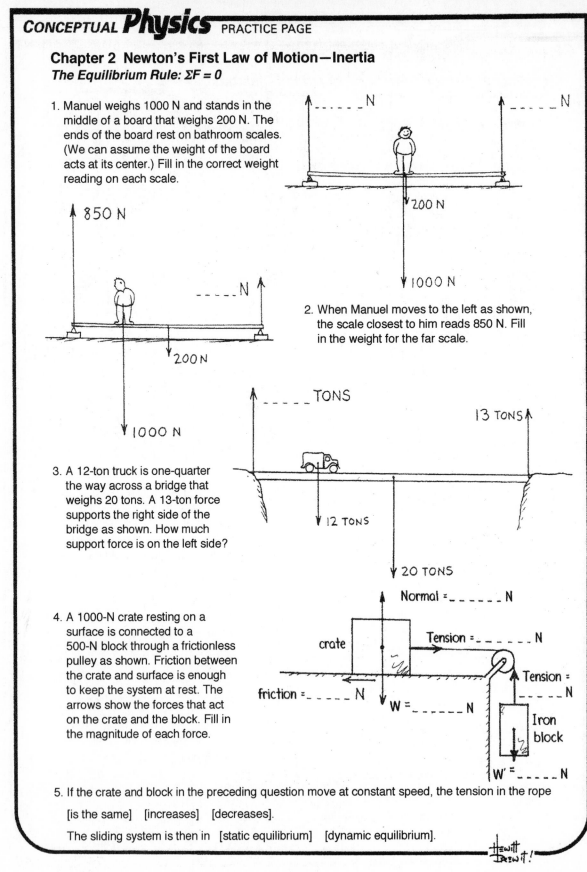

850 N

____ N

200 N

1000 N

N

200 N

1000 N

2. When Manuel moves to the left as shown, the scale closest to him reads 850 N. Fill in the weight for the far scale.

TONS

13 TONS

3. A 12-ton truck is one-quarter the way across a bridge that weighs 20 tons. A 13-ton force supports the right side of the bridge as shown. How much support force is on the left side?

12 TONS

20 TONS

Normal = ____ N

Tension = ____ N

crate

Tension = ____ N

friction = ____ N

W = ____ N

Iron block

4. A 1000-N crate resting on a surface is connected to a 500-N block through a frictionless pulley as shown. Friction between the crate and surface is enough to keep the system at rest. The arrows show the forces that act on the crate and the block. Fill in the magnitude of each force.

W' = ____ N

5. If the crate and block in the preceding question move at constant speed, the tension in the rope

[is the same]   [increases]   [decreases].

The sliding system is then in   [static equilibrium]   [dynamic equilibrium].

4

CONCEPTUAL *Physics* PRACTICE PAGE

Chapter 2 Newton's First Law of Motion—Inertia
Vectors and Equilibrium

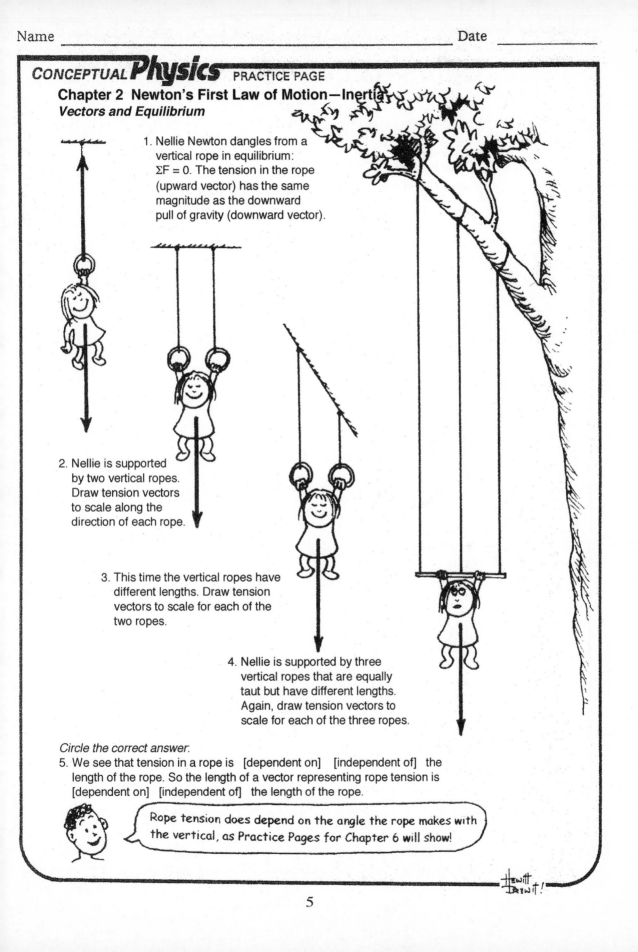

1. Nellie Newton dangles from a vertical rope in equilibrium: $\Sigma F = 0$. The tension in the rope (upward vector) has the same magnitude as the downward pull of gravity (downward vector).

2. Nellie is supported by two vertical ropes. Draw tension vectors to scale along the direction of each rope.

3. This time the vertical ropes have different lengths. Draw tension vectors to scale for each of the two ropes.

4. Nellie is supported by three vertical ropes that are equally taut but have different lengths. Again, draw tension vectors to scale for each of the three ropes.

Circle the correct answer.

5. We see that tension in a rope is [dependent on]   [independent of]   the length of the rope. So the length of a vector representing rope tension is [dependent on]   [independent of]   the length of the rope.

Rope tension does depend on the angle the rope makes with the vertical, as Practice Pages for Chapter 6 will show!

Name ______________________________ Date ____________

CONCEPTUAL Physics PRACTICE PAGE

Chapter 3 Linear Motion

Free Fall Speed

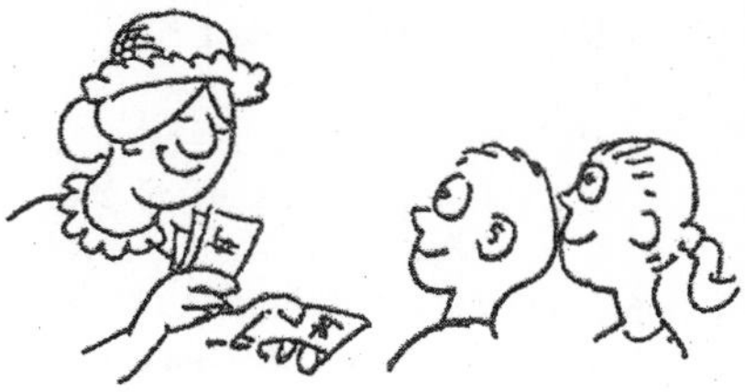

1. Aunt Minnie gives you $10 per second for 4 seconds.
   How much money do you have after 4 seconds? ____________

2. A ball dropped from rest picks up speed at 10 m/s per second.
   After it falls for 4 seconds, how fast is it going? ____________

3. You have $20, and Uncle Harry gives you $10 each second for 3 seconds.
   How much money do you have after 3 seconds? ____________

4. A ball is thrown straight down with an initial speed of 20 m/s.
   After 3 seconds, how fast is it going? ____________

5. You have $50, and you pay Aunt Minnie $10/second.
   When will your money run out? ____________

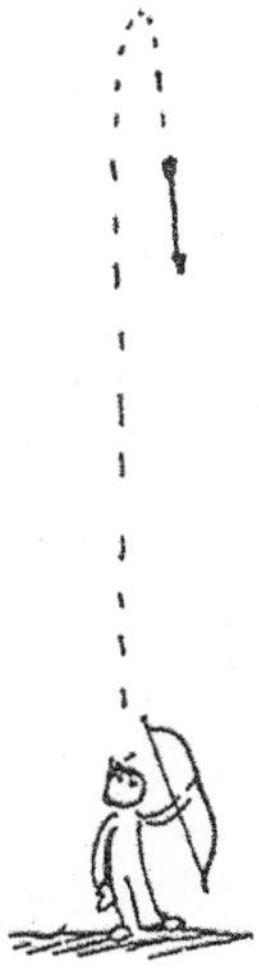

6. You shoot an arrow straight up at 50 m/s.
   When will it run out of speed? ____________

7. So what will be the arrow's speed 5 seconds after you shoot it? ____________

8. What will its speed be 6 seconds after you shoot it? ____________

   Speed after 7 seconds? ____________

Free Fall Distance

1. Speed is one thing; distance is another. How high is the arrow
   when you shoot up at 50 m/s when it runs out of speed? ____________

2. How high will the arrow be 7 seconds after being shot up at 50 m/s? ____________

3.a. Aunt Minnie drops a penny into a wishing well, and it falls for 3 seconds before hitting the water. How fast is it going when it hits? ____________

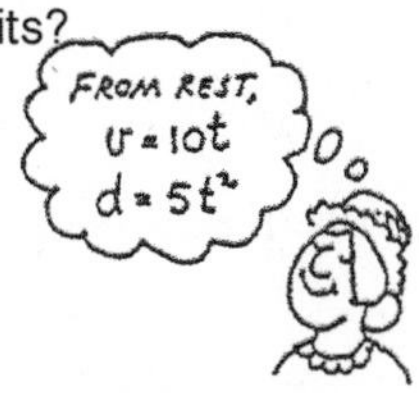

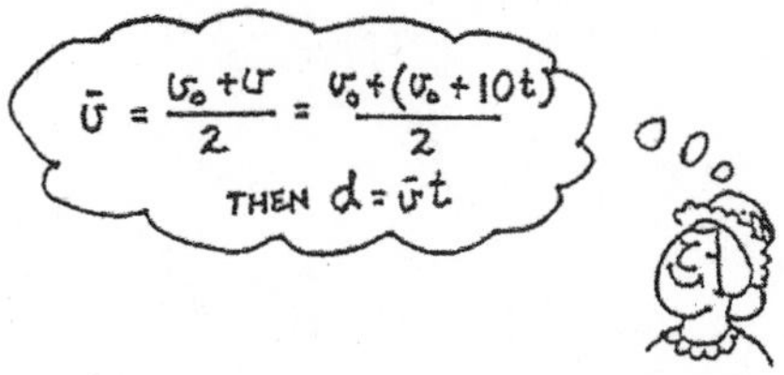

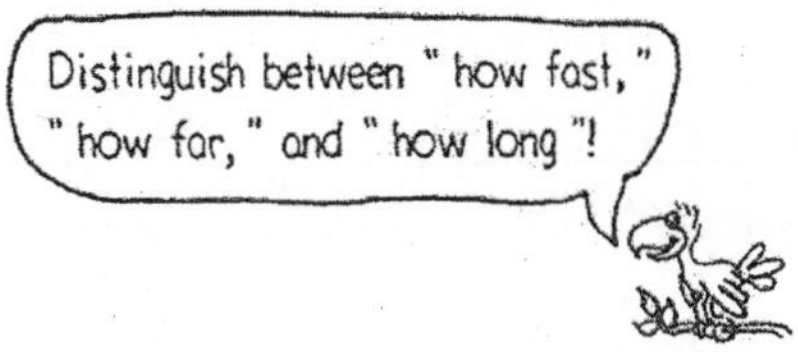

FROM REST,
$v = 10t$
$d = 5t^2$

b. What is the penny's average speed during its 3-second drop? ____________

c. How far down is the water surface? ____________

4. Aunt Minnie didn't get her wish, so she goes to a deeper wishing well and throws a penny straight down into it at 10 m/s. How far does this penny go in 3 seconds? ____________

$\bar{v} = \frac{v_0 + v}{2} = \frac{v_0 + (v_0 + 10t)}{2}$
THEN $d = \bar{v}t$

Distinguish between "how fast," "how far," and "how long"!

Hewitt Drew it!

Chapter 3 Linear Motion
Acceleration of Free Fall

A rock dropped from the top of a cliff picks up speed as it falls. Pretend that a speedometer and odometer are attached to the rock to indicate readings of speed and distance at 1-second intervals. Both speed and distance are zero at time = zero (see sketch). Note that after falling 1 second, the speed reading is 10 m/s and the distance fallen is 5 m. The readings of succeeding seconds of fall are not shown and are left for you to complete. So draw the position of the speedometer pointer and write in the correct odometer reading for each time. Use $g = 10$ m/s^2 and neglect air resistance.

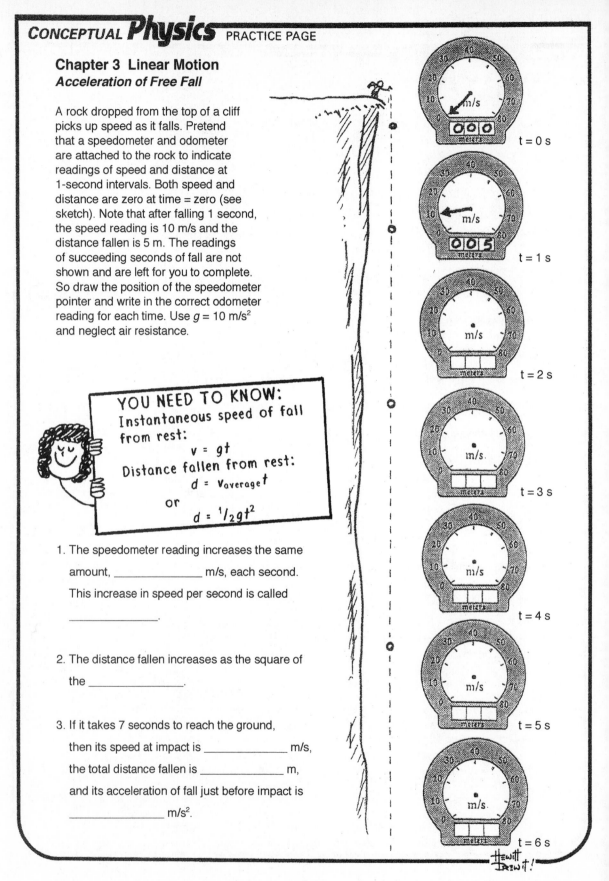

YOU NEED TO KNOW:
Instantaneous speed of fall from rest:
$$v = gt$$
Distance fallen from rest:
$$d = v_{average}t$$
or
$$d = \tfrac{1}{2}gt^2$$

1. The speedometer reading increases the same amount, _____ m/s, each second. This increase in speed per second is called _____.

2. The distance fallen increases as the square of the _____.

3. If it takes 7 seconds to reach the ground, then its speed at impact is _____ m/s, the total distance fallen is _____ m, and its acceleration of fall just before impact is _____ m/s^2.

t = 0 s

t = 1 s

t = 2 s

t = 3 s

t = 4 s

t = 5 s

t = 6 s

Name _____   Date _____

CONCEPTUAL **Physics** PRACTICE PAGE

Chapter 3 Linear Motion
Hang Time

Some athletes and dancers have great jumping ability. When leaping, they seem to momentarily "hang in the air" and defy gravity. The time that a jumper is airborne with feet off the ground is called hang time. Ask your friends to estimate the hang time of the great jumpers. They may say two or three seconds. But surprisingly, the hang time of the greatest jumpers is most always less than 1 second! A longer time is one of many illusions we have about nature.

To better understand this, find the answers to the following questions:

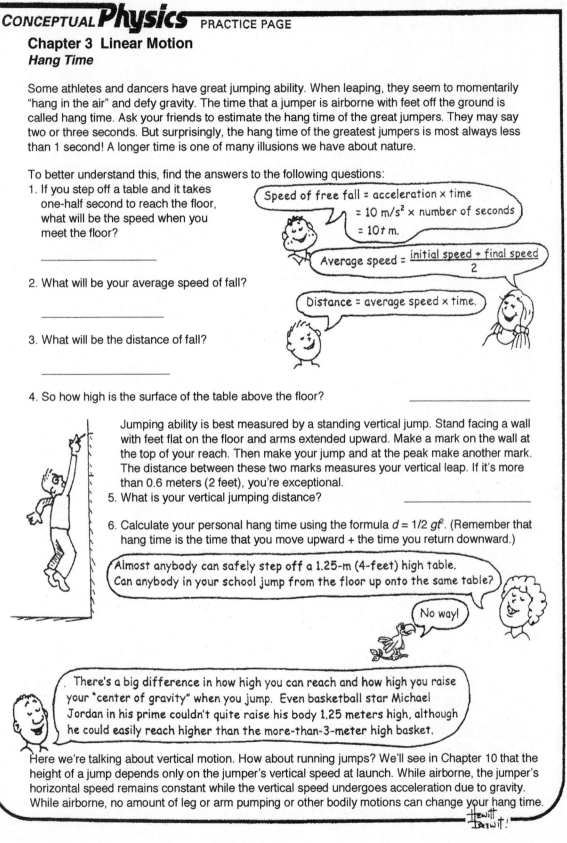

1. If you step off a table and it takes one-half second to reach the floor, what will be the speed when you meet the floor?

   _____

Speed of free fall = acceleration × time
= 10 m/s^2 × number of seconds
= 10t m.

2. What will be your average speed of fall?

   _____

Average speed = $\dfrac{\text{initial speed + final speed}}{2}$

3. What will be the distance of fall?

   _____

Distance = average speed × time.

4. So how high is the surface of the table above the floor?   _____

Jumping ability is best measured by a standing vertical jump. Stand facing a wall with feet flat on the floor and arms extended upward. Make a mark on the wall at the top of your reach. Then make your jump and at the peak make another mark. The distance between these two marks measures your vertical leap. If it's more than 0.6 meters (2 feet), you're exceptional.

5. What is your vertical jumping distance?   _____

6. Calculate your personal hang time using the formula $d = 1/2\, gt^2$. (Remember that hang time is the time that you move upward + the time you return downward.)

Almost anybody can safely step off a 1.25-m (4-feet) high table. Can anybody in your school jump from the floor up onto the same table?

No way!

There's a big difference in how high you can reach and how high you raise your "center of gravity" when you jump. Even basketball star Michael Jordan in his prime couldn't quite raise his body 1.25 meters high, although he could easily reach higher than the more-than-3-meter high basket.

Here we're talking about vertical motion. How about running jumps? We'll see in Chapter 10 that the height of a jump depends only on the jumper's vertical speed at launch. While airborne, the jumper's horizontal speed remains constant while the vertical speed undergoes acceleration due to gravity. While airborne, no amount of leg or arm pumping or other bodily motions can change your hang time.

Chapter 3 Linear Motion
Non-Accelerated Motion

1. The sketch shows a ball rolling at constant velocity along a level floor. The ball rolls from the first position shown to the second in 1 second. The two positions are 1 meter apart. Sketch the ball at successive 1-second intervals all the way to the wall (neglect resistance).

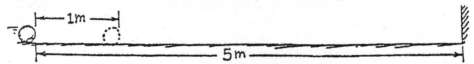

   a. Did you draw successive ball positions evenly spaced, farther apart, or closer together? Why?

   _____

   b. The ball reaches the wall with a speed of _____ m/s and takes a time of _____ seconds.

2. Table I shows data of sprinting speeds of some animals. Make whatever computations necessary to complete the table.

TABLE I

ANIMAL	DISTANCE	TIME	SPEED
CHEETAH	75 m	3 s	25 m/s
GREYHOUND	160 m	10 s	
GAZELLE	1 km		100 km/h
TURTLE		30 s	1 cm/s

Accelerated Motion

3. An object starting from rest gains a speed $v = at$ when it undergoes uniform acceleration. The distance it covers is $d = 1/2\ at^2$. Uniform acceleration occurs for a ball rolling down an inclined plane. The plane below is tilted so a ball picks up a speed of 2 m/s each second; then its acceleration $a = 2$ m/s^2. The positions of the ball are shown at 1-second intervals. Complete the six blank spaces for distance covered and the four blank spaces for speeds.

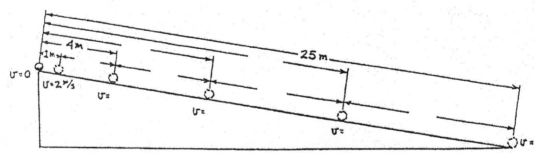

   a. Do you see that the total distance from the starting point increases as the square of the time? This was discovered by Galileo. If the incline were to continue, predict the ball's distance from the starting point for the next 3 seconds.

   _____

   b. Note the increase of distance between ball positions with time. Do you see an odd-integer pattern (also discovered by Galileo) for this increase? If the incline were to continue, predict the successive distances between ball positions for the next 3 seconds.

   _____

CONCEPTUAL *Physics* PRACTICE PAGE

Chapter 4 Newton's Second Law of Motion
Mass and Weight

Learning physics is learning the connections among concepts in nature, and also learning to distinguish between closely-related concepts. Velocity and acceleration, previously treated, are often confused. Similarly in this chapter, we find that mass and weight are often confused. They aren't the same! Please review the distinction between mass and weight in your textbook. To reinforce your understanding of this distinction, circle the correct answers below.

Comparing the concepts of mass and weight, one is basic—fundamental—depending only on the internal makeup of an object and the number and kind of atoms that compose it. The concept that is fundamental is   [mass]   [weight].

The concept that additionally depends on location in a gravitational field is   [mass]   [weight].

[Mass]   [Weight]   is a measure of the amount of matter in an object and only depends on the number and kind of atoms that compose it.

It can correctly be said that   [mass]   [weight]   is a measure of "laziness" of an object.

[Mass]   [Weight]   is related to the gravitational force acting on the object.

[Mass]   [Weight]   depends on an object's location, whereas   [mass]   [weight]   does not.

In other words, a stone would have the same   [mass]   [weight]   whether it is on the surface of Earth or on the surface of the Moon. However, its   [mass]   [weight]   depends on its location.

On the Moon's surface, where gravity is only about 1/6th Earth gravity   [mass]   [weight] [both the mass and the weight]   of the stone would be the same as on Earth.

While mass and weight are not the same, they are   [directly proportional]   [inversely proportional] to each other. In the same location, twice the mass has   [twice]   [half]   the weight.

The Standard International (SI) unit of mass is the   [kilogram]   [newton],   and the SI unit of force is the   [kilogram]   [newton].

In the United States, it is common to measure the mass of something by measuring its gravitational pull to Earth, its weight. The common unit of weight in the U.S. is the   [pound]   [kilogram]   [newton].

Pull of gravity

Support Force

When I step on a weighing scale, two forces act on it; a downward pull of gravity, and an upward support force. These equal and opposite forces effectively compress a spring inside the scale that is calibrated to show weight. When in equilibrium, my weight = *mg*.

thanx to Daniela Taylor

Chapter 4 Newton's Second Law of Motion
Converting Mass to Weight

Objects with mass also have weight (although they can be weightless under special conditions). If you know the mass of something in **kilograms** and want its weight in **newtons**, at Earth's surface, you can take advantage of the formula that relates weight and mass.

Weight = mass × acceleration due to gravity
$W = mg$

This is in accord with Newton's 2nd law, written as $F = ma$. When the force of gravity is the only force, the acceleration of any object of mass m will be g, the acceleration of free fall. Importantly, g acts as a proportionality constant, 9.8 N/kg, which is equivalent to 9.8 m/s^2.

Sample Question:
How much does a 1-kg bag of nails weigh on Earth?

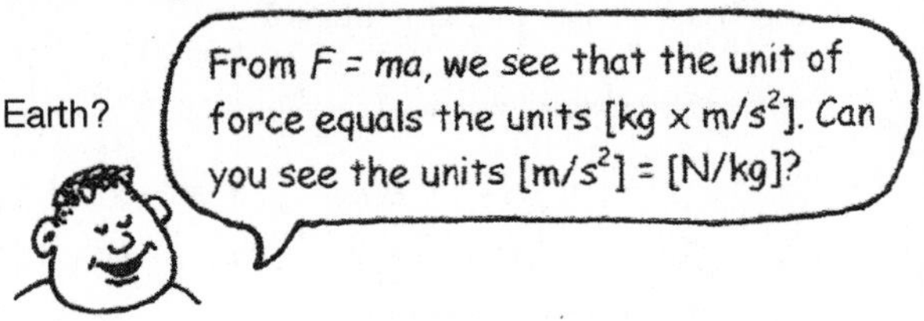

From $F = ma$, we see that the unit of force equals the units [kg × m/s^2]. Can you see the units [m/s^2] = [N/kg]?

$W = mg = (1 \text{ kg})(9.8 \text{ m/s}^2) = 9.8 \text{ m/s}^2 = 9.8 \text{ N}.$
or simply, $W = mg = (1 \text{ kg})(9.8 \text{ N/kg}) = 9.8 \text{ N}.$

Answer the following questions:
Felicia the ballet dancer has a mass of 45.0 kg.

1. What is Felicia's weight in newtons at Earth's surface? _____

2. Given that 1 kilogram of mass corresponds to 2.2 pounds at Earth's surface,
    what is Felicia's weight in pounds on Earth? _____

3. What would be Felicia's mass on the surface of Jupiter? _____

4. What would be Felicia's weight on Jupiter's surface,
    where the acceleration due to gravity is 25.0 m/s^2? _____

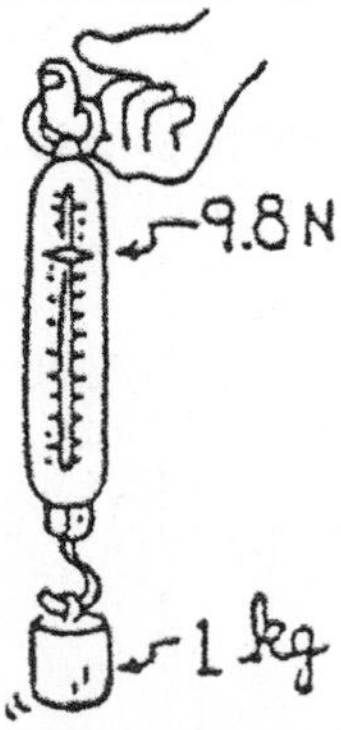

Different masses are hung on a spring scale calibrated in newtons.
The force exerted by gravity on 1 kg = 9.8 N.

9.8 N

5. The force exerted by gravity on 5 kg = _____ N.

6. The force exerted by gravity on _____ kg = 98 N.

Make up your own mass and show the corresponding weight:
The force exerted by gravity on _____ kg = _____ N.

1 kg

By whatever means (spring scales, measuring balances, etc.), find the mass of your physics book. Then complete the table.

OBJECT	MASS	WEIGHT
MELON	1 kg	
APPLE		1 N
BOOK		
A FRIEND	60 kg	

Hewitt Drewit!

CONCEPTUAL **Physics** PRACTICE PAGE

Chapter 4 Newton's Second Law of Motion
A Day at the Races with a = F/m

In each situation below, Cart A has a mass of **1 kg**. *Circle the correct answer* (A, B, or Same for both).

1. Cart A is pulled with a force of **1 N**.
   Cart B also has a mass of **1 kg** and is
   pulled with a force of **2 N**.
   Which undergoes the greater acceleration?

   [A]   [B]   [Same for both]

2. Cart A is pulled with a force of **1 N**.
   Cart B has a mass of **2 kg** and is also
   pulled with a force of **1 N**.
   Which undergoes the greater acceleration?

   [A]   [B]   [Same for both]

3. Cart A is pulled with a force of **1 N**.
   Cart B has a mass of **2 kg** and is pulled
   with a force of **2 N**.
   Which undergoes the greater acceleration?

   [A]   [B]   [Same for both]

4. Cart A is pulled with a force of **1 N**.
   Cart B has a mass of **3 kg** and is pulled
   with a force of **3 N**.
   Which undergoes the greater acceleration?

   [A]   [B]   [Same for both]

5. This time Cart A is pulled with a force of **4 N**.
   Cart B has a mass of **4 kg** and is pulled with
   a force of **4 N**.
   Which undergoes the greater acceleration?

   [A]   [B]   [Same for both]

6. Cart A is pulled with a force of **2 N**.
   Cart B has a mass of **4 kg** and is pulled
   with a force of **3 N**.
   Which undergoes the greater acceleration?

   [A]   [B]   [Same for both]

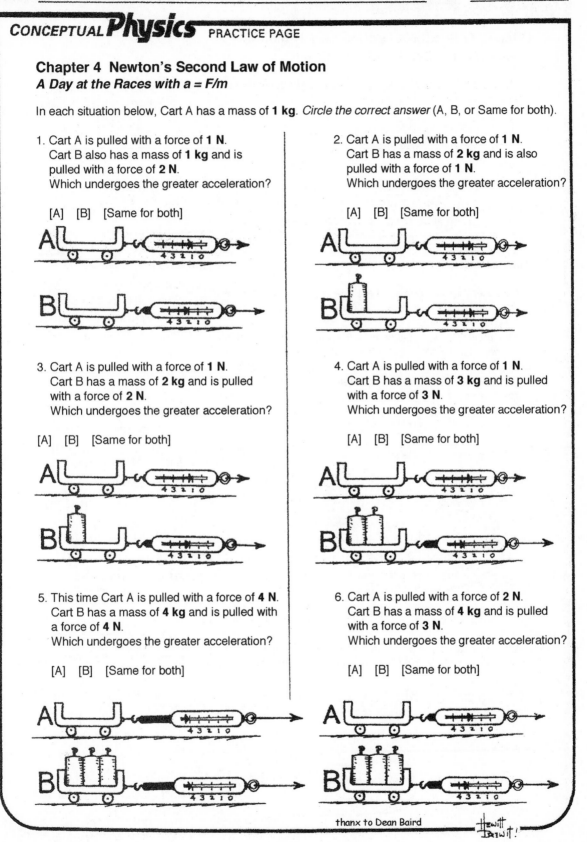

thanx to Dean Baird

Chapter 4 Newton's Second Law of Motion
Dropping Masses and Accelerating Cart

1. Consider a 1-kg cart being pulled by a 10-N applied force.
   According to Newton's 2nd law, acceleration of the cart is

$$a = \frac{F}{m} = \frac{10\,N}{1\,kg} = 10\ m/s^2.$$

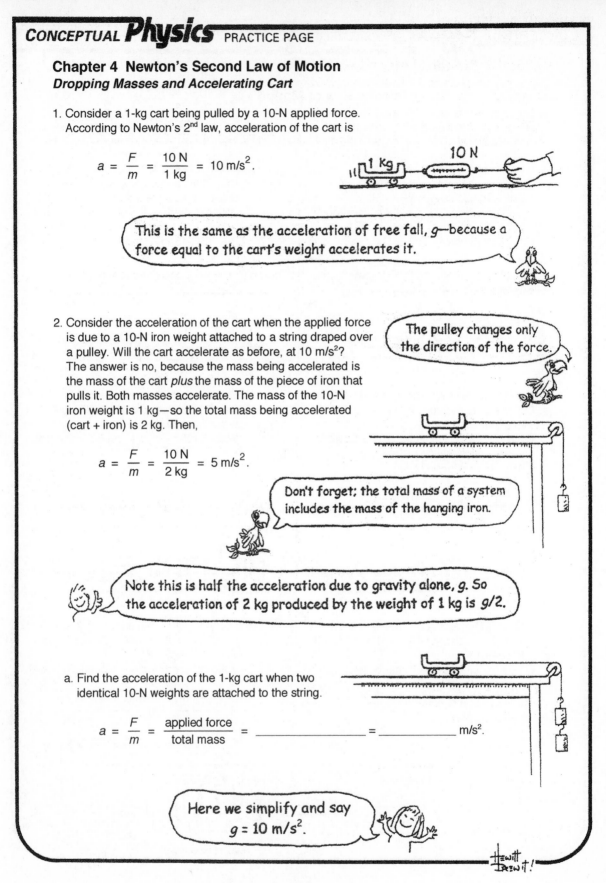

This is the same as the acceleration of free fall, *g*—because a force equal to the cart's weight accelerates it.

2. Consider the acceleration of the cart when the applied force is due to a 10-N iron weight attached to a string draped over a pulley. Will the cart accelerate as before, at 10 m/s²? The answer is no, because the mass being accelerated is the mass of the cart *plus* the mass of the piece of iron that pulls it. Both masses accelerate. The mass of the 10-N iron weight is 1 kg—so the total mass being accelerated (cart + iron) is 2 kg. Then,

$$a = \frac{F}{m} = \frac{10\,N}{2\,kg} = 5\ m/s^2.$$

The pulley changes only the direction of the force.

Don't forget; the total mass of a system includes the mass of the hanging iron.

Note this is half the acceleration due to gravity alone, *g*. So the acceleration of 2 kg produced by the weight of 1 kg is *g*/2.

a. Find the acceleration of the 1-kg cart when two identical 10-N weights are attached to the string.

$$a = \frac{F}{m} = \frac{\text{applied force}}{\text{total mass}} = \underline{\hspace{4cm}} = \underline{\hspace{3cm}}\ m/s^2.$$

Here we simplify and say
g = 10 m/s².

Chapter 4 Newton's Second Law of Motion
Dropping Masses and Accelerating Cart—continued

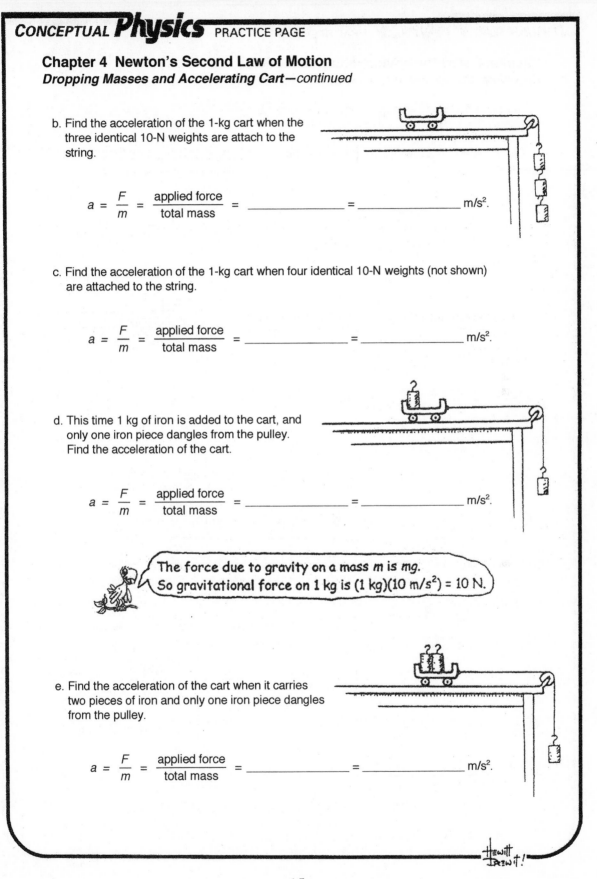

b. Find the acceleration of the 1-kg cart when the three identical 10-N weights are attach to the string.

$$a = \frac{F}{m} = \frac{\text{applied force}}{\text{total mass}} = \underline{\hspace{2cm}} = \underline{\hspace{2cm}} \text{ m/s}^2.$$

c. Find the acceleration of the 1-kg cart when four identical 10-N weights (not shown) are attached to the string.

$$a = \frac{F}{m} = \frac{\text{applied force}}{\text{total mass}} = \underline{\hspace{2cm}} = \underline{\hspace{2cm}} \text{ m/s}^2.$$

d. This time 1 kg of iron is added to the cart, and only one iron piece dangles from the pulley. Find the acceleration of the cart.

$$a = \frac{F}{m} = \frac{\text{applied force}}{\text{total mass}} = \underline{\hspace{2cm}} = \underline{\hspace{2cm}} \text{ m/s}^2.$$

The force due to gravity on a mass m is mg.
So gravitational force on 1 kg is (1 kg)(10 m/s²) = 10 N.

e. Find the acceleration of the cart when it carries two pieces of iron and only one iron piece dangles from the pulley.

$$a = \frac{F}{m} = \frac{\text{applied force}}{\text{total mass}} = \underline{\hspace{2cm}} = \underline{\hspace{2cm}} \text{ m/s}^2.$$

Chapter 4 Newton's Second Law of Motion
Dropping Masses and Accelerating Cart—continued

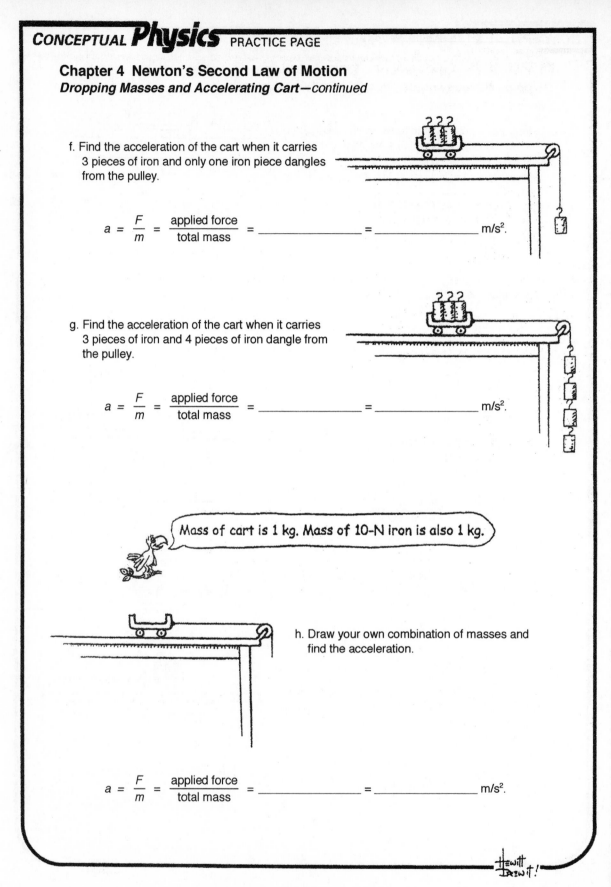

f. Find the acceleration of the cart when it carries 3 pieces of iron and only one iron piece dangles from the pulley.

$$a = \frac{F}{m} = \frac{\text{applied force}}{\text{total mass}} = \underline{\hspace{3cm}} = \underline{\hspace{3cm}} \text{ m/s}^2.$$

g. Find the acceleration of the cart when it carries 3 pieces of iron and 4 pieces of iron dangle from the pulley.

$$a = \frac{F}{m} = \frac{\text{applied force}}{\text{total mass}} = \underline{\hspace{3cm}} = \underline{\hspace{3cm}} \text{ m/s}^2.$$

Mass of cart is 1 kg. Mass of 10-N iron is also 1 kg.

h. Draw your own combination of masses and find the acceleration.

$$a = \frac{F}{m} = \frac{\text{applied force}}{\text{total mass}} = \underline{\hspace{3cm}} = \underline{\hspace{3cm}} \text{ m/s}^2.$$

CONCEPTUAL *Physics* PRACTICE PAGE

Chapter 4 Newton's Second Law of Motion
Force and Acceleration

1. Skelly the skater, total mass 25 kg, is propelled by rocket power.

   a. Complete Table I (neglect resistance).

   TABLE I

FORCE	ACCELERATION
100 N	
200 N	
	10 m/s²

   b. Complete Table II for a constant 50-N resistance.

   TABLE II

FORCE	ACCELERATION
50 N	0 m/s²
100 N	
200 N	

2. Block A on a horizontal friction-free table is accelerated by a force from a string attached to Block B of the same mass. Block B falls vertically and drags Block A horizontally. (Neglect the string's mass).

   Circle the correct answers:
   a. The *mass* of the system (A + B) is   [*m*]   [2 *m*].

   b. The *force* that accelerates (A + B) is the weight of   [A]   [B]   [A + B].

   c. The weight of B is   [*mg*/2]   [*mg*]   [2 *mg*].

   d. Acceleration of (A + B) is   [less than *g*]   [*g*]   [more than *g*].

   e. Use $a = \dfrac{F}{m}$ to show the acceleration of (A + B) as a fraction of *g*. _____

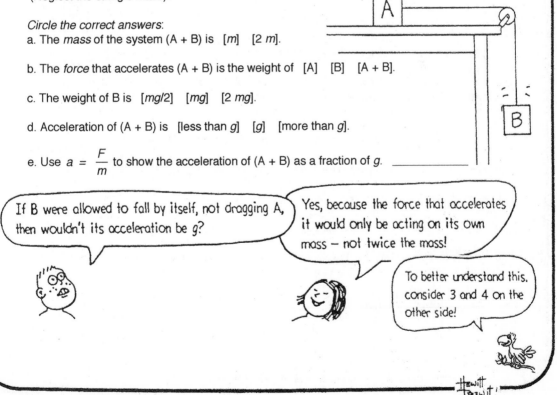

If B were allowed to fall by itself, not dragging A, then wouldn't its acceleration be *g*?

Yes, because the force that accelerates it would only be acting on its own mass — not twice the mass!

To better understand this, consider 3 and 4 on the other side!

Chapter 4 Newton's Second Law of Motion
Force and Acceleration—continued

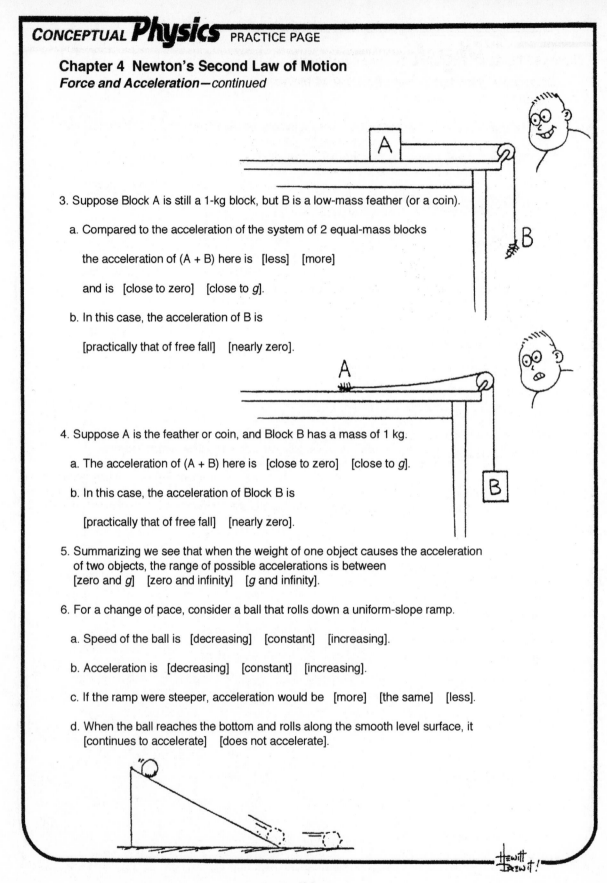

3. Suppose Block A is still a 1-kg block, but B is a low-mass feather (or a coin).

   a. Compared to the acceleration of the system of 2 equal-mass blocks

      the acceleration of (A + B) here is [less] [more]

      and is [close to zero] [close to g].

   b. In this case, the acceleration of B is

      [practically that of free fall] [nearly zero].

4. Suppose A is the feather or coin, and Block B has a mass of 1 kg.

   a. The acceleration of (A + B) here is [close to zero] [close to g].

   b. In this case, the acceleration of Block B is

      [practically that of free fall] [nearly zero].

5. Summarizing we see that when the weight of one object causes the acceleration
   of two objects, the range of possible accelerations is between
   [zero and g] [zero and infinity] [g and infinity].

6. For a change of pace, consider a ball that rolls down a uniform-slope ramp.

   a. Speed of the ball is [decreasing] [constant] [increasing].

   b. Acceleration is [decreasing] [constant] [increasing].

   c. If the ramp were steeper, acceleration would be [more] [the same] [less].

   d. When the ball reaches the bottom and rolls along the smooth level surface, it
      [continues to accelerate] [does not accelerate].

CONCEPTUAL **Physics** PRACTICE PAGE

Chapter 4 Newton's Second Law of Motion
Friction

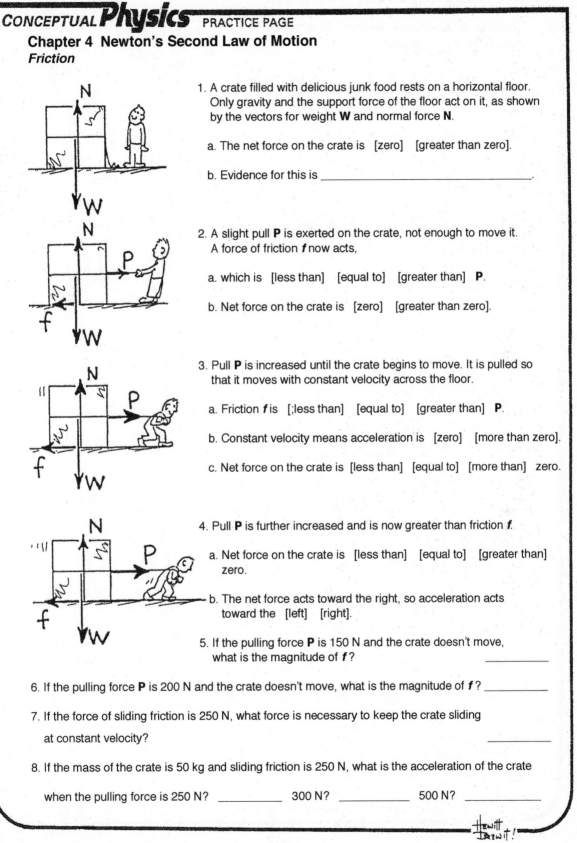

1. A crate filled with delicious junk food rests on a horizontal floor. Only gravity and the support force of the floor act on it, as shown by the vectors for weight **W** and normal force **N**.

   a. The net force on the crate is   [zero]   [greater than zero].

   b. Evidence for this is _____.

2. A slight pull **P** is exerted on the crate, not enough to move it. A force of friction *f* now acts,

   a. which is   [less than]   [equal to]   [greater than]   **P**.

   b. Net force on the crate is   [zero]   [greater than zero].

3. Pull **P** is increased until the crate begins to move. It is pulled so that it moves with constant velocity across the floor.

   a. Friction *f* is   [;less than]   [equal to]   [greater than]   **P**.

   b. Constant velocity means acceleration is   [zero]   [more than zero].

   c. Net force on the crate is   [less than]   [equal to]   [more than]   zero.

4. Pull **P** is further increased and is now greater than friction *f*.

   a. Net force on the crate is   [less than]   [equal to]   [greater than]   zero.

   b. The net force acts toward the right, so acceleration acts toward the   [left]   [right].

5. If the pulling force **P** is 150 N and the crate doesn't move, what is the magnitude of *f*? _____

6. If the pulling force **P** is 200 N and the crate doesn't move, what is the magnitude of *f*? _____

7. If the force of sliding friction is 250 N, what force is necessary to keep the crate sliding

   at constant velocity? _____

8. If the mass of the crate is 50 kg and sliding friction is 250 N, what is the acceleration of the crate

   when the pulling force is 250 N? _____ 300 N? _____ 500 N? _____

Chapter 4 Newton's Second Law of Motion
Falling and Air Resistance

Bronco skydives and parachutes from a stationary
helicopter. Various stages of fall are shown in
positions *a* through *f*. Using Newton's 2nd law,

$$a = \frac{F_{net}}{m} = \frac{W - R}{m}$$

find Bronco's acceleration at each position
(answer in the blanks to the right). You need to know
that Bronco's mass *m* is 100 kg so his weight is a
constant 1000 N. Air resistance *R* varies with speed
and cross-sectional area as shown.

Circle the correct answers:

1. When Bronco's speed is least, his acceleration is

   [least]   [most].

2. In which position(s) does Bronco experience a
   downward acceleration?

   [a]   [b]   [c]   [d]   [e]   [f]

3. In which position(s) does Bronco experience an
   upward acceleration?

   [a]   [b]   [c]   [d]   [e]   [f]

4. When Bronco experiences an upward acceleration,

   his velocity is   [still downward]   [upward also].

5. In which position(s) is Bronco's velocity constant?

   [a]   [b]   [c]   [d]   [e]   [f]

6. In which position(s) does Bronco experience terminal
   velocity?

   [a]   [b]   [c]   [d]   [e]

7. In which position(s) is terminal velocity greatest?

   [a]   [b]   [c]   [d]   [e]

8. If Bronco were heavier, his terminal velocity would be

   [greater]   [less]   [the same].

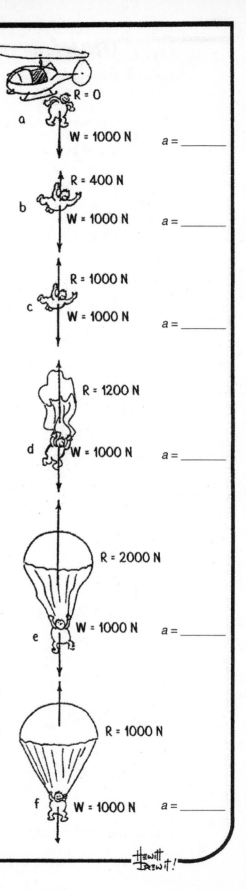

R = 0
a
W = 1000 N   a = _____

R = 400 N
b
W = 1000 N   a = _____

R = 1000 N
c
W = 1000 N   a = _____

R = 1200 N
d
W = 1000 N   a = _____

R = 2000 N
e
W = 1000 N   a = _____

R = 1000 N
f
W = 1000 N   a = _____

CONCEPTUAL *Physics* PRACTICE PAGE

Chapter 5 Newton's Third Law of Motion
Action and Reaction Pairs

1. In the example below, the action-reaction pair is shown by the arrows (vectors), and the action-reaction described in words. In *a* through *g*, draw the other arrow (vector) and state the reaction to the given action. Then make up your own example in *h*.

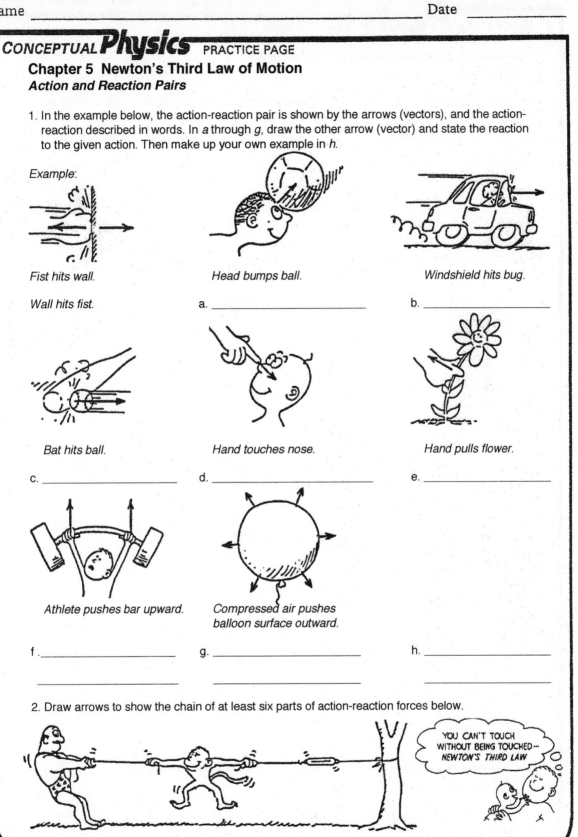

Example:

Fist hits wall.

Wall hits fist.

Head bumps ball.

a. _____

Windshield hits bug.

b. _____

Bat hits ball.

c. _____

Hand touches nose.

d. _____

Hand pulls flower.

e. _____

Athlete pushes bar upward.

Compressed air pushes
balloon surface outward.

f. _____
_____

g. _____
_____

h. _____
_____

2. Draw arrows to show the chain of at least six parts of action-reaction forces below.

YOU CAN'T TOUCH
WITHOUT BEING TOUCHED—
NEWTON'S THIRD LAW

Chapter 5 Newton's Third Law of Motion
Interactions

1. Nellie Newton holds an apple weighing 1 newton at rest on the palm of her hand. The force vectors shown are the forces that act on the apple.

a. To say the weight of the apple is 1 N is to say that a downward gravitational force of 1 N is exerted on the apple by   [Earth]   [her hand].

b. Nellie's hand supports the apple with normal force **N**, which acts in a direction opposite to **W**. We can say **N**

[equals **W**]   [has the same magnitude as **W**].

c. Since the apple is at rest, the net force on the apple is   [zero]   [nonzero].

d. Since **N** is equal and opposite to **W**, we   [can]   [cannot]   say that **N** and **W**

comprise an action-reaction pair. The reason is because action and reaction always

[act on the same object]   [act on different objects],   and here we see **N** and **W**

[both acting on the apple]   [acting on different objects].

e. In accord with the rule, "If ACTION is A acting on B, then REACTION is B acting on A," if we say *action* is Earth pulling down on the apple, then *reaction* is

[the apple pulling up on Earth]   [**N**, Nellie's hand pushing up on the apple].

f. To repeat for emphasis, we see that **N** and **W** are equal and opposite to each other

[and comprise an action-reaction pair]   [but do not comprise an action-reaction pair].

> To identify a pair of action-reaction forces in any situation, first identify the pair of interacting objects involved. Something is interacting with something else. In this case the whole Earth is interacting (gravitationally) with the apple. So Earth pulls downward on the apple (call it action). while the apple pulls upward on Earth (reaction).

> Simply put, Earth pulls on apple (action); apple pulls on Earth (reaction).

> Better put, apple and Earth *pull on each other* with equal and opposite forces that comprise a *single* interaction.

g. Another pair of forces is **N** as shown, and the downward force of the apple against Nellie's hand, not shown. This force pair   [is]   [isn't]   an action-reaction pair.

h. Suppose Nellie now pushes upward on the apple with a force of 2 N. The apple

[is still in equilibrium]   [accelerates upward],   and compared to **W**, the magnitude of **N** is

[the same]   [twice]   [not the same, and not twice].

i. Once the apple leaves Nellie's hand, **N** is   [zero]   [still twice the magnitude of **W**],   and

the net force on the apple is   [zero]   [only **W**]   [still **W** - **N**, a negative force].

CONCEPTUAL **Physics** PRACTICE PAGE

Chapter 5 Newton's Third Law of Motion
Vectors and the Parallelogram Rule

1. When two vectors **A** and **B** are at an angle to each other, they add to produce the resultant **C** by the *parallelogram rule*. Note that **C** is the diagonal of a parallelogram where **A** and **B** are adjacent sides. Resultant **C** is shown in the first two diagrams, *a* and *b*. Construct resultant **C** in diagrams *c* and *d*. Note that in diagram *d* you form a rectangle (a special case of a parallelogram).

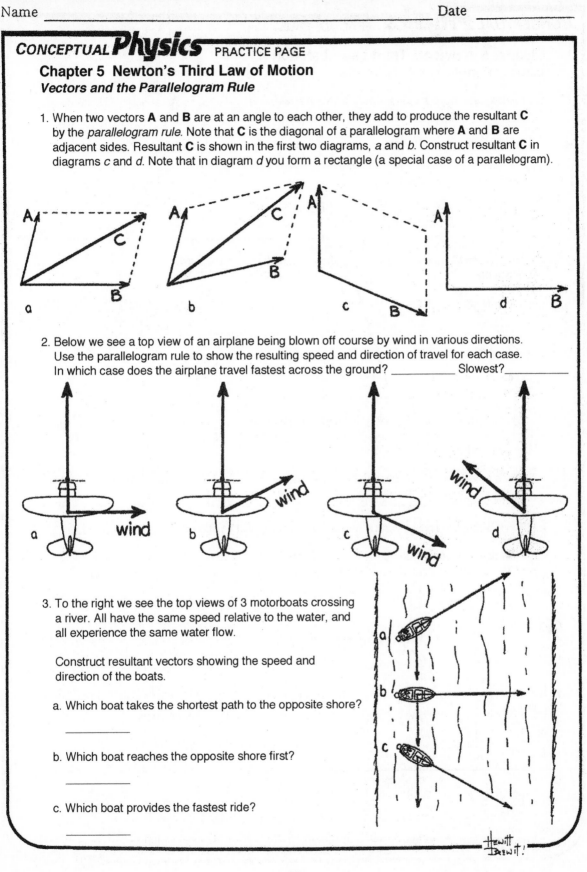

2. Below we see a top view of an airplane being blown off course by wind in various directions. Use the parallelogram rule to show the resulting speed and direction of travel for each case. In which case does the airplane travel fastest across the ground? _____ Slowest?_____

3. To the right we see the top views of 3 motorboats crossing a river. All have the same speed relative to the water, and all experience the same water flow.

   Construct resultant vectors showing the speed and direction of the boats.

   a. Which boat takes the shortest path to the opposite shore?

   _____

   b. Which boat reaches the opposite shore first?

   _____

   c. Which boat provides the fastest ride?

   _____

Chapter 5 Newton's Third Law of Motion
Velocity Vectors and Components

1. Draw the resultants of the four sets of vectors below.

2. Draw the horizontal and vertical components of the four vectors below.

I was only a scalar until you came along and gave me direction! ≥sigh≤

3. She tosses the ball along the dashed path. The velocity vector, complete with its horizontal and vertical components, is shown at position A. Carefully sketch the appropriate components for positions B and C.

   a. Since there is no acceleration in the horizontal direction, how does the horizontal component of velocity compare for positions A, B, and C? _____

   b. What is the value of the vertical component of velocity at position B? _____

   c. How does the vertical component of velocity at position C compare with that of position A?

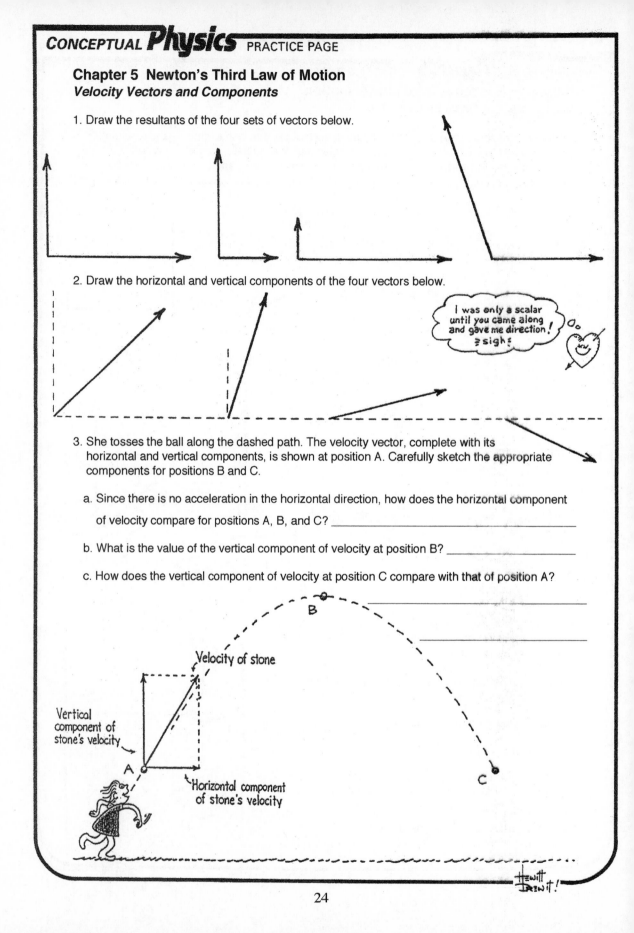

Velocity of stone

Vertical component of stone's velocity

Horizontal component of stone's velocity

CONCEPTUAL **Physics** PRACTICE PAGE

Chapter 5 Newton's Third Law of Motion
Force and Velocity Vectors

1. Draw sample vectors to represent the force of gravity on the ball in the positions shown below after it leaves the thrower's hand. (Neglect air resistance.)

2. Draw sample bold vectors to represent the velocity of the ball in the positions shown below. With lighter vectors, show the horizontal and vertical components of velocity for each position.

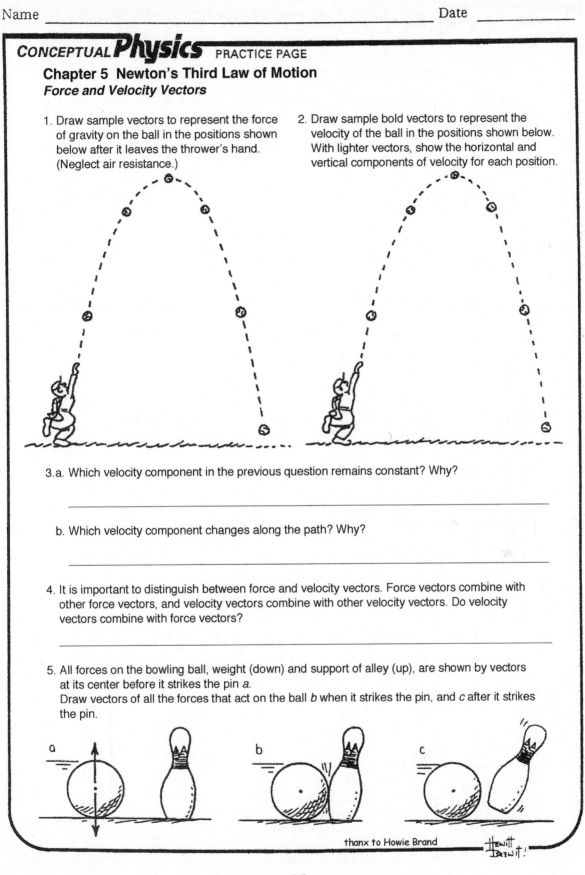

3.a. Which velocity component in the previous question remains constant? Why?

_____

b. Which velocity component changes along the path? Why?

_____

4. It is important to distinguish between force and velocity vectors. Force vectors combine with other force vectors, and velocity vectors combine with other velocity vectors. Do velocity vectors combine with force vectors?

_____

5. All forces on the bowling ball, weight (down) and support of alley (up), are shown by vectors at its center before it strikes the pin *a*.
Draw vectors of all the forces that act on the ball *b* when it strikes the pin, and *c* after it strikes the pin.

thanx to Howie Brand

25

Chapter 5 Newton's Third Law of Motion
Force Vectors and the Parallelogram Rule

1. The heavy ball is supported in each case by two strands of rope. The tension in each strand is shown by the vectors. Use the parallelogram rule to find the resultant of each vector pair.

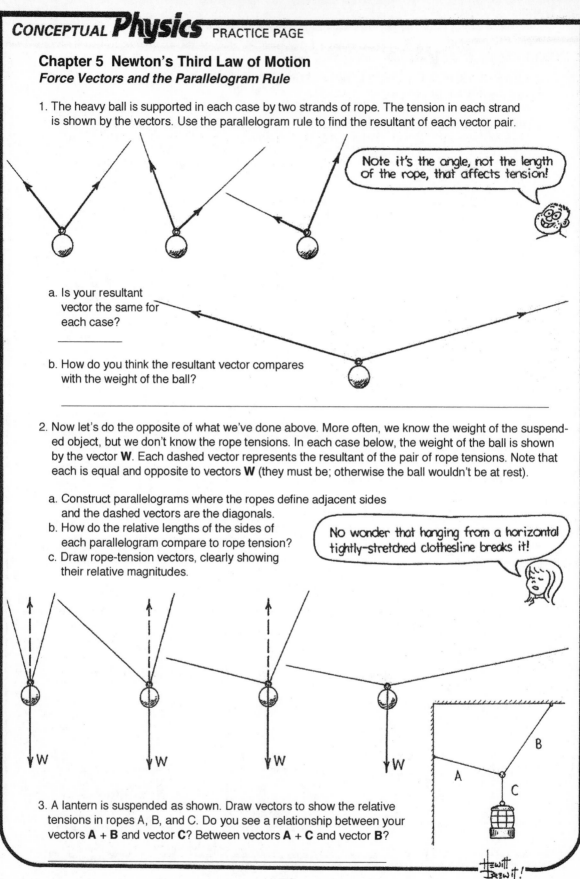

Note it's the angle, not the length of the rope, that affects tension!

a. Is your resultant vector the same for each case?

b. How do you think the resultant vector compares with the weight of the ball?

2. Now let's do the opposite of what we've done above. More often, we know the weight of the suspended object, but we don't know the rope tensions. In each case below, the weight of the ball is shown by the vector **W**. Each dashed vector represents the resultant of the pair of rope tensions. Note that each is equal and opposite to vectors **W** (they must be; otherwise the ball wouldn't be at rest).

a. Construct parallelograms where the ropes define adjacent sides and the dashed vectors are the diagonals.
b. How do the relative lengths of the sides of each parallelogram compare to rope tension?
c. Draw rope-tension vectors, clearly showing their relative magnitudes.

No wonder that hanging from a horizontal tightly-stretched clothesline breaks it!

3. A lantern is suspended as shown. Draw vectors to show the relative tensions in ropes A, B, and C. Do you see a relationship between your vectors **A** + **B** and vector **C**? Between vectors **A** + **C** and vector **B**?

Name _____ Date _____

Chapter 5 Newton's Third Law of Motion
Force-Vector Diagrams

In each case, a rock is acted on by one or more forces. Using a pencil and a ruler, draw an accurate vector diagram showing all forces acting on the rock, and no other forces. The first two cases are done as examples. The parallelogram rule in case 2 shows that the vector sum of **A** + **B** is equal and opposite to **W** (that is, **A** + **B** = -**W**). Do the same for cases 3 and 4. Draw and label vectors for the weight and normal support forces in cases 5 to 10, and for the appropriate forces in cases 11 and 12.

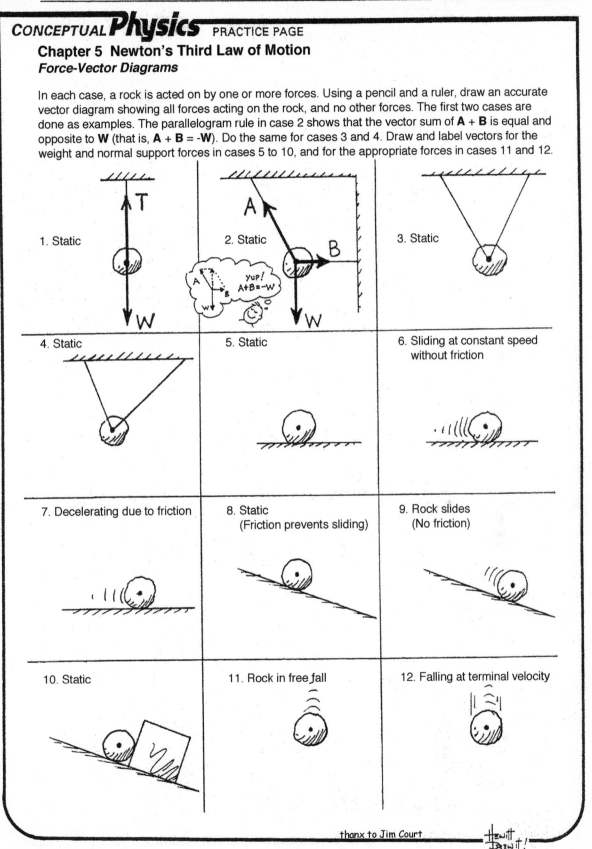

1. Static

2. Static

3. Static

4. Static

5. Static

6. Sliding at constant speed without friction

7. Decelerating due to friction

8. Static (Friction prevents sliding)

9. Rock slides (No friction)

10. Static

11. Rock in free fall

12. Falling at terminal velocity

thanx to Jim Court

Chapter 5 Newton's Third Law of Motion
More on Vectors

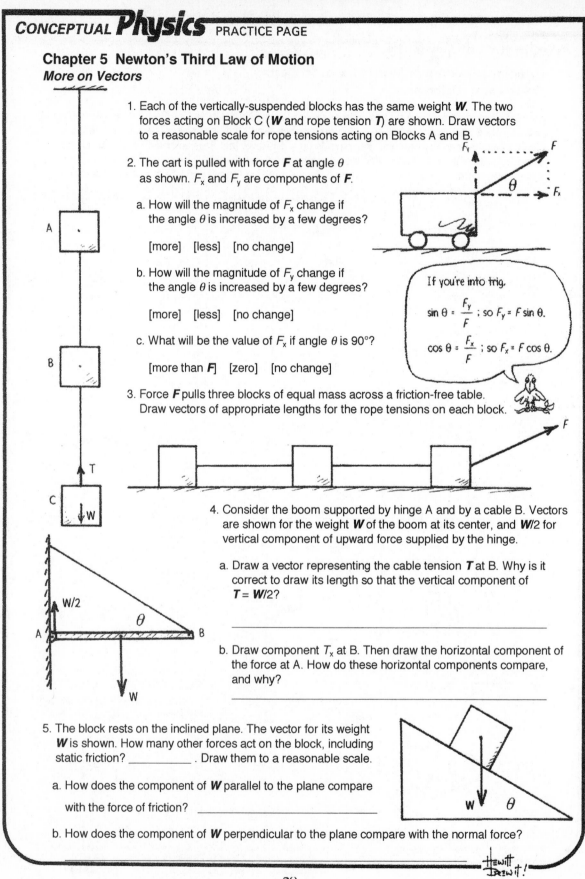

1. Each of the vertically-suspended blocks has the same weight **W**. The two forces acting on Block C (**W** and rope tension **T**) are shown. Draw vectors to a reasonable scale for rope tensions acting on Blocks A and B.

2. The cart is pulled with force **F** at angle θ as shown. F_x and F_y are components of **F**.

   a. How will the magnitude of F_x change if the angle θ is increased by a few degrees?

   [more]   [less]   [no change]

   b. How will the magnitude of F_y change if the angle θ is increased by a few degrees?

   [more]   [less]   [no change]

   c. What will be the value of F_x if angle θ is 90°?

   [more than **F**]   [zero]   [no change]

   If you're into trig,

   $\sin \theta = \dfrac{F_y}{F}$; so $F_y = F \sin \theta$.

   $\cos \theta = \dfrac{F_x}{F}$; so $F_x = F \cos \theta$.

3. Force **F** pulls three blocks of equal mass across a friction-free table. Draw vectors of appropriate lengths for the rope tensions on each block.

4. Consider the boom supported by hinge A and by a cable B. Vectors are shown for the weight **W** of the boom at its center, and **W**/2 for vertical component of upward force supplied by the hinge.

   a. Draw a vector representing the cable tension **T** at B. Why is it correct to draw its length so that the vertical component of **T** = **W**/2?

   _____

   b. Draw component T_x at B. Then draw the horizontal component of the force at A. How do these horizontal components compare, and why?

   _____

5. The block rests on the inclined plane. The vector for its weight **W** is shown. How many other forces act on the block, including static friction? _____ . Draw them to a reasonable scale.

   a. How does the component of **W** parallel to the plane compare with the force of friction? _____

   b. How does the component of **W** perpendicular to the plane compare with the normal force?

   _____

CONCEPTUAL *Physics* PRACTICE PAGE

Appendix D More About Vectors
Vectors and Sailboats

(Please do not attempt this until you have studied Appendix D!)

1. The sketch shows a top view of a small railroad car pulled by a rope. The force **F** that the rope exerts on the car has one component along the track, and another component perpendicular to the track.

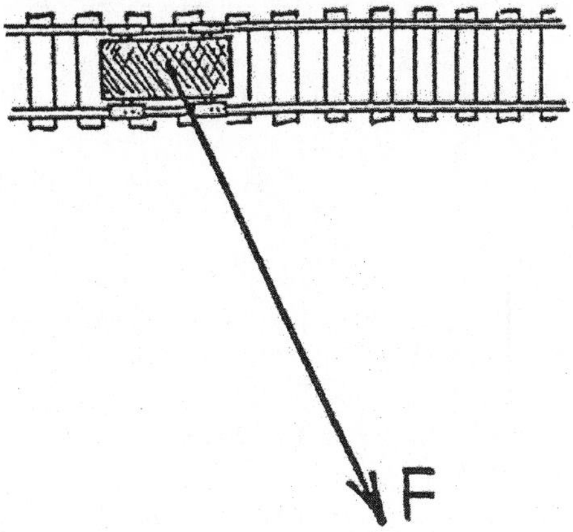

   a. Draw these components on the sketch. Which component is larger?

   _____

   b. Which component produces acceleration?

   _____

   c. What would be the effect of pulling on the rope if it were perpendicular to the track?

   _____

2. The sketches below represent simplified top views of sailboats in a cross-wind direction. The impact of the wind produces a FORCE vector on each as shown.
   (We do NOT consider *velocity* vectors here!)

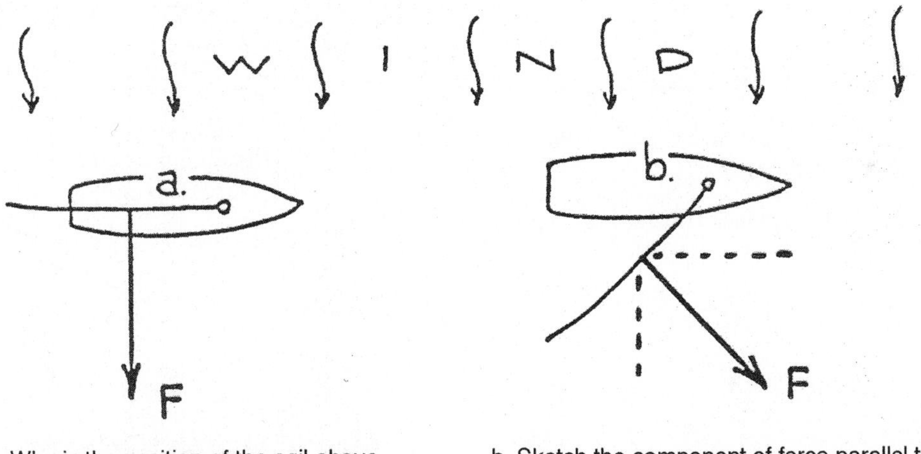

   a. Why is the position of the sail above useless for propelling the boat along its forward direction? (Relate this to Question 1.c above where the train is constrained by tracks to move in one direction, and the boat is similarly constrained to move along one direction by its deep vertical fin—the *keel*.)

   _____

   _____

   b. Sketch the component of force parallel to the to the direction of the boat's motion (along its keel), and the component perpendicular to its motion. Will the boat move in a forward direction? (Relate this to Question 1.b above.)

   _____

   _____

29

Appendix D More About Vectors
Vectors and Sailboats—continued

3. The boat to the right is oriented at an angle into the wind. Draw the force vector and its forward and perpendicular components.

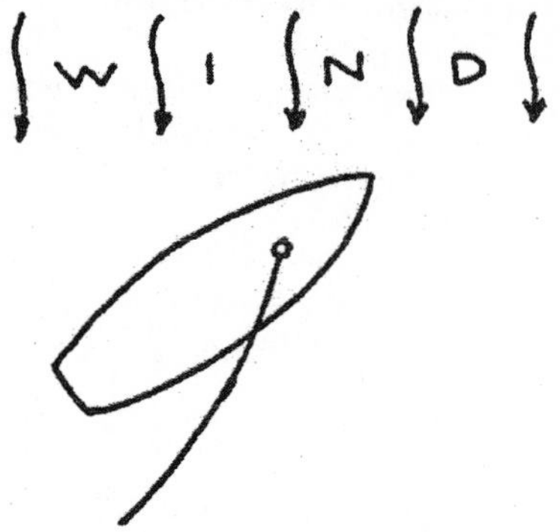

   a. Will the boat move in a forward direction and tack into the wind? Why or why not?

   _____

   _____

   _____

4. The sketch below is a top view of five identical sailboats. Where they exist, draw force vectors to represent wind impact on the sails. Then draw components parallel and perpendicular to the keels of each boat. 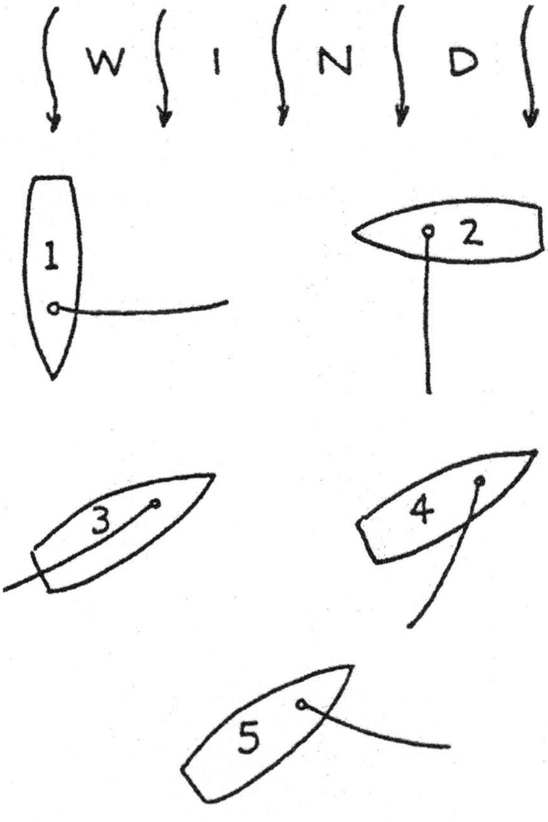
   a. Which boat will sail the fastest in a forward direction?

   _____

   b. Which will respond least to the wind?

   _____

   c. Which will move in a backward direction?

   _____

   d. Which will experience decreasing wind impact with increasing speed?

   _____

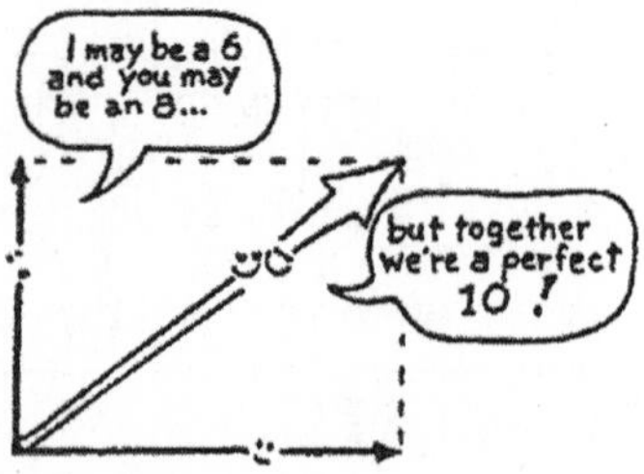

I may be a 6 and you may be an 8...

but together we're a perfect 10 !

CONCEPTUAL *Physics* PRACTICE PAGE

Chapter 6 Momentum
Changing Momentum

1. A moving car has momentum. If it moves twice as fast, its momentum is

   _____ as much.

2. Two cars, one twice as heavy as the other, move down a hill at the same speed. Compared

   with the lighter car, the momentum of the heavier car is _____ as much.

3. The recoil momentum of a cannon that kicks is

   [more than]   [less than]   [the same as]

   the momentum of the cannonball it fires.
   (Here we neglect friction and the momentum
   of the gases.)

4. Suppose you are traveling in a bus at highway speed on a nice summer day and the momentum
   of an unlucky bug is suddenly changed as it splatters onto the front window.

   a. Compared to the force that acts on the bug,
      how much force acts on the bus?

      [more]   [less]   [the same]

   b. The time of impact is the same for both the
      bug and the bus. Compared to the impulse
      on the bug, this means the impulse on the
      bus is

      [more]   [less]   [the same].

   c. Although the momentum of the bus is very
      large compared to the momentum of the
      bug, the *change* in momentum of the bus,
      compared to the *change* of momentum of
      the bug is

      [more]   [less]   [the same].

   d. Which undergoes the greater acceleration?

      [bus]   [both the same]   [bug]

   e. Which therefore, suffers the greater damage?

      [bus]   [both the same]   [bug of course!]

   Isn't it amazing, that in a collision
   between two very different entities
   — a bug and a bus, that three
   opposite quantities remain equal:
   impact forces, impulses, and changes
   in momentum!

Chapter 6 Momentum
Changing Momentum—continued

5. Granny whizzes around the rink and is suddenly confronted with Ambrose at rest directly in her path. Rather than knock him over, she picks him up and continues in motion without "braking."

Consider both Granny and Ambrose as two parts of one system. Since no outside forces act on the system, the momentum of the system before collision equals the momentum of the system after collision.

a. Complete the before-collision data in the table below.

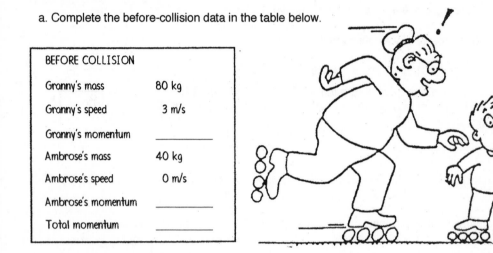

BEFORE COLLISION	
Granny's mass	80 kg
Granny's speed	3 m/s
Granny's momentum	_____
Ambrose's mass	40 kg
Ambrose's speed	0 m/s
Ambrose's momentum	_____
Total momentum	_____

b. After collision, Granny's speed   [increases]   [decreases].

c. After collision, Ambrose's speed   [increases]   [decreases].

d. After collision, the total mass of Granny + Ambrose is   _____.

e. After collision, the total momentum of Granny + Ambrose is

_____

f. Use the conservation of momentum law to find the speed of Granny and Ambrose together after collision.
(Show your work in the space below.)

New speed _____

Chapter 6 Momentum
Systems

1. When the compressed spring is released, Blocks A and B will slide apart. There are 3 systems to consider, indicated by the closed dashed lines below—A, B, and A + B. Ignore the vertical forces of gravity and the support force of the table.

   a. Does an external force act on System A? [Y] [N]

      Will the momentum of System A change? [Y] [N]

   b. Does an external force act on System B? [Y] [N]

      Will the momentum of System B change? [Y] [N]

   c. Does an external force act on System A + B?
                                            [Y] [N]

      Will the momentum of System A + B change?
                                            [Y] [N]

2. Billiard ball A collides with billiard ball B at rest. Isolate each system with a closed dashed line. Draw only the external force vectors that act on each system.

   System A   System B   System A + B

   Note that external forces on System A and System B are internal to System A+B, so they cancel!

   a. Upon collision, the momentum of System A   [increases] [decreases] [remains unchanged].

   b. Upon collision, the momentum of System B   [increases] [decreases] [remains unchanged].

   c. Upon collision, the momentum of System A + B [increases] [decreases] [remains unchanged].

3.a. A girl jumps upward. In the left sketch, draw a closed dashed line to indicate the system of the girl.
     Is there an external force acting on her?   [Y] [N]

     Does her momentum change?   [Y] [N]

     Is the girl's momentum conserved?   [Y] [N]

   b. In the right sketch, draw a closed dashed line to indicate the system (girl + Earth). Is there an external force acting on the system due to the interaction between the girl and Earth?
                                                       [Y] [N]

4. A block strikes a blob of jelly. Isolate 3 systems with a closed dashed line and show the external force on each. In which system is momentum conserved?

5. A truck crashes into a wall. Isolate 3 systems with a closed dashed line and show the external force on each. In which system is momentum conserved?

MOMENTUM TRANSFER   MOMENTUM TRANSFER   MOMENTUM TRANSFER

thanx to Cedric Linder

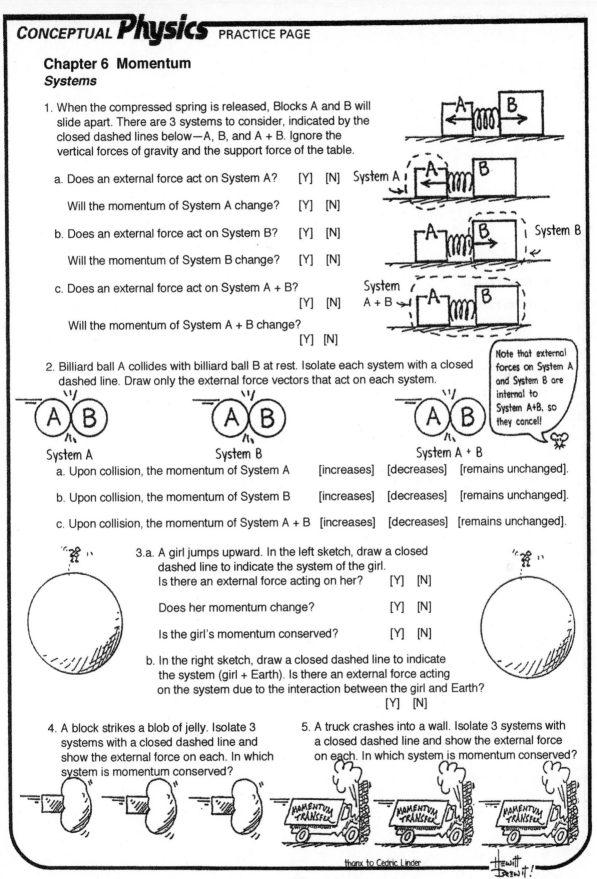

33

Name _____ Date _____

Chapter 7 Energy
Work and Energy

1. How much work (energy) is needed to lift an object that weighs 200 N to a height of 4 meters?

_____

2. How much power is needed to lift the 200-N object to a height of 4 m in 4 seconds? _____

3. What is the power output of an engine that does 60,000 J of work in 10 seconds? _____

4. The block of ice weighs 500 newtons. (Neglect friction.)

   a. How much force parallel to the incline is needed to push it to the top? _____

   b. How much work is required to push it to the top of the incline? _____

   c. What is the potential energy of the block relative to ground level? _____

   d. What would be the potential energy if the block were simply lifted vertically 3 m? _____

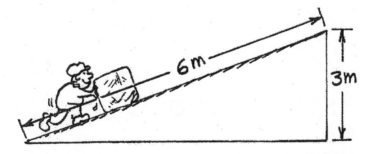

5. All the ramps below are 5 meters high. We know that the KE of the block at the bottom of each ramp will be equal to the loss of PE (conservation of energy).
   Find the speed of the block at ground level in each case. (Hint: Do you recall from earlier chapters how much time it takes something to fall a vertical distance of 5 m from a position of rest assuming $g = 10$ m/s^2 and how much speed a falling object acquires in this time?) This gives you the answer to Case 1.
   Discuss with your classmates how energy conservation provides the answers to Cases 2 and 3.

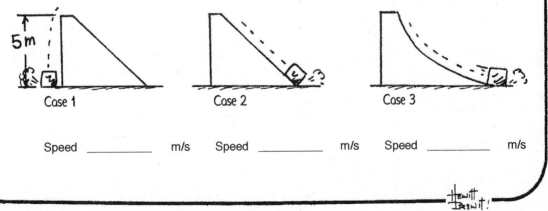

| Case 1 | Case 2 | Case 3 |

Speed _____ m/s   Speed _____ m/s   Speed _____ m/s

35

Chapter 7 Energy
Work and Energy—continued

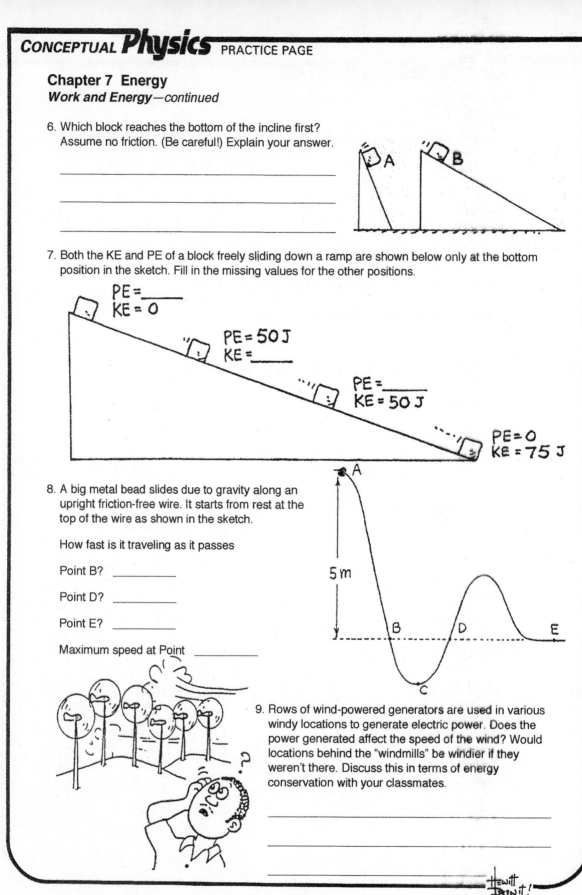

6. Which block reaches the bottom of the incline first? Assume no friction. (Be careful!) Explain your answer.

_____

_____

_____

7. Both the KE and PE of a block freely sliding down a ramp are shown below only at the bottom position in the sketch. Fill in the missing values for the other positions.

PE = _____
KE = 0

PE = 50 J
KE = _____

PE = _____
KE = 50 J

PE = 0
KE = 75 J

8. A big metal bead slides due to gravity along an upright friction-free wire. It starts from rest at the top of the wire as shown in the sketch.

   How fast is it traveling as it passes

   Point B? _____

   Point D? _____

   Point E? _____

   Maximum speed at Point _____

   5 m

9. Rows of wind-powered generators are used in various windy locations to generate electric power. Does the power generated affect the speed of the wind? Would locations behind the "windmills" be windier if they weren't there. Discuss this in terms of energy conservation with your classmates.

_____

_____

_____

CONCEPTUAL *Physics* PRACTICE PAGE

Chapter 7 Energy
Conservation of Energy

1. Fill in the blanks for the six systems.

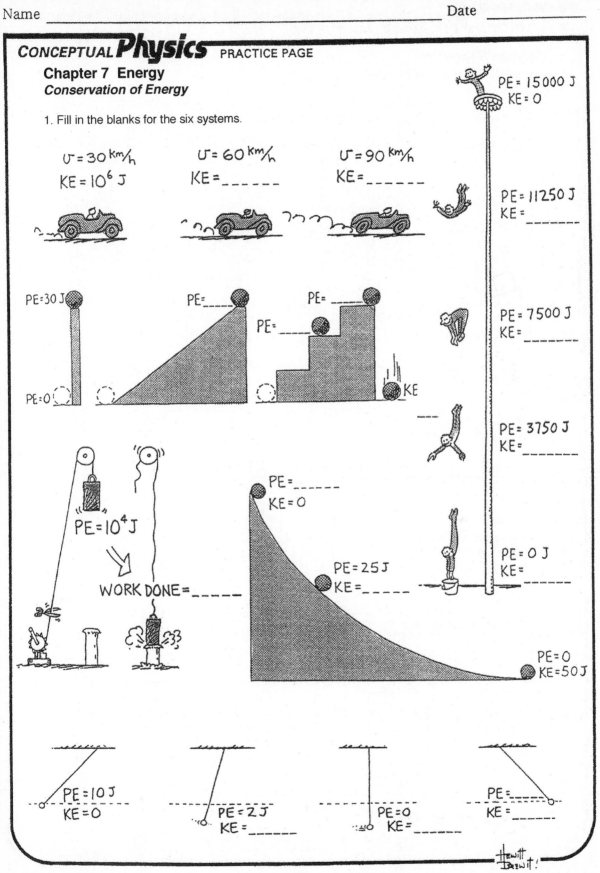

$v = 30 \frac{km}{h}$
$KE = 10^6$ J

$v = 60 \frac{km}{h}$
$KE = _____$

$v = 90 \frac{km}{h}$
$KE = _____$

PE = 15000 J
KE = 0

PE = 11250 J
KE = _____

PE = 7500 J
KE = _____

PE = 3750 J
KE = _____

PE = 0 J
KE = _____

PE = 30 J

PE = _____

PE = _____

PE = _____

PE = 0

KE

PE = 10⁴ J → $PE = 10^4$ J

WORK DONE = _____

PE = _____
KE = 0

PE = 25 J
KE = _____

PE = 0
KE = 50 J

PE = 10 J
KE = 0

PE = 2 J
KE = _____

PE = 0
KE = _____

PE = _____
KE = _____

37

Chapter 7 Energy
Conservation of Energy—continued

2. The woman supports a 100-N load with the friction-free pulley systems shown below. Fill in the spring-scale readings that show how much force she must exert.

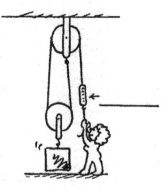

3. A 600-N block is lifted by the friction-free pulley system shown.

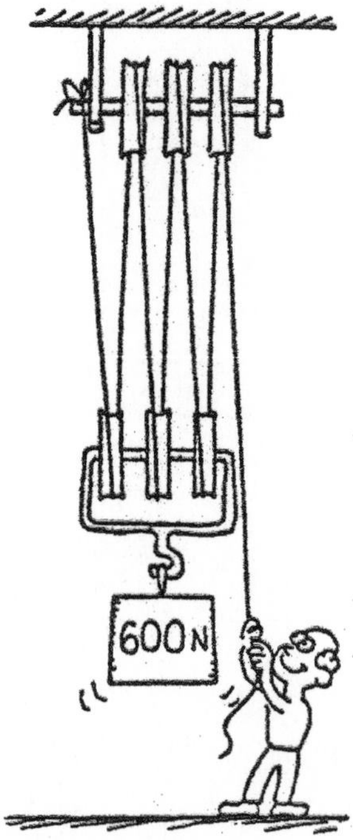

  a. How many strands of rope support the 600-N weight?

    _____

  b. What is the tension in each strand?

    _____

  c. What is the tension in the end held by the man?

    _____

  d. If the man pulls his end down 60 cm, how many cm will the weight rise?

    _____

  e. If the man does 60 joules of work, what will be the increase of PE of the 600-N weight?

    _____

4. Why don't balls bounce as high during the second bounce as they do in the first bounce?

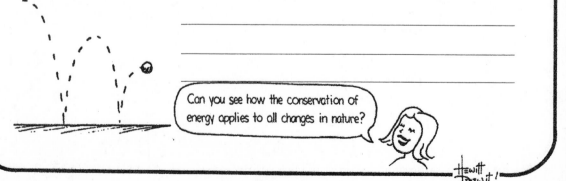

    _____

    _____

    _____

Can you see how the conservation of energy applies to all changes in nature?

CONCEPTUAL *Physics* PRACTICE PAGE

Chapter 7 Energy
Momentum and Energy

Bronco Brown wants to put $Ft = \Delta\,mv$ to the test and try bungee jumping. Bronco leaps from a high cliff and experiences 3 s of free fall. Then the bungee cord begins to stretch, reducing his speed to zero in 2 s. Fortunately, the cord stretches to its maximum length just short of the ground below.

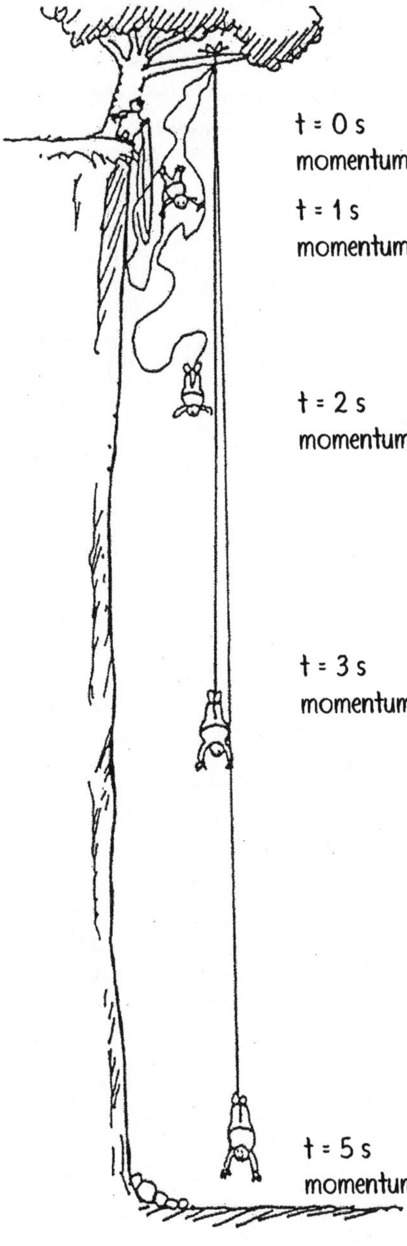

$t = 0$ s $v =$ _____
momentum = _____

Fill in the blanks:
Bronco's mass is 100 kg.
Acceleration of free fall is 10 m/s².

$t = 1$ s $v =$ _____
momentum = _____

Express values in SI units (*distance* in m, *velocity* in m/s, *momentum* in kg•m/s, *impulse* in N•s, and *deceleration* in m/s²).

$t = 2$ s $v =$ _____
momentum = _____

The 3-s free-fall distance of Bronco just before the bungee cord begins to stretch
= _____

$\Delta\,mv$ during the 3 to 5-s interval of free fall
= _____

$t = 3$ s $v =$ _____
momentum = _____

$\Delta\,mv$ during the 3 to 5-s of slowing down
= _____

Impulse during the 3 to 5-s of slowing down
= _____

Average force exerted by the cord during the 3 to 5-s interval of slowing down
= _____

How about *work* and *energy*? How much KE does Bronco have 3 s after he first jumps?

_____

$t = 5$ s $v =$ _____
momentum = _____

How much does gravitational PE decrease during this 3 s?

_____

What two kinds of PE are changing during the 3 to 5-s slowing-down interval?

_____

_____

Chapter 7 Energy
Energy and Momentum

A MiniCooper and a Lincoln Town Car are initially at rest on a horizontal parking lot at the edge of a steep cliff. For simplicity, we assume that the Town Car has twice as much mass as the MiniCooper. Equal constant forces are applied to each car and they accelerate across equal distances (we ignore the effects of friction). When they reach the far end of the lot, the force is suddenly removed, whereupon they sail through the air and crash to the ground below. (The cars are wrecks to begin with, and this is a scientific experiment!)

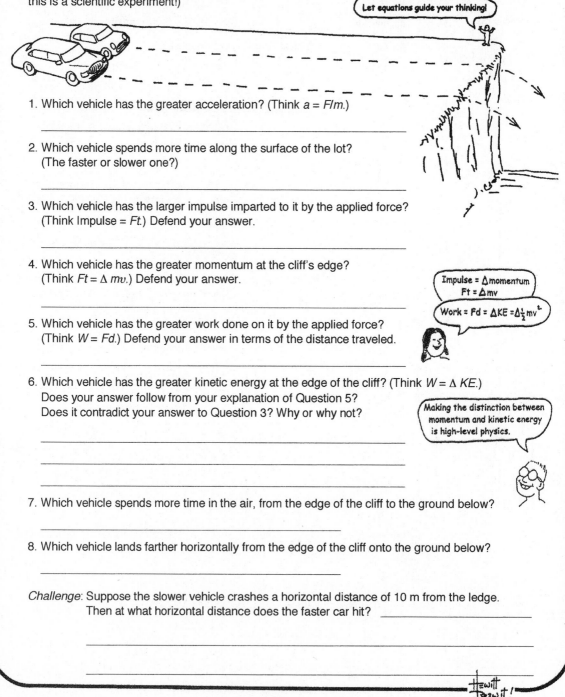

Let equations guide your thinking!

1. Which vehicle has the greater acceleration? (Think $a = F/m$.)

_____

2. Which vehicle spends more time along the surface of the lot?
   (The faster or slower one?)

_____

3. Which vehicle has the larger impulse imparted to it by the applied force?
   (Think Impulse = Ft.) Defend your answer.

_____

4. Which vehicle has the greater momentum at the cliff's edge?
   (Think $Ft = \Delta mv$.) Defend your answer.

_____

Impulse = Δ momentum
$Ft = \Delta mv$

Work = Fd = $\Delta KE = \Delta \frac{1}{2}mv^2$

5. Which vehicle has the greater work done on it by the applied force?
   (Think $W = Fd$.) Defend your answer in terms of the distance traveled.

_____

6. Which vehicle has the greater kinetic energy at the edge of the cliff? (Think $W = \Delta KE$.)
   Does your answer follow from your explanation of Question 5?
   Does it contradict your answer to Question 3? Why or why not?

_____

_____

Making the distinction between momentum and kinetic energy is high-level physics.

7. Which vehicle spends more time in the air, from the edge of the cliff to the ground below?

_____

8. Which vehicle lands farther horizontally from the edge of the cliff onto the ground below?

_____

Challenge: Suppose the slower vehicle crashes a horizontal distance of 10 m from the ledge.
   Then at what horizontal distance does the faster car hit? _____

_____

_____

CONCEPTUAL **Physics** PRACTICE PAGE

Chapter 8 Rotational Motion
Torques

1. Apply what you know about torques by making a mobile. Shown below are five horizontal arms with fixed 1- and 2-kg masses attached, and four hangers with ends that fit in the loops of the arms, lettered *A* through *R*. You are to determine where the loops should be attached so that when the whole system is suspended from the spring scale at the top, it will hang as a proper mobile, with its arms suspended horizontally. This is best done by working from the bottom upward. Circle the loops where the hangers should be attached. When the mobile is complete, how many kilograms will be indicated on the scale? (Assume the horizontal struts and connecting hooks are practically massless compared with the 1- and 2-kg masses.) On a separate sheet of paper, make a sketch of your completed mobile.

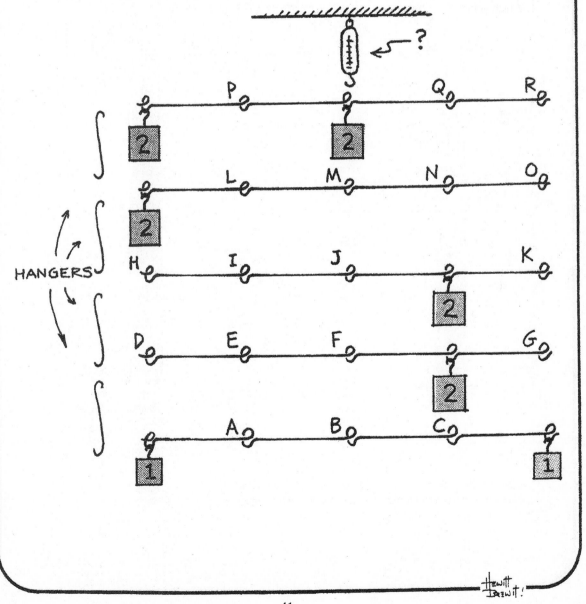

Chapter 8 Rotational Motion
Torques—continued

2. Complete the data for the three seesaws in equilibrium.

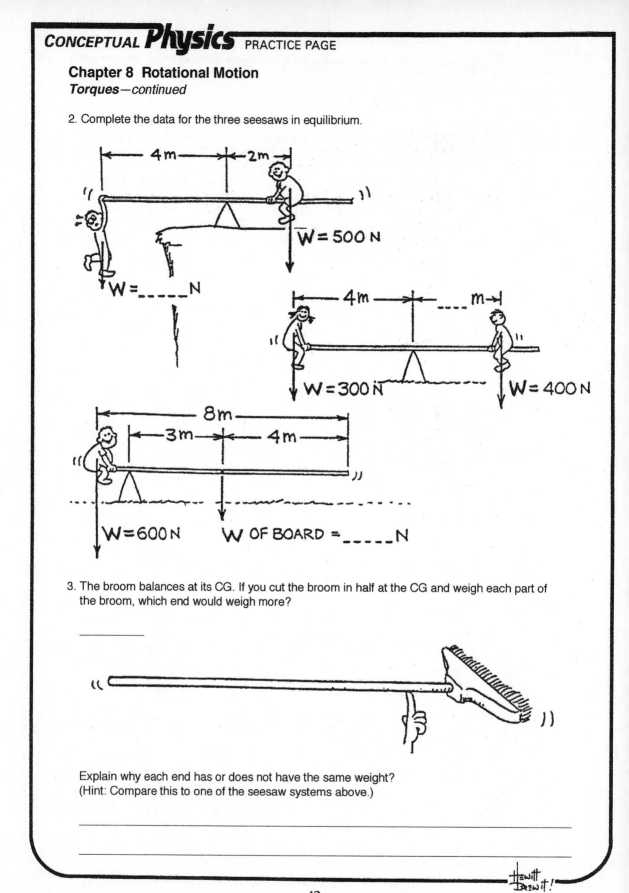

|←——— 4 m ———→|←— 2 m —→|

W = 500 N

W = _____ N

|←——— 4 m ———→|←— _____ m —→|

W = 300 N   W = 400 N

|←——————— 8 m ———————→|

|←— 3 m —→|←—— 4 m ——→|

W = 600 N   W OF BOARD = _____ N

3. The broom balances at its CG. If you cut the broom in half at the CG and weigh each part of the broom, which end would weigh more?

_____

Explain why each end has or does not have the same weight?
(Hint: Compare this to one of the seesaw systems above.)

_____

_____

Name _____   Date _____

Chapter 8 Rotational Motion
Torques and Rotation

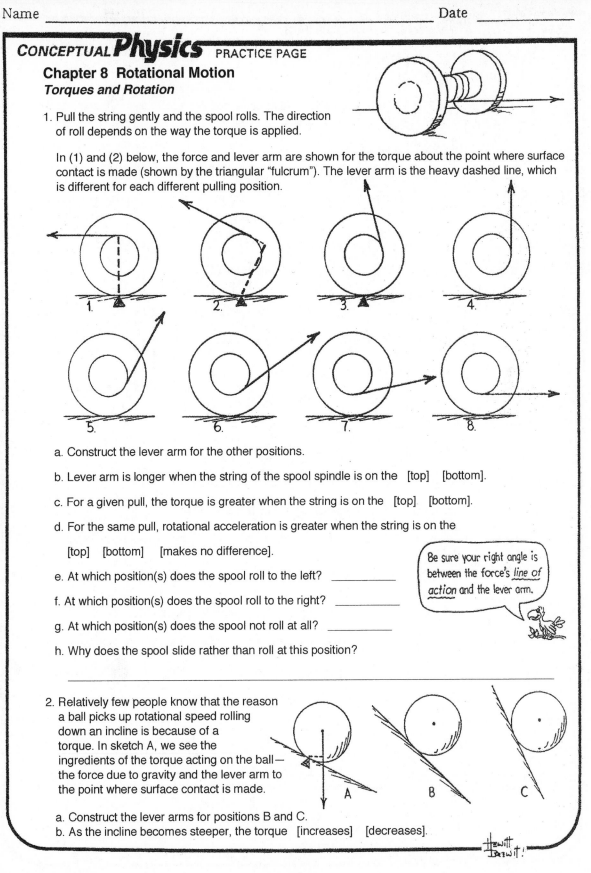

1. Pull the string gently and the spool rolls. The direction
   of roll depends on the way the torque is applied.

   In (1) and (2) below, the force and lever arm are shown for the torque about the point where surface
   contact is made (shown by the triangular "fulcrum"). The lever arm is the heavy dashed line, which
   is different for each different pulling position.

   a. Construct the lever arm for the other positions.

   b. Lever arm is longer when the string of the spool spindle is on the   [top]   [bottom].

   c. For a given pull, the torque is greater when the string is on the   [top]   [bottom].

   d. For the same pull, rotational acceleration is greater when the string is on the

      [top]   [bottom]   [makes no difference].

   e. At which position(s) does the spool roll to the left?   _____

   f. At which position(s) does the spool roll to the right?   _____

   g. At which position(s) does the spool not roll at all?   _____

   h. Why does the spool slide rather than roll at this position?

   _____

   Be sure your right angle is
   between the force's *line of
   action* and the lever arm.

2. Relatively few people know that the reason
   a ball picks up rotational speed rolling
   down an incline is because of a
   torque. In sketch A, we see the
   ingredients of the torque acting on the ball—
   the force due to gravity and the lever arm to
   the point where surface contact is made.

   A   B   C

   a. Construct the lever arms for positions B and C.
   b. As the incline becomes steeper, the torque   [increases]   [decreases].

Chapter 8 Rotational Motion
Acceleration and Circular Motion

Newton's 2nd law, $a = F/m$, tells us that net force and its corresponding acceleration are always in the same direction. But force and acceleration vectors are not always in the direction of velocity (another vector).

1. You're in a car at a traffic light. The light turns green and the driver "steps on the gas."
   The sketch shows the top view of the car. Note the direction of the velocity and acceleration vectors.

   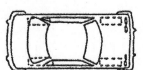

   a. Your body tends to lurch   [forward]   [not at all]   [backward].

   b. The car accelerates   [forward]   [not at all]   [backward].

   c. The force on the car acts   [forward]   [not at all]   [backward].

2. You're driving along and approach a stop sign. The driver steps on the brakes.
   The sketch shows the top view of the car. Draw vectors for velocity and acceleration.

   a. Your body tends to lurch   [forward]   [not at all]   [backward].

   b. The car accelerates   [forward]   [not at all]   [backward].

3. You continue driving, and round a sharp curve to the left at

   constant speed.

   a. Your body tends to lean   [inward]   [not at all]   [outward].

   b. The direction of the car's acceleration is   [inward]   [not at all]   [outward].

   c. The force on the car acts   [inward]   [not at all]   [outward].

   Draw vectors for velocity and acceleration of the car.

4. In general, the directions of lurch and acceleration, and therefore
   the directions of lurch and force are   [the same]   [not relate]   [opposite].

5. The whirling stone's direction of motion keeps changing.

   a. If it moves faster, its direction changes   [faster]   [slower].

   b. This indicates that as speed increases, acceleration

   [increases]   [decreases]   [stays the same].

5. Like Question 4, consider whirling the stone on a shorter string—that is, of smaller radius.

   a. For a given speed, the rate that the stone changes direction is   [less]   [more]   [the same].

   b. This indicates that as the radius decreases, acceleration

   [increases]   [decreases]   [stays the same].

thanx to Jim Harper

CONCEPTUAL **Physics** PRACTICE PAGE

Chapter 8 Rotational Motion
The Flying Pig

The toy pig flies in a circle at constant speed. This arrangement is called a conical pendulum because the supporting string sweeps out a cone. Neglecting the action of its flapping wings, only two forces act on the pig—gravitational *mg*, and string tension *T*.

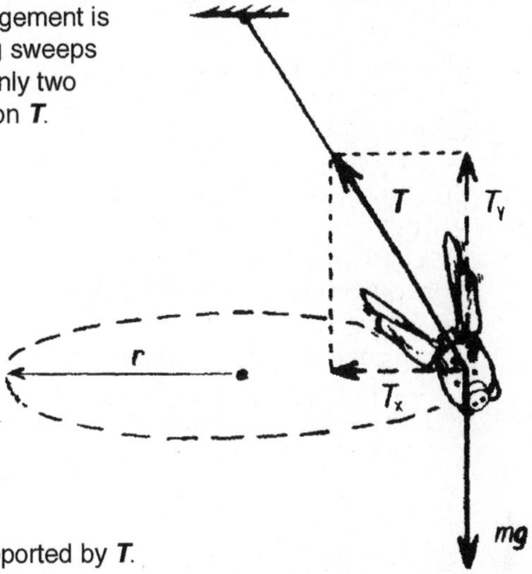

Vector Component Analysis:
Note that vector ***T*** can be resolved into two components—horizontal T_x, and vertical T_y. These vector components are dashed to distinguish them from the tension vector ***T***.

Circle the correct answers:
1. If ***T*** were somehow replaced with T_x and T_y the pig

   [would]   [would not]   behave identically to being supported by ***T***.

2. Since the pig doesn't accelerate vertically, compared with the magnitude of *mg*, component T_y,

   must be   [greater]   [less]   [equal and opposite].

3. The velocity of the pig at any instant is   [along the radius of]   [tangent to]   its circular path.

4. Since the pig continues in circular motion, component T_x must be a

   [centripetal]   [centrifugal]   [nonexistent]   force, which equals   [zero]   [mv^2/r].

   Furthermore, T_x is   [along the radius]   [tangent to]   the circle swept out.

Vector Resultant Analysis:
5. Rather than resolving ***T*** into horizontal and vertical components, use your pencil to sketch the resultant of *mg* and ***T*** using the *parallelogram rule*.

6. The resultant lies in a   [horizontal]   [vertical]

   direction, and   [toward]   [away from]   the

   center of the circular path. The resultant of *mg*

   and ***T*** is a   [centripetal]   [centrifugal]   force.

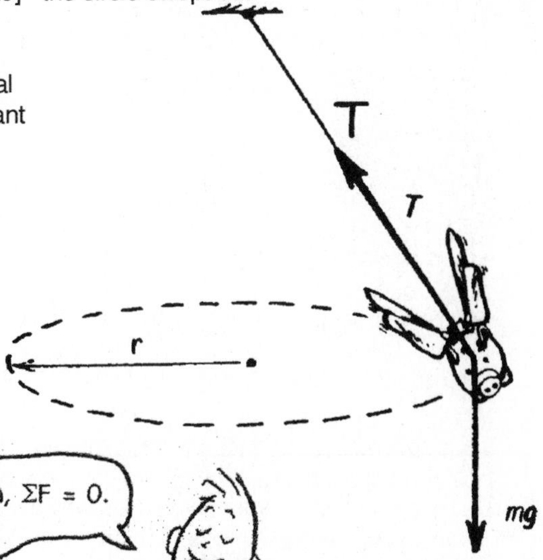

> For straight-line motion with no acceleration, $\Sigma F = 0$.
> But for uniform circular motion, $\Sigma F = mv^2/r$.

thanx to Pablo Robinson and Miss Piggy

Chapter 8 Rotational Motion
Banked Airplanes

An airplane banks as it turns along a horizontal circular path in the air. Except for the thrust of its engines and air resistance, the two significant forces on the plane are gravitational mg (vertical), and lift L (perpendicular to the wings).

Vector Component Analysis:
With a ruler and a pencil, resolve vector L into two perpendicular components, horizontal L_x, and vertical L_y. Make these vectors dashed to distinguish them from L.

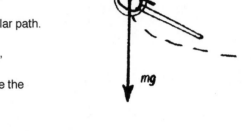

Circle the correct answers:
1. The velocity of the airplane at any instant is

   [along the radius of]   [tangent to]   its circular path.

2. If L were somehow replaced with L_x and L_y,

   the airplane   [would]   [would not]   behave the

   same as being supported by L.

3. Since the airplane doesn't accelerate vertically, component L_y must be

   [greater than]   [less than]   [equal and opposite to] mg.

4. Since the plane continues in circular motion, component L_x must equal   [zero]   [mv^2/r]   , and be a

   [centripetal]   [centrifugal]   [nonexistent]   force. Furthermore, L_x is

   [along the radius of]   [tangent to]   the circular path.

Vector Resultant Analysis:
5. Rather than resolving L into horizontal and vertical components, use your pencil to sketch the resultant of mg and L using the *parallelogram rule*.

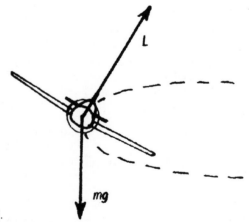

6. The resultant lies in a   [horizontal]   [vertical]

   direction, and   [toward]   [away from]   the center

   of the circular path. The resultant of mg and L is a

   [centripetal]   [centrifugal]   force.

7. The resultant of mg and L is the same as   [L_x]   [L_y].

Challenge: Explain in your own words why the resultant of two vectors can be the same as a single component of one of them.

_____

Chapter 8 Rotational Motion
Banked Track

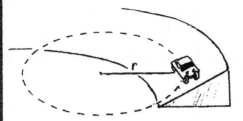

A car rounds a banked curve with just the right speed so that it has no tendency to slide down or up the banked road surface. Shown below are two main forces that act on the car perpendicular to its motion—gravitational mg and the normal force N (the support force of the surface).

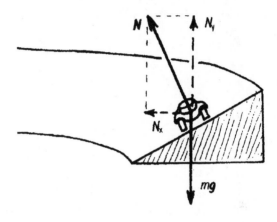

Vector Component Analysis:
Note that vector N is resolved into two perpendicular components, horizontal N_x, and vertical N_y. As usual, these vectors are dashed to distinguish them from N.

Circle the correct answers:

1. If N were somehow replaced with

   N_x and N_y, the car   [would]   [would not]

   behave identically to being supported by N.

2. Since the car doesn't accelerate vertically, component N_y must be

   [greater than]   [equal and opposite to]   [less than] mg.

3. The velocity of the car at any instant is   [along the radius of]   [tangent to]   its circular path.

4. Since the car continues in uniform circular motion, component N_x must equal   [zero]   [mv^2/r]

   and be a   [centripetal]   [centrifugal]   [nonexistent]   force. Furthermore, N_x

   [lies along the radius of]   [is tangent to]   the circular path.

Vector Resultant Analysis:

5. Rather than resolving N into horizontal and vertical components, use your pencil to sketch the resultant of mg and N using the *parallelogram rule*.

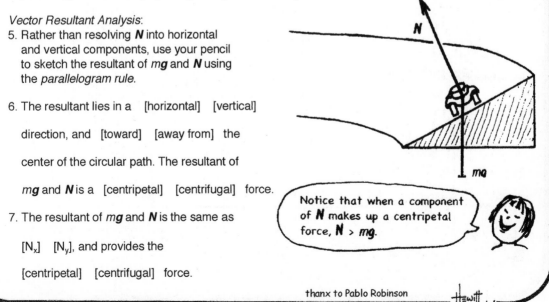

6. The resultant lies in a   [horizontal]   [vertical]

   direction, and   [toward]   [away from]   the

   center of the circular path. The resultant of

   mg and N is a   [centripetal]   [centrifugal]   force.

7. The resultant of mg and N is the same as

   [N_x]   [N_y], and provides the

   [centripetal]   [centrifugal]   force.

Notice that when a component of N makes up a centripetal force, $N > mg$.

thanx to Pablo Robinson

Hewitt Drew it!

Chapter 8 Circular and Rotational Motion
Leaning On

When turning a corner on a bicycle, everyone knows that you've got to lean "into the curve."
What is the physics of this leaning? It involves torque, friction, and centripetal force (mv^2/r).

First, consider the simple case of riding a bicycle along a straight-line path. Except
for the force that propels the bike forward (friction of the road in the direction of
motion) and air resistance (friction of air against the direction of motion), only two
significant forces act: weight *mg* and the normal force **N**. (The vectors are drawn
side-by-side, but actually lie along a single vertical line.)

Circle the correct answers:

1. Since there is no vertical acceleration, we can say that the magnitude of

   [**N** > *mg*]   [**N** < *mg*]   [**N** = *mg*],   which means that in the vertical direction,

   [$\Sigma F_y > 0$]   [$\Sigma F_y < 0$]   [$\Sigma F_y = 0$].

2. Since the bike doesn't rotate or change in its rotational state, then the total

   torque is   [zero]   [not zero].

Now consider the same bike rounding a corner. In order to safely make the turn, the bicyclist leans
in the direction of the turn. A force of friction pushes sideways on the tire toward the center of the curve.

3. The friction force, *f*, provides the centripetal force that produces a

   curved path. Then   [*f* = mv^2/r]   [*f* ≠ mv^2/r].

4. Consider the net torque about the center of mass (*CM*) of the
   bike-rider system. Gravity produces no torque about this point,
   but **N** and *f* do. The torque involving **N** tends to produce

   [clockwise]   [counterclockwise]   rotation, and the one involving *f*

   tends to produce   [clockwise]   [counterclockwise]   rotation.

   These torques cancel each other when the resultant of vectors
   N and *f* pass through the *CM*.

5. With your pencil, use the parallelogram rule and sketch in the
   resultant of vectors **N** and *f*. Label your resultant **R**. Note the **R**
   passes through the center of mass of the bike-rider system. That

   means that **R** produces   [a clockwise]   [a counterclockwise]   [no]

   torque about the *CM*. Therefore the bike-rider system

   [topples clockwise]   [topples counterclockwise]   [doesn't topple].

When learning how to turn on a bike, you lean so that the
sum of the torques about your CM is zero. You may not be
calculating torques, but your body learns to feel them.

thanx to Pablo Robinson

Name _____   Date _____

CONCEPTUAL **Physics** PRACTICE PAGE

Chapter 8 Rotational Motion
Simulated Gravity and Frames of Reference

Suzie Spacewalker and Bob Biker are in outer space. Bob
experiences Earth-normal gravity in a rotating habitat, where
centripetal force on his feet provides a normal support force
that feels like weight. Suzie hovers outside in a weightless
condition, motionless relative to the stars and the center of
the habitat.

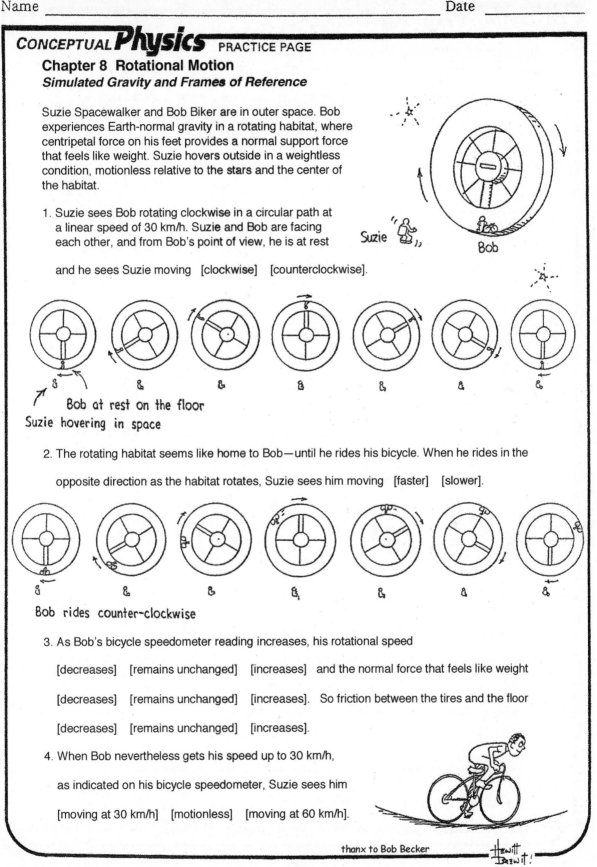

1. Suzie sees Bob rotating clockwise in a circular path at
   a linear speed of 30 km/h. Suzie and Bob are facing
   each other, and from Bob's point of view, he is at rest

   and he sees Suzie moving   [clockwise]   [counterclockwise].

Bob at rest on the floor

Suzie hovering in space

2. The rotating habitat seems like home to Bob—until he rides his bicycle. When he rides in the

   opposite direction as the habitat rotates, Suzie sees him moving   [faster]   [slower].

Bob rides counter-clockwise

3. As Bob's bicycle speedometer reading increases, his rotational speed

   [decreases]   [remains unchanged]   [increases]   and the normal force that feels like weight

   [decreases]   [remains unchanged]   [increases].   So friction between the tires and the floor

   [decreases]   [remains unchanged]   [increases].

4. When Bob nevertheless gets his speed up to 30 km/h,

   as indicated on his bicycle speedometer, Suzie sees him

   [moving at 30 km/h]   [motionless]   [moving at 60 km/h].

thanx to Bob Becker

49

Chapter 8 Rotational Motion
Simulated Gravity and Frames of Reference—continued

5. Bounding off the floor a bit while riding at 30 km/h, and neglecting wind effects, Bob

   [drifts toward the ceiling in midspace as the floor whizzes by him at 30 km/h]

   [falls as he would on Earth]

   [slams onto the floor with increased force]

   and finds himself

   [in the same frame of reference as Suzie]

   [as if he rode at 30 km/h on Earth's surface]

   [pressed harder against the bicyclist seat].

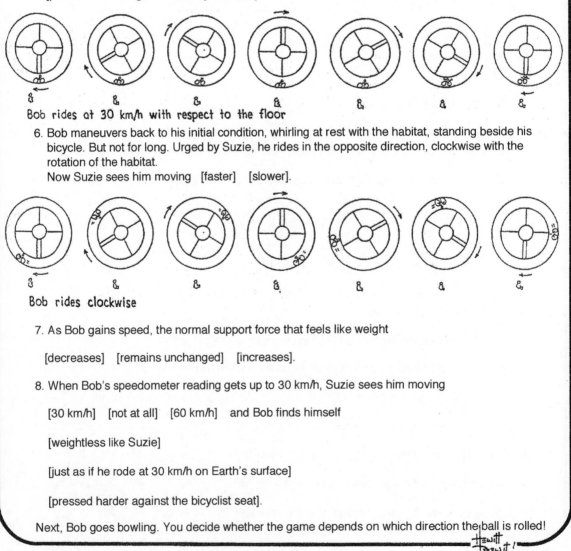

Bob rides at 30 km/h with respect to the floor

6. Bob maneuvers back to his initial condition, whirling at rest with the habitat, standing beside his bicycle. But not for long. Urged by Suzie, he rides in the opposite direction, clockwise with the rotation of the habitat.
   Now Suzie sees him moving [faster] [slower].

Bob rides clockwise

7. As Bob gains speed, the normal support force that feels like weight

   [decreases]   [remains unchanged]   [increases].

8. When Bob's speedometer reading gets up to 30 km/h, Suzie sees him moving

   [30 km/h]   [not at all]   [60 km/h]   and Bob finds himself

   [weightless like Suzie]

   [just as if he rode at 30 km/h on Earth's surface]

   [pressed harder against the bicyclist seat].

Next, Bob goes bowling. You decide whether the game depends on which direction the ball is rolled!

Name _____ Date _____

Chapter 9 Gravity
Inverse-Square Law

1. Paint spray travels radially away from the nozzle of the can in straight lines. Like gravity, the strength (intensity) of the spray obeys an inverse-square law. Complete the diagram by filling in the blank spaces.

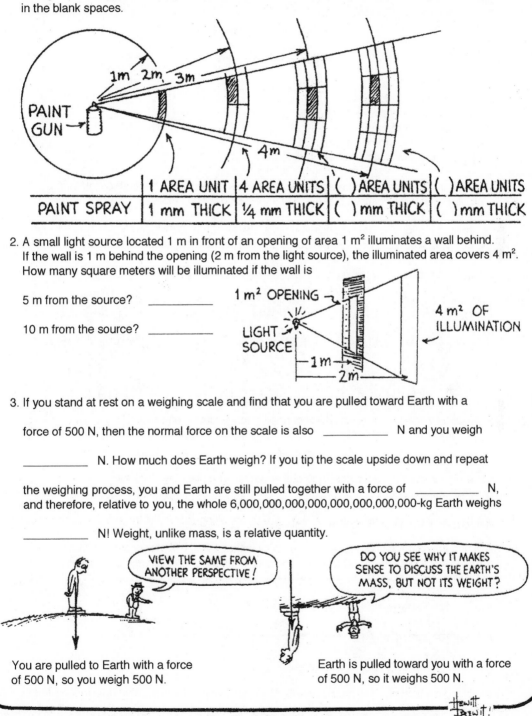

	1 AREA UNIT	4 AREA UNITS	( ) AREA UNITS	( ) AREA UNITS
PAINT SPRAY	1 mm THICK	¼ mm THICK	( ) mm THICK	( ) mm THICK

2. A small light source located 1 m in front of an opening of area 1 m² illuminates a wall behind. If the wall is 1 m behind the opening (2 m from the light source), the illuminated area covers 4 m². How many square meters will be illuminated if the wall is

   5 m from the source? _____

   10 m from the source? _____

   1 m² OPENING

   LIGHT SOURCE

   4 m² OF ILLUMINATION

   1 m

   2 m

3. If you stand at rest on a weighing scale and find that you are pulled toward Earth with a

   force of 500 N, then the normal force on the scale is also _____ N and you weigh

   _____ N. How much does Earth weigh? If you tip the scale upside down and repeat

   the weighing process, you and Earth are still pulled together with a force of _____ N, and therefore, relative to you, the whole 6,000,000,000,000,000,000,000,000-kg Earth weighs

   _____ N! Weight, unlike mass, is a relative quantity.

   VIEW THE SAME FROM ANOTHER PERSPECTIVE!

   DO YOU SEE WHY IT MAKES SENSE TO DISCUSS THE EARTH'S MASS, BUT NOT ITS WEIGHT?

   You are pulled to Earth with a force of 500 N, so you weigh 500 N.

   Earth is pulled toward you with a force of 500 N, so it weighs 500 N.

Chapter 9 Gravity
Inverse-Square Law—continued

4. The spaceship is attracted to both the planet and the planet's moon. The planet has four times the mass of its moon. The force of attraction of the spaceship to the planet is shown by the vector.

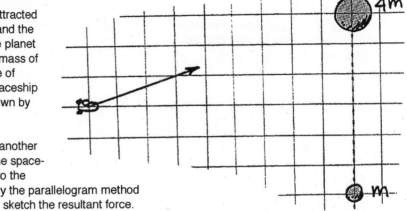

a. Carefully sketch another vector to show the space-ship's attraction to the moon. Then apply the parallelogram method of Chapter 3 and sketch the resultant force.

b. Determine the location between the planet and its moon (along the dotted line) where gravitational forces cancel. Make a sketch of the spaceship there.

5. Consider a planet of uniform density that has a straight tunnel from the North Pole through the center to the South Pole. At the surface of the planet, an object weighs 1 ton.

a. Fill in the gravitational force on the object when it is halfway to the center, then at the center.

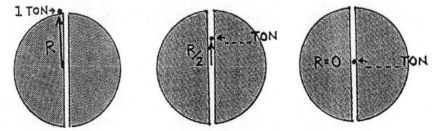

b. Describe the motion you would experience if you fell into the tunnel.

_____

6. Consider an object that weighs 1 ton at the surface of a planet, just before the planet gravitationally collapses.

a. Fill in the weights of the object on the planet's shrinking surface at the radial values shown.

b. When the planet has collapsed to 1/10 of its initial radius, a ladder is erected that puts the object as far from its center as the object was originally. Fill in its weight at this position.

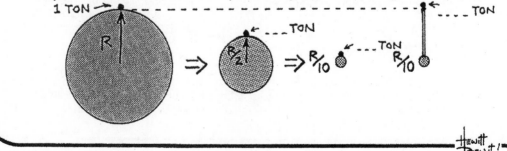

Name _____   Date _____

CONCEPTUAL **Physics** PRACTICE PAGE

Chapter 9 Gravity
Our Ocean Tides

1. Consider two equal-mass blobs of water, A and B, initially at rest in the Moon's gravitational field. The vector shows the gravitational force of the Moon on A.

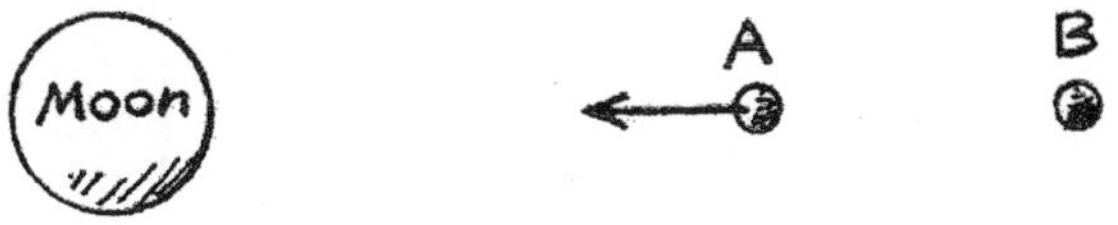

   a. Draw a force vector on B due to the Moon's gravity.

   b. Is the force on B more or less than the force on A? _____

   c. Why? _____

   d. The blobs accelerate toward the Moon. Which has the greater acceleration?   [A]   [B]

   e. Because of the different accelerations, with time

      [A gets farther ahead of B]   [A and B gain identical speeds]   and the distance between A and B

      [increases]   [stays the same]   [decreases].

   f. If A and B were connected by a rubber band, with time the rubber band would

      [stretch]   [not stretch].

   g. This   [stretching]   [nonstretching]   is due to the   [difference]   [nondifference] in the Moon's gravitational pulls.

   h. The two blobs will eventually crash into the Moon. To orbit around the Moon instead of crashing into it, the blobs should move

      [away from the Moon]   [tangentially].   Then their accelerations will consist of changes in

      [speed]   [direction].

2. Now consider the same two blobs located on opposite sides of Earth.

   a. Because of difference in the Moon's pull on the blobs,

      they tend to   [spread away from each other]   [approach each other].

   b. Does this spreading produce ocean tides?   [Yes]   [No]

   c. If Earth and Moon were closer, gravitational force between them would be

      [more]   [the same]   [less], and the difference in gravitational forces on the near and far parts

      of the ocean would be   [more]   [the same]   [less].

   d. Because Earth's orbit about the Sun is slightly elliptical, Earth and Sun are closer in December than in June. Taking the Sun's tidal force into account, on a world average, ocean tides are

      greater in   [December]   [June]   [no difference].

53

CONCEPTUAL Physics PRACTICE PAGE

Chapter 10 Projectile and Satellite Motion
Independence of Horizontal and Vertical Components of Motion

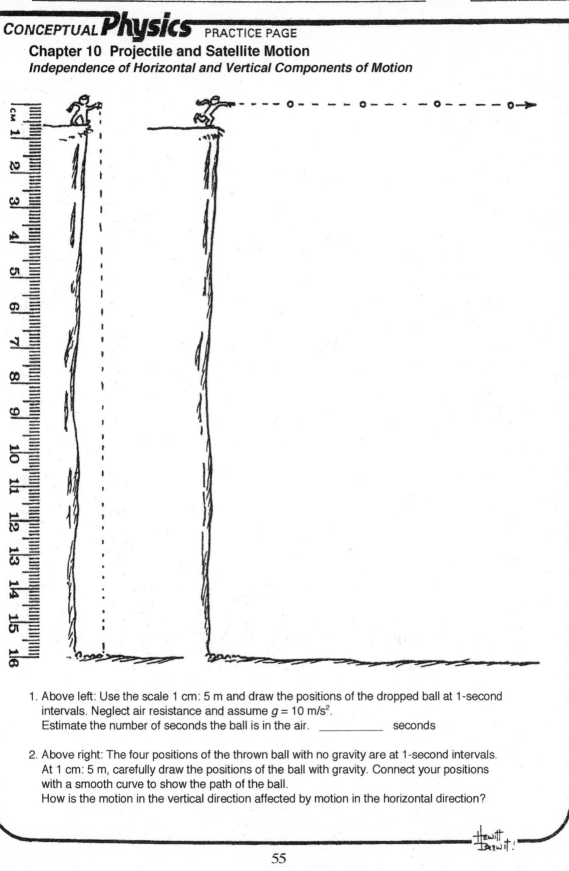

1. Above left: Use the scale 1 cm: 5 m and draw the positions of the dropped ball at 1-second intervals. Neglect air resistance and assume $g = 10$ m/s^2.
   Estimate the number of seconds the ball is in the air. _____ seconds

2. Above right: The four positions of the thrown ball with no gravity are at 1-second intervals. At 1 cm: 5 m, carefully draw the positions of the ball with gravity. Connect your positions with a smooth curve to show the path of the ball.
   How is the motion in the vertical direction affected by motion in the horizontal direction?

Chapter 10 Projectile and Satellite Motion
Independence of Horizontal and Vertical Components of Motion—continued

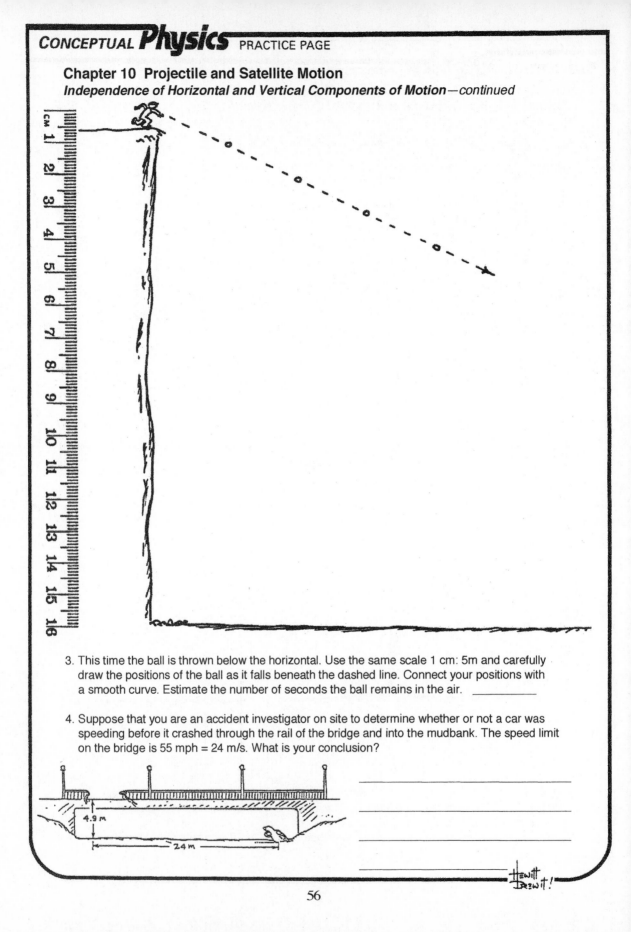

3. This time the ball is thrown below the horizontal. Use the same scale 1 cm: 5m and carefully draw the positions of the ball as it falls beneath the dashed line. Connect your positions with a smooth curve. Estimate the number of seconds the ball remains in the air. _____

4. Suppose that you are an accident investigator on site to determine whether or not a car was speeding before it crashed through the rail of the bridge and into the mudbank. The speed limit on the bridge is 55 mph = 24 m/s. What is your conclusion?

4.9 m

24 m

CONCEPTUAL *Physics* PRACTICE PAGE

Chapter 10 Projectile and Satellite Motion
Tossed Ball

A ball tossed upward has initial velocity components 30 m/s vertical, and 5 m/s horizontal. The location of the ball is shown at 1-second intervals. Air resistance is negligible, and $g = 10$ m/s^2. Write the values in the boxes for ascending velocity components, and your calculated resultant descending velocities.

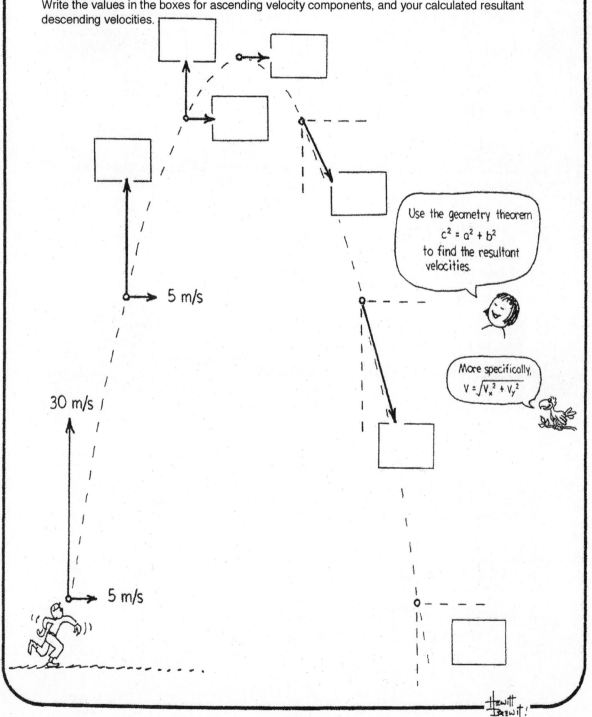

Use the geometry theorem
$$c^2 = a^2 + b^2$$
to find the resultant velocities.

More specifically,
$$V = \sqrt{V_x^2 + V_y^2}$$

5 m/s

30 m/s

5 m/s

CONCEPTUAL **Physics** PRACTICE PAGE

Chapter 10 Projectile and Satellite Motion
Satellite in Circular Orbit

1. Figure A shows "Newton's Mountain," so high that its top is above the drag of the atmosphere. The cannonball is fired and hits the ground.

   a. Draw a likely path that the cannonball might take if it were fired a little bit faster.

   b. Repeat for a still greater speed, but less than 8 km/s.

   c. Then draw its orbital path for a speed of 8 km/s.

   d. What is the shape of the 8-km/s curve?

   _____

Figure A

   e. What would be the shape of the orbital path if the cannonball were fired at a speed of 9 km/s?

   _____

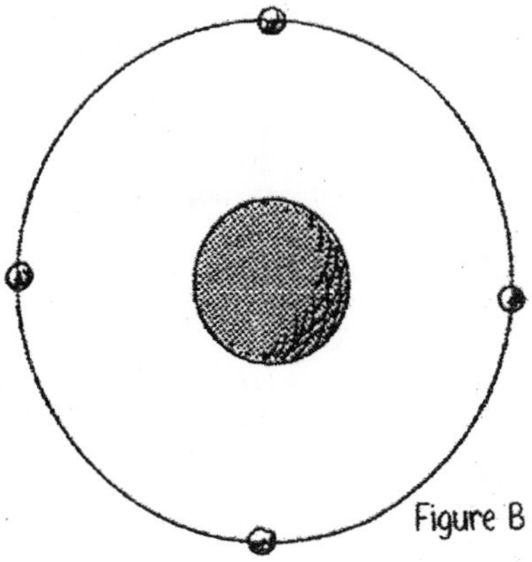

2. Figure B shows a satellite in circular orbit.

   a. At each of the four positions, draw a vector that represents the gravitational *force* exerted on the satellite.

   b. Label the force vectors *F*.

   c. Then draw a vector at each location to represent the v*elocity* of the satellite, and label it *V*.

   d. Are all four *F* vectors the same length? Why or why not?

   _____

Figure B

   e. Are all four *V* vectors the same length? Why or why not?

   _____

   f. What is the angle between your *F* and *V* vectors? _____

   g. Is there any component of *F* parallel to *V*? _____

   h. What does this indicate about the work the force of gravity can do on the satellite?

   _____

   i. Does the KE of the satellite in Figure B remain constant or does it vary? _____

   j. Does the PE of the satellite remain constant or does it vary? _____

Chapter 10 Projectile and Satellite Motion
Satellite in Elliptical Orbit

3. Repeat the procedure you used for the circular orbit, drawing vectors **F** and **V** for each position in Figure C, including proper labeling. Show greater magnitudes with greater lengths. Don't bother making the scale accurate.

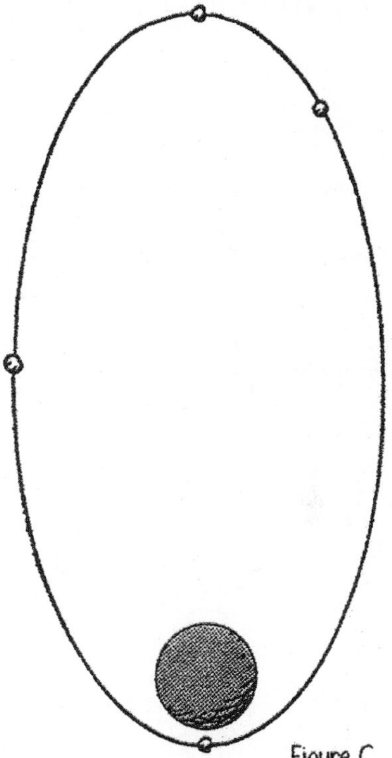

a. Are your vectors **F** all the same magnitude? Why or why not?

_____

_____

b. Are your vectors **V** all the same magnitude? Why or why not?

_____

_____

c. Is the angle between vectors **F** and **V** everywhere the same, or does it vary?

_____

_____

d. Are there places where there is a component of **F** parallel to **V**?

_____

_____

Figure C

e. Is work done on the satellite where there is a component of **F** parallel to **V**? If so, does this change the KE of the satellite?

_____

f. Where there is a component of **F** parallel to or in the direction of **V**, does this increase or decrease the KE of the satellite?

_____

_____

Be very very careful when placing both velocity and force vectors on the same diagram. Not a good practice. for one may construct the resultant of the vectors— ouch!

g. What can you say about the sum of KE + PE along the orbit?

_____

_____

CONCEPTUAL *Physics* PRACTICE PAGE

Mechanics Overview—Chapters 1 to 10

1. The sketch shows the elliptical path described by a satellite about Earth. In which of the labeled positions, A - D, (place an "S" for "same everywhere") does the satellite experience the maximum

   a. gravitational force?　　　　　　 _____

   b. speed?　　　　　　　　　　　 _____

   c. momentum?　　　　　　　　　 _____

   d. kinetic energy?　　　　　　　　 _____

   e. gravitational potential energy? _____

   f. total energy (KE + PE)?　　　　 _____

   g. acceleration?　　　　　　　　　 _____

   h. angular momentum?　　　　　　 _____

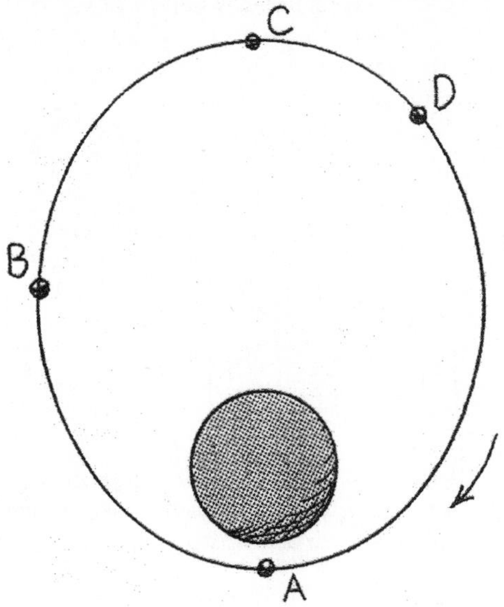

2. Answer the above questions for a satellite in circular orbit.

   a. _____ b. _____ c. _____ d. _____

   e. _____ f. _____ g. _____ h. _____

3. In which position(s) is there momentarily no work being done on the satellite by the force of gravity? Why?

   _____

4. Work changes energy. Let the equation for work, $W = Fd$, guide your thinking on the following: Defend your answers in terms of $W = Fd$.

   a. In which position will a several-minutes thrust of rocket engines pushing the satellite forward do the most work on the satellite and give it the greatest change in kinetic energy?
   (Hint: Think about where the most distance will be traveled during the application of a several-minutes thrust?)

   _____

   b. In which position will a several-minutes thrust of rocket engines pushing the satellite forward do the least work on the satellite and give it the least boost in kinetic energy?

   _____

   c. In which position will a several-minutes thrust of a retro-rocket (pushing opposite to the satellite's direction of motion) do the most work on the satellite and change its kinetic energy the most?

   _____

CONCEPTUAL *Physics* PRACTICE PAGE

Chapter 11 The Atomic Nature of Matter
Atoms and Atomic Nuclei

> ATOMS ARE CLASSIFIED BY THEIR ATOMIC NUMBER, WHICH IS THE SAME AS THE NUMBER OF _____ IN THE NUCLEUS.

> TO CHANGE THE ATOMS OF ONE ELEMENT INTO THOSE OF ANOTHER, _____ MUST BE ADDED OR SUBTRACTED !

Use the periodic table in your text to help you answer the following questions.

1. When the atomic nuclei of hydrogen and lithium are squashed together (nuclear fusion) the element that is produced is

   _____

2. When the atomic nuclei of a pair of lithium nuclei are fused, the element produced is

   _____

3. When the atomic nuclei of a pair of aluminum nuclei are fused, the element produced is

   _____

4. When the nucleus of a nitrogen atom absorbs a proton, the resulting element is

   _____

5. What element is produced when a gold nucleus gains a proton?   _____

6. What element is produced when a gold nucleus loses a proton?   _____

7. What element is produced when a uranium nucleus ejects an elementary particle composed of two protons and two neutrons?

   _____

8. If a uranium nucleus breaks into two pieces (nuclear fission) and one of the pieces is zirconium (atomic number 40), the other piece is the element

   _____

9. Which has more mass, a nitrogen molecule (N_2) or an oxygen molecule (O_2)?

   _____

> I LIKE THE WAY YOUR ATOMS ARE PUT TOGETHER !

> ÷SIGH÷

10. Which has the greater number of atoms, a gram of helium or a gram of neon?

    _____

Chapter 11 The Atomic Nature of Matter
Subatomic Particles

Three fundamental particles of the atom are the _____ , _____ , and

_____ . At the center of each atom lies the atomic _____ which

consists of _____ and _____ . The atomic number refers to

the number of _____ in the nucleus. All atoms of the same element have the same

number of _____ , hence, the same atomic number.

Isotopes are atoms that have the same number of _____ but a different number of

_____ . An isotope is identified by its atomic mass number, which is the total number

of _____ and _____ in the nucleus. A carbon isotope that has

6 _____ and _____ is identified as carbon-12, where 12 is the atomic

mass number. A carbon isotope having 6 _____ and 8 _____ , on the
other hand is carbon-14.

1. *Complete the following table*:

ISOTOPE	ELECTRONS	NUMBER OF PROTONS	NEUTRONS
Hydrogen-1	1		
Chlorine-36		17	
Nitrogen-14			7
Potassium-40	19		
Arsenic-75		33	
Gold-197			118

2. Which results in a more valuable product—
   adding or *subtracting* protons from gold nuclei?

   _____

3. Which has more mass, a lead atom or
   a uranium atom?

   _____

4. Which has a greater number of atoms,
   a gram of lead or a gram of uranium?

   _____

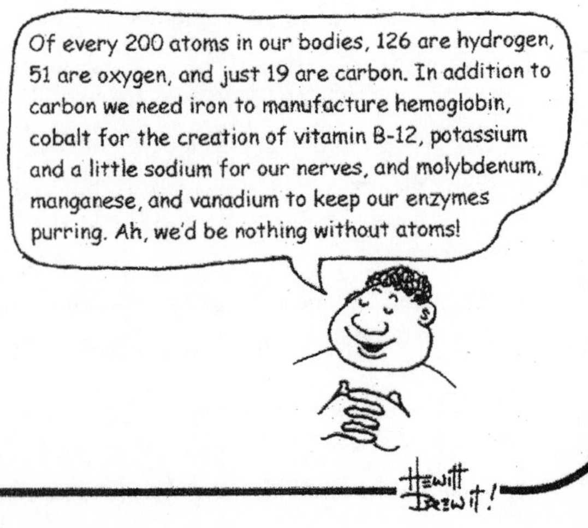

Of every 200 atoms in our bodies, 126 are hydrogen, 51 are oxygen, and just 19 are carbon. In addition to carbon we need iron to manufacture hemoglobin, cobalt for the creation of vitamin B-12, potassium and a little sodium for our nerves, and molybdenum, manganese, and vanadium to keep our enzymes purring. Ah, we'd be nothing without atoms!

CONCEPTUAL *Physics* PRACTICE PAGE

Chapter 12 Solids
Scaling

1. Consider a cube 1 cm × 1 cm × 1 cm (a very small sugar cube). Its volume is 1 cm^3. The surface area of one of its faces is 1 cm^2. The total surface area of the cube is 6 cm^2 because it has 6 sides. Now consider a second cube, scaled up by a factor of 2 so it is 2 cm × 2 cm × 2 cm.

   a. What is the total surface area of each cube?

   1st cube _____ cm^2; 2nd cube _____ cm^2

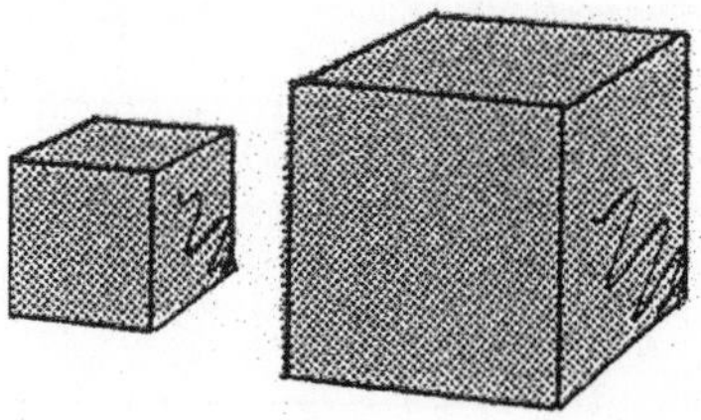

   b. What is the volume of each cube?

   1st cube _____ cm^3; 2nd cube _____ cm^3

   c. Compare the ratio of surface area to volume for each cube.

   1st cube of $\dfrac{\text{surface area}}{\text{volume}}$ = _____; 2nd cube of $\dfrac{\text{surface area}}{\text{volume}}$ = _____

2. Now consider a third cube, scaled up by a factor of 3 so it is 3 cm × 3 cm × 3 cm.

   a. What is its total surface area? _____ cm^2

   b. What is its volume? _____ cm^3

   c. What is its ratio of surface area to volume?

   $\dfrac{\text{surface area}}{\text{volume}}$ = _____

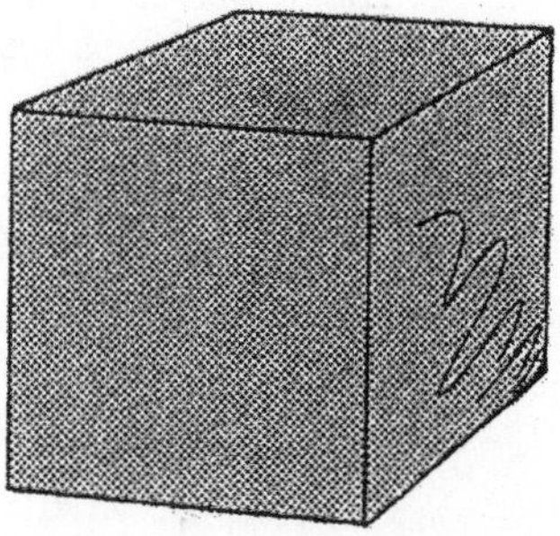

3. When the size of a cube is scaled up by a certain factor (2 and then 3 for the above examples), the area increases as the _____ of the factor, and the volume increases as the _____ of the factor.

4. Does the ratio of surface area to volume increase or decrease as things are scaled up?

   _____

5. Does the rule for the scaling up of cubes also apply to other shapes? _____ Would your answers have been different if we started with a sphere of diameter 1 cm and scaled it up to a sphere of diameter 2 cm, and then 3 cm? _____

6. The effects of scaling are beneficial to some creatures and detrimental to others. Check either (B) for beneficial or (D) for detrimental for each of the following:

   a. an insect falling from a tree _____   d. a big fish chasing a small fish _____

   b. an elephant falling from the same tree _____   e. a hungry mouse _____

   c. a small fish trying to flee from a big fish _____   f. an insect that falls in the water _____

Chapter 12 Solids
Scaling Circles

1. Complete the table below.

CIRCLES		
RADIUS	CIRCUMFERENCE	AREA
1 cm	$2\pi(1cm) = 2\pi$ cm	$\pi(1cm)^2 = \pi cm^2$
2 cm		
3 cm		
10 cm		

FOR THE CIRCUMFERENCE OF A CIRCLE, $C = 2\pi r$

AND FOR THE AREA OF A CIRCLE, $A = \pi r^2$

2. From your completed table, when the radius of a circle is doubled, its area increases by _____.
   When the radius is increased by a factor of 10, the area increases by _____.

3. Consider a small pizza that costs $5.00. Another pizza of the same thickness has twice the diameter. How much should the larger pizza cost?

_____

Circle one:

4. [True]   [False]   If the radius of a circle is increased by a certain factor, say 5, then the area increases by the *square* of the factor, in this case 5^2 or 25.

Fill in the blank:

So if you scale up the radius of a circle by a factor of 10, its area will increase by

_____.

Application:

5. Suppose you raise chickens and purchase $50.00 worth of wire for a chicken pen. The shape of the pen that will accommodate the most number of chickens will be

[square]   [circular]   [either, for both provide the same area].

CONCEPTUAL **Physics** PRACTICE PAGE

Chapter 13 Liquids
Archimedes' Principle I

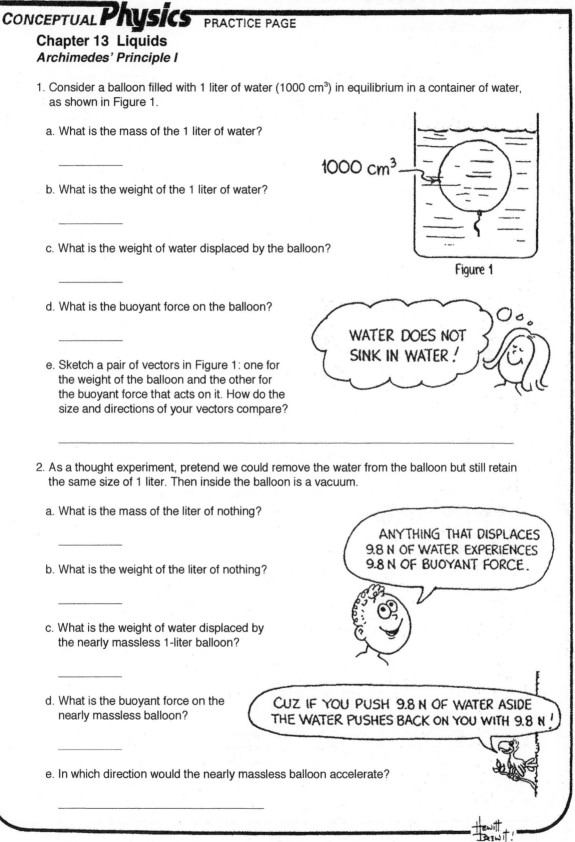

1. Consider a balloon filled with 1 liter of water (1000 cm³) in equilibrium in a container of water, as shown in Figure 1.

   a. What is the mass of the 1 liter of water?

   _____

   b. What is the weight of the 1 liter of water?

   _____

   c. What is the weight of water displaced by the balloon?

   _____

   1000 cm³

   d. What is the buoyant force on the balloon?

   _____

   Figure 1

   e. Sketch a pair of vectors in Figure 1: one for the weight of the balloon and the other for the buoyant force that acts on it. How do the size and directions of your vectors compare?

   WATER DOES NOT SINK IN WATER!

   _____

2. As a thought experiment, pretend we could remove the water from the balloon but still retain the same size of 1 liter. Then inside the balloon is a vacuum.

   a. What is the mass of the liter of nothing?

   _____

   b. What is the weight of the liter of nothing?

   ANYTHING THAT DISPLACES 9.8 N OF WATER EXPERIENCES 9.8 N OF BUOYANT FORCE.

   _____

   c. What is the weight of water displaced by the nearly massless 1-liter balloon?

   _____

   d. What is the buoyant force on the nearly massless balloon?

   CUZ IF YOU PUSH 9.8 N OF WATER ASIDE THE WATER PUSHES BACK ON YOU WITH 9.8 N!

   _____

   e. In which direction would the nearly massless balloon accelerate?

   _____

Chapter 13 Liquids
Archimedes' Principle I—continued

3. Assume the balloon is replaced by a 0.5-kilogram piece of wood that has exactly the same volume (1000 cm^3), as shown in Figure 2. The wood is held in the same submerged position beneath the surface of the water.

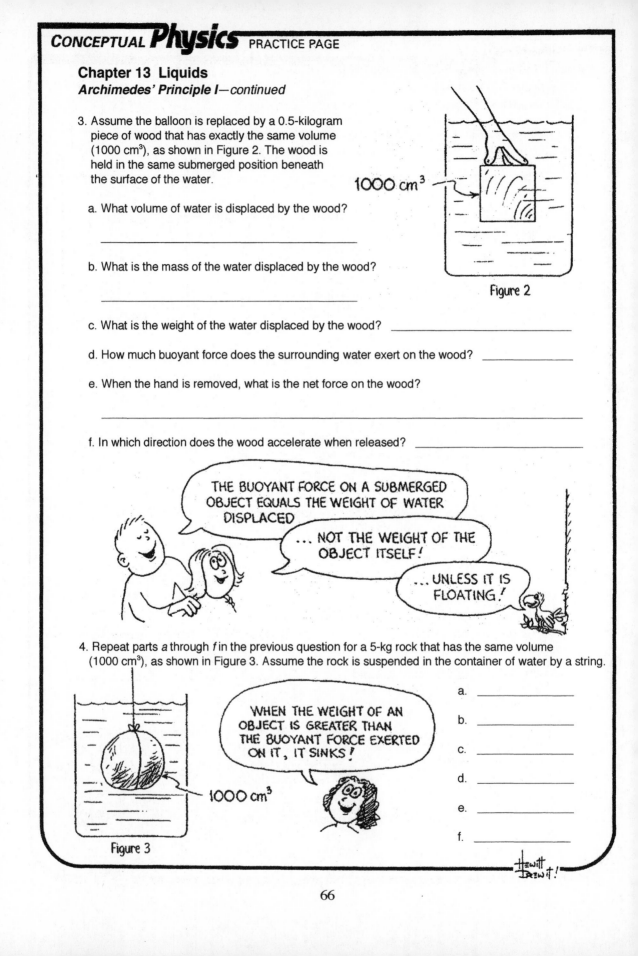

1000 cm^3

Figure 2

a. What volume of water is displaced by the wood?

_____

b. What is the mass of the water displaced by the wood?

_____

c. What is the weight of the water displaced by the wood? _____

d. How much buoyant force does the surrounding water exert on the wood? _____

e. When the hand is removed, what is the net force on the wood?

_____

f. In which direction does the wood accelerate when released? _____

THE BUOYANT FORCE ON A SUBMERGED OBJECT EQUALS THE WEIGHT OF WATER DISPLACED

... NOT THE WEIGHT OF THE OBJECT ITSELF!

... UNLESS IT IS FLOATING!

4. Repeat parts *a* through *f* in the previous question for a 5-kg rock that has the same volume (1000 cm^3), as shown in Figure 3. Assume the rock is suspended in the container of water by a string.

WHEN THE WEIGHT OF AN OBJECT IS GREATER THAN THE BUOYANT FORCE EXERTED ON IT, IT SINKS!

1000 cm^3

Figure 3

a. _____

b. _____

c. _____

d. _____

e. _____

f. _____

CONCEPTUAL **Physics** PRACTICE PAGE

Chapter 13 Liquids
Archimedes' Principle II

1. The water lines for the first three cases are shown. Sketch in the appropriate water lines for cases *d* and *e*, and make up your own for case *f*.

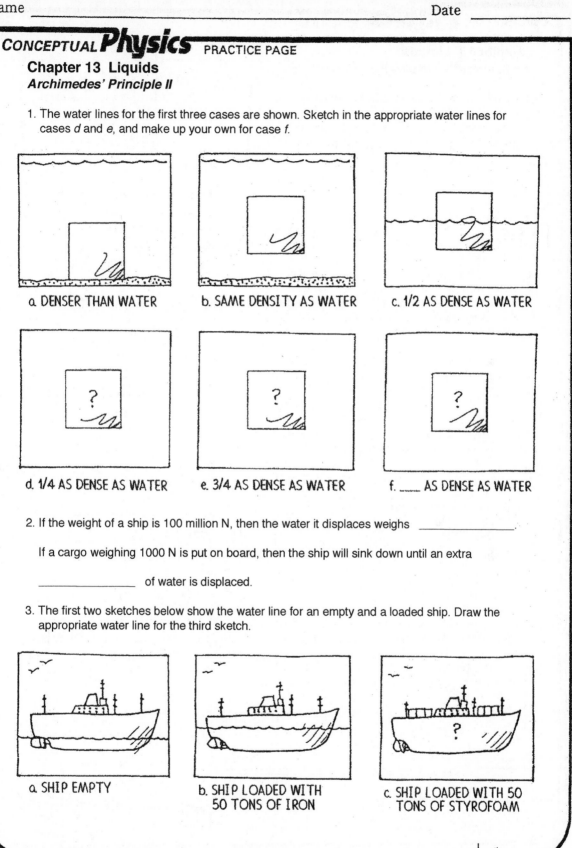

a. DENSER THAN WATER

b. SAME DENSITY AS WATER

c. 1/2 AS DENSE AS WATER

d. 1/4 AS DENSE AS WATER

e. 3/4 AS DENSE AS WATER

f. ____ AS DENSE AS WATER

2. If the weight of a ship is 100 million N, then the water it displaces weighs _____.

   If a cargo weighing 1000 N is put on board, then the ship will sink down until an extra

   _____ of water is displaced.

3. The first two sketches below show the water line for an empty and a loaded ship. Draw the appropriate water line for the third sketch.

a. SHIP EMPTY

b. SHIP LOADED WITH 50 TONS OF IRON

c. SHIP LOADED WITH 50 TONS OF STYROFOAM

Chapter 13 Liquids
Archimedes' Principles II—continued

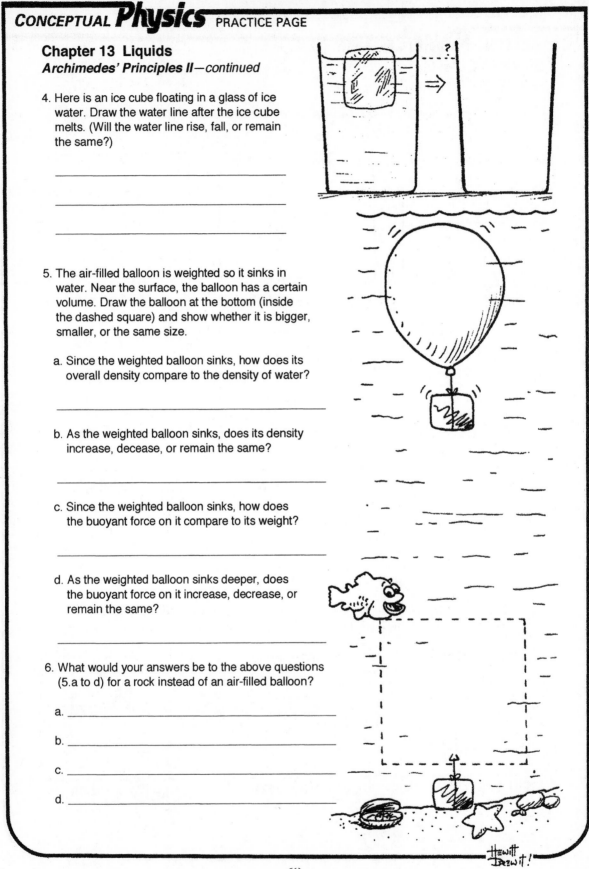

4. Here is an ice cube floating in a glass of ice water. Draw the water line after the ice cube melts. (Will the water line rise, fall, or remain the same?)

_____

_____

_____

5. The air-filled balloon is weighted so it sinks in water. Near the surface, the balloon has a certain volume. Draw the balloon at the bottom (inside the dashed square) and show whether it is bigger, smaller, or the same size.

a. Since the weighted balloon sinks, how does its overall density compare to the density of water?

_____

b. As the weighted balloon sinks, does its density increase, decease, or remain the same?

_____

c. Since the weighted balloon sinks, how does the buoyant force on it compare to its weight?

_____

d. As the weighted balloon sinks deeper, does the buoyant force on it increase, decrease, or remain the same?

_____

6. What would your answers be to the above questions (5.a to d) for a rock instead of an air-filled balloon?

a. _____

b. _____

c. _____

d. _____

Name _____   Date _____

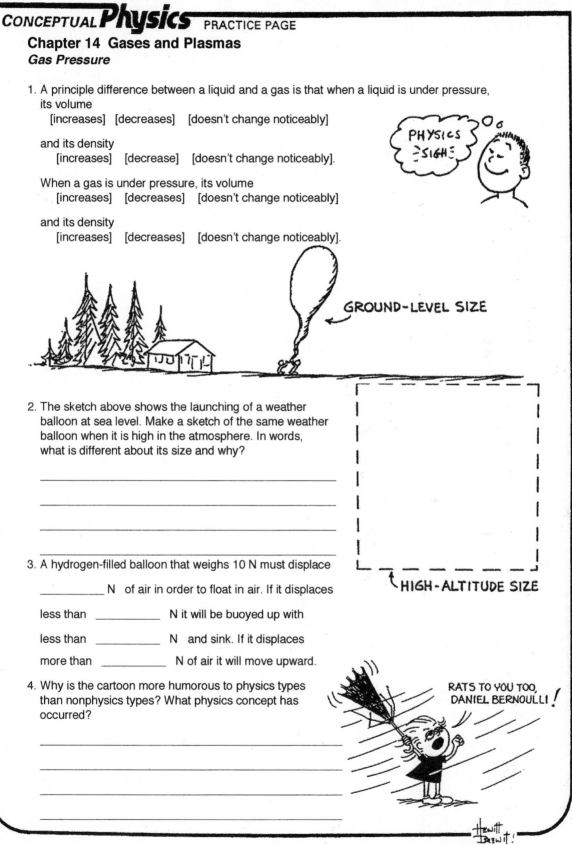

CONCEPTUAL **Physics** PRACTICE PAGE

Chapter 14 Gases and Plasmas
Gas Pressure

1. A principle difference between a liquid and a gas is that when a liquid is under pressure, its volume
   [increases]   [decreases]   [doesn't change noticeably]

   and its density
   [increases]   [decrease]   [doesn't change noticeably].

   When a gas is under pressure, its volume
   [increases]   [decreases]   [doesn't change noticeably]

   and its density
   [increases]   [decreases]   [doesn't change noticeably].

PHYSICS SIGH!

GROUND-LEVEL SIZE

2. The sketch above shows the launching of a weather balloon at sea level. Make a sketch of the same weather balloon when it is high in the atmosphere. In words, what is different about its size and why?

   _____

   _____

   _____

   _____

HIGH-ALTITUDE SIZE

3. A hydrogen-filled balloon that weighs 10 N must displace

   _____ N of air in order to float in air. If it displaces

   less than _____ N it will be buoyed up with

   less than _____ N and sink. If it displaces

   more than _____ N of air it will move upward.

4. Why is the cartoon more humorous to physics types than nonphysics types? What physics concept has occurred?

   _____

   _____

   _____

   _____

RATS TO YOU TOO, DANIEL BERNOULLI!

69

Name _____   Date _____

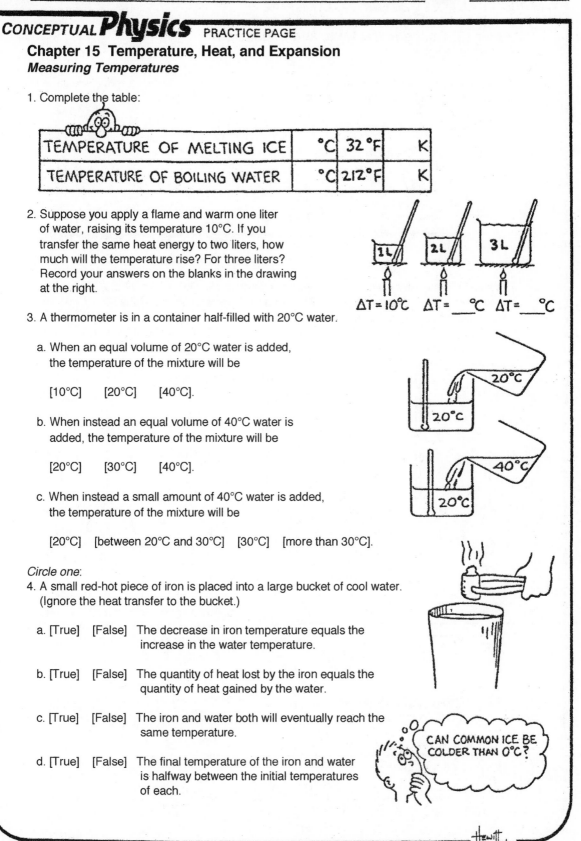

CONCEPTUAL **Physics** PRACTICE PAGE

Chapter 15 Temperature, Heat, and Expansion
Measuring Temperatures

1. Complete the table:

TEMPERATURE OF MELTING ICE	°C	32 °F	K
TEMPERATURE OF BOILING WATER	°C	212°F	K

2. Suppose you apply a flame and warm one liter of water, raising its temperature 10°C. If you transfer the same heat energy to two liters, how much will the temperature rise? For three liters? Record your answers on the blanks in the drawing at the right.

ΔT = 10°C   ΔT = ___ °C   ΔT = ___ °C

3. A thermometer is in a container half-filled with 20°C water.

   a. When an equal volume of 20°C water is added, the temperature of the mixture will be

   [10°C]   [20°C]   [40°C].

   b. When instead an equal volume of 40°C water is added, the temperature of the mixture will be

   [20°C]   [30°C]   [40°C].

   c. When instead a small amount of 40°C water is added, the temperature of the mixture will be

   [20°C]   [between 20°C and 30°C]   [30°C]   [more than 30°C].

Circle one:
4. A small red-hot piece of iron is placed into a large bucket of cool water. (Ignore the heat transfer to the bucket.)

   a. [True]   [False]   The decrease in iron temperature equals the increase in the water temperature.

   b. [True]   [False]   The quantity of heat lost by the iron equals the quantity of heat gained by the water.

   c. [True]   [False]   The iron and water both will eventually reach the same temperature.

   d. [True]   [False]   The final temperature of the iron and water is halfway between the initial temperatures of each.

CAN COMMON ICE BE COLDER THAN 0°C?

Chapter 15 Temperature, Heat, and Expansion
Thermal Expansion

1. The weight hangs above the floor from the copper wire. When a candle is moved along the wire and warms it, what happens to the height of the weight above the floor? Why?

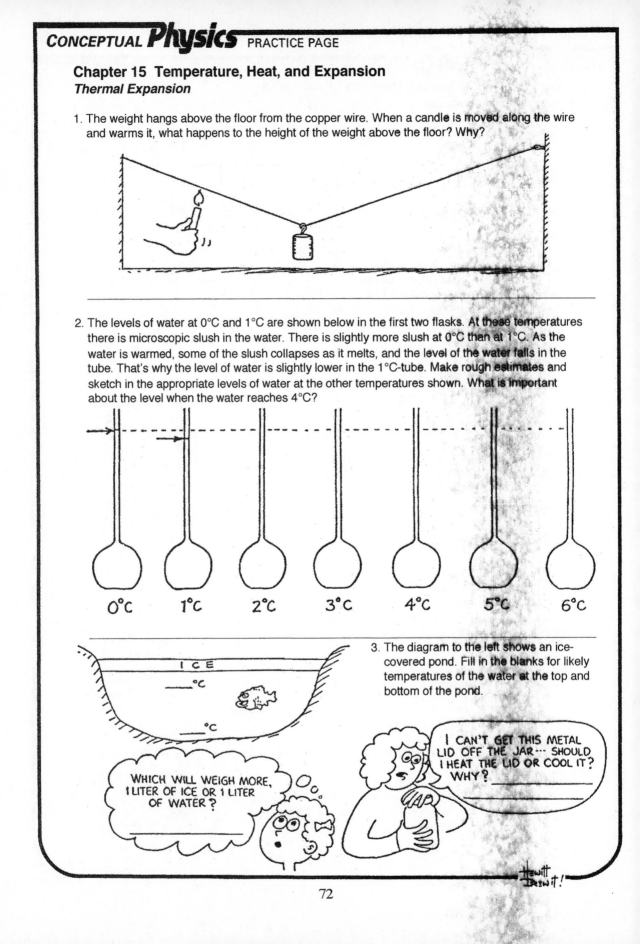

2. The levels of water at 0°C and 1°C are shown below in the first two flasks. At these temperatures there is microscopic slush in the water. There is slightly more slush at 0°C than at 1°C. As the water is warmed, some of the slush collapses as it melts, and the level of the water falls in the tube. That's why the level of water is slightly lower in the 1°C-tube. Make rough estimates and sketch in the appropriate levels of water at the other temperatures shown. What is important about the level when the water reaches 4°C?

0°C   1°C   2°C   3°C   4°C   5°C   6°C

I C E
____°C

____°C

3. The diagram to the left shows an ice-covered pond. Fill in the blanks for likely temperatures of the water at the top and bottom of the pond.

WHICH WILL WEIGH MORE, 1 LITER OF ICE OR 1 LITER OF WATER?
____

I CAN'T GET THIS METAL LID OFF THE JAR --- SHOULD I HEAT THE LID OR COOL IT? WHY? _____
_____

CONCEPTUAL **Physics** PRACTICE PAGE

Chapter 16 Heat Transfer
Transmission of Heat

Circle one:

1. The tips of both brass rods are held in the gas flame.

a. [True] [False] Heat is conducted only
along Rod A.

b. [True] [False] Heat is conducted only
along Rod B.

c. [True] [False] Heat is conducted equally along
both Rod A and Rod B.

d. [True] [False] The idea that "heat rises" applies to heat transfer by *convection*, not by *conduction*.

2. Why does a bird fluff its feathers to keep warm on a cold day?

_____

3. Why does a down-filled sleeping bag keep you warm on a cold night?
Why is it useless if the down is wet?

_____

4. What does *convection* have to do with the holes in the shade of the
desk lamp?

_____

5. The warmth of equatorial regions and coldness of polar regions
on Earth can be understood by considering light from a flashlight
striking a surface. If it strikes perpendicularly, light energy is more
concentrated as it covers a smaller area; if it strikes at an angle,
the energy spreads over a larger area. So the energy per unit
area is less.

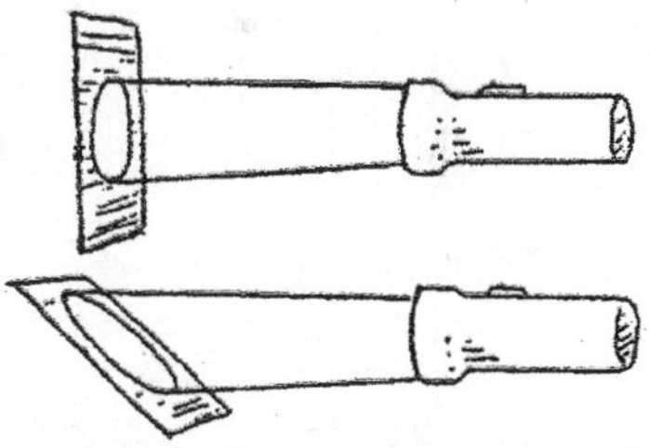

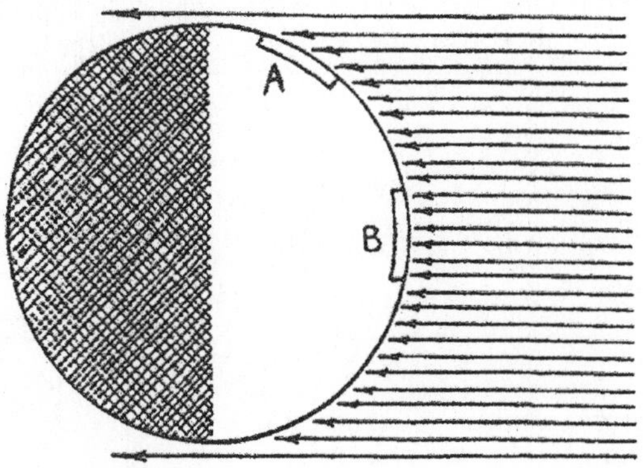

The arrows represent rays of light from
the distant Sun incident upon Earth. Two
areas of equal size are shown, Area A
near the North Pole and Area B near the
equator. Count the rays that reach each
area, and explain why B is warmer than A.

_____

_____

_____

Chapter 16 Heat Transfer
Transmission of Heat

6. The Earth's seasons arise from the 23.5-degree tilt of Earth's daily spin axis as it orbits the Sun. When Earth is at the position shown on the right in the sketch below (not to scale), the Northern Hemisphere tilts toward the Sun, and sunlight striking it is strong (more rays per area). Sunlight striking Southern Hemisphere is weak (fewer rays per area). Days in the north are warmer, and daylight is longer. You can see this by imagining Earth making its complete daily 24-hour spin.

Do two things on the sketch:
(i) Shade the part of Earth in nighttime darkness for all positions, as is already done in the left position.
(ii) Label each position with the proper month—March, June, September, or December.

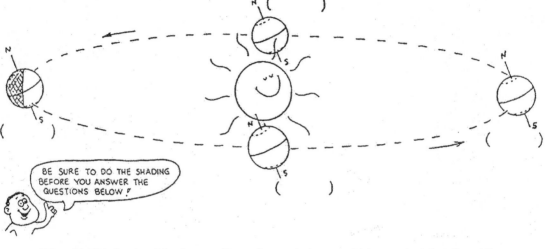

BE SURE TO DO THE SHADING BEFORE YOU ANSWER THE QUESTIONS BELOW !

a. When Earth is in any of the four positions shown, during one 24-hour spin, a location at the equator receives sunlight half the time and is in darkness the other half the time. This means

that regions at the equator always receive about _____ hours of sunlight and

_____ hours of darkness.

b. Can you see that in the June position regions farther north have longer daylight hours and shorter nights? Locations north of the Arctic Circle (dotted line in Northern Hemisphere) are

continually in view of the Sun as Earth spins, so they get daylight _____ hours a day.

c. How many hours of light and darkness are there in June at regions south of the Antarctic Circle (dotted line in Southern Hemisphere)?

_____

d. Six months later, when Earth is at the December position, is the situation in the Antarctic Circle the same or is it the reverse?

_____

e. Why do South America and Australia enjoy warm weather in December instead of June?

_____

Name _____ Date _____

Chapter 17 Change of Phase
Ice, Water, and Steam

All matter can exist in the solid, liquid, or gaseous phases. The solid phase normally exists at relatively low temperatures, the liquid phase at higher temperatures, and the gaseous phase at still higher temperatures. Water is the most common example, not only because of its abundance but also because the temperatures for all three phases are common. Study "Energy and Changes of Phase" in your textbook and then answer the following:

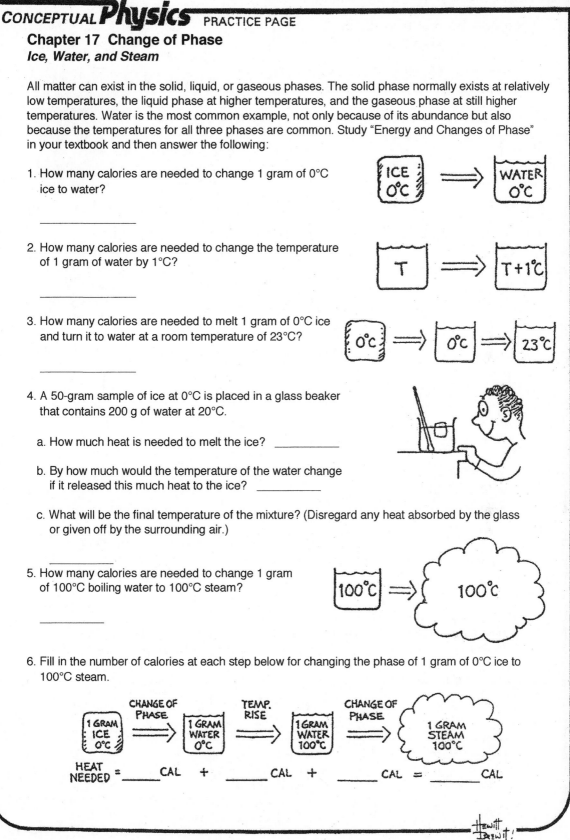

1. How many calories are needed to change 1 gram of 0°C ice to water?

   _____

2. How many calories are needed to change the temperature of 1 gram of water by 1°C?

   _____

3. How many calories are needed to melt 1 gram of 0°C ice and turn it to water at a room temperature of 23°C?

   _____

4. A 50-gram sample of ice at 0°C is placed in a glass beaker that contains 200 g of water at 20°C.

   a. How much heat is needed to melt the ice? _____

   b. By how much would the temperature of the water change if it released this much heat to the ice? _____

   c. What will be the final temperature of the mixture? (Disregard any heat absorbed by the glass or given off by the surrounding air.)

   _____

5. How many calories are needed to change 1 gram of 100°C boiling water to 100°C steam?

   _____

6. Fill in the number of calories at each step below for changing the phase of 1 gram of 0°C ice to 100°C steam.

   CHANGE OF PHASE | TEMP. RISE | CHANGE OF PHASE

   1 GRAM ICE 0°C ⟹ 1 GRAM WATER 0°C ⟹ 1 GRAM WATER 100°C ⟹ 1 GRAM STEAM 100°C

   HEAT NEEDED = _____ CAL + _____ CAL + _____ CAL = _____ CAL

Chapter 17 Change of Phase
Ice, Water, and Steam—continued

7. One gram of steam at 100°C condenses, and the water cools to 22°C.

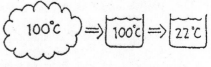

   a. How much heat is released when the steam condenses? _____

   b. How much heat is released when the water cools from 100°C to 22°C? _____

   c. How much heat is released altogether? _____

8. In a household radiator 1000 g of steam at 100°C condenses, and the water cools to 90°C.

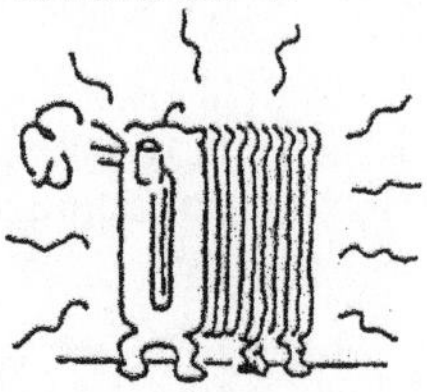

   a. How much heat is released when the steam condenses? _____

   b. How much heat is released when the water cools from 100°C to 90°C?

   _____

   c. How much heat is released altogether? _____

9. Why is it difficult to brew tea on the top of a high mountain?

   _____

10. How many calories are given up by 1 gram of 100°C steam that condenses to 100°C water?

    _____

11. How many calories are given up by 1 gram of 100°C steam that condenses and drops in temperature to 22°C water?

    _____

12. How many calories are given to a household radiator when 1000 grams of 100°C steam condenses, and drops in temperature to 90°C water?

    _____

13. To get water from the ground, even in the hot desert, dig a hole about a half meter wide and a half meter deep. Place a cup at the bottom. Spread a sheet of plastic wrap over the hole and place stones along the edge to hold it secure. Weight the center of the plastic with a stone so it forms a cone shape. Why will water collect in the cup? (Physics can save your life if you're ever stranded in a desert!)

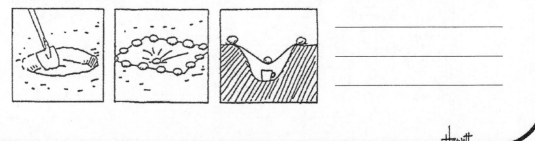

   _____

   _____

   _____

Name _____ Date _____

Chapter 17 Change of Phase
Evaporation

1. Why do you feel colder when you swim in a pool on a windy day?

   _____

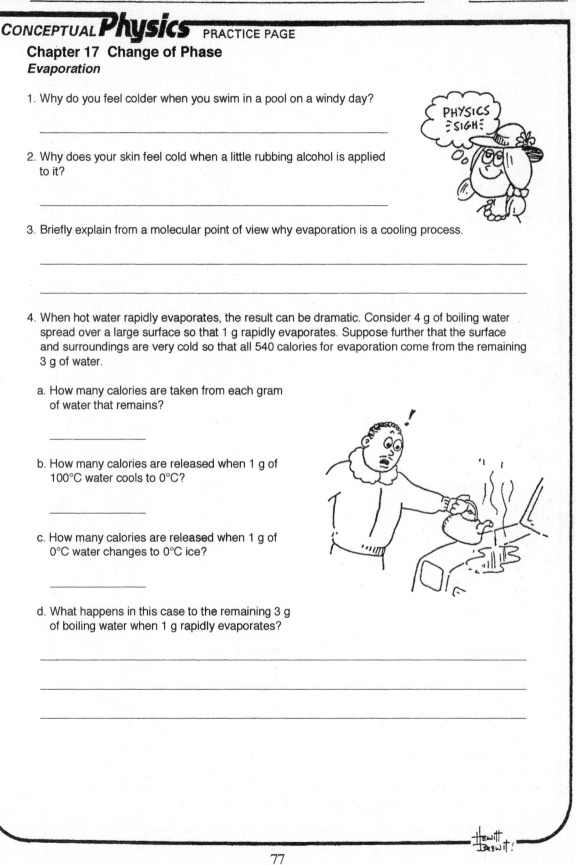

2. Why does your skin feel cold when a little rubbing alcohol is applied to it?

   _____

3. Briefly explain from a molecular point of view why evaporation is a cooling process.

   _____

   _____

4. When hot water rapidly evaporates, the result can be dramatic. Consider 4 g of boiling water spread over a large surface so that 1 g rapidly evaporates. Suppose further that the surface and surroundings are very cold so that all 540 calories for evaporation come from the remaining 3 g of water.

   a. How many calories are taken from each gram of water that remains?

   _____

   b. How many calories are released when 1 g of 100°C water cools to 0°C?

   _____

   c. How many calories are released when 1 g of 0°C water changes to 0°C ice?

   _____

   d. What happens in this case to the remaining 3 g of boiling water when 1 g rapidly evaporates?

   _____

   _____

   _____

CONCEPTUAL **Physics** PRACTICE PAGE

Chapter 17 Change of Phase
Our Earth's Hot Interior

A major puzzle faced scientists in the 19th century. Volcanoes
showed that Earth is molten beneath its crust. Penetration into
the crust by bore holes and mines showed that Earth's
temperature increases with depth. Scientists found that heat
flows from the interior to the surface. They assumed that the
source of Earth's internal heat was primordial, the afterglow of
its fiery birth. Measurements of cooling rates indicated a
relatively young Earth—some 25 to 30 millions years in age.
But geological evidence indicated an older Earth. This puzzle
wasn't solved until the discovery of radioactivity. Then it was
learned that the interior is kept hot by the energy of radioactive
decay. We now know the age of Earth is some 4.5 billions years—
a much older Earth.

All rock contains trace amounts of radioactive minerals. Those in common granite release energy
at the rate 0.03 Joule/kilogram•year. Granite at Earth's surface transfers this energy to the
surroundings as fast as it is generated, so we don't find granite warm to the touch. But what if a
sample of granite were thermally insulated? That is, suppose the increase of internal energy due
to radioactivity were contained. Then it would get hotter. How much? Let's figure it out, using
790 joule/kilogram kelvin as the specific heat of granite.

Calculations to make:
1. How many joules are required to increase the temperature of 1 kg
   of granite by 1000 K?

   _____

2. How many years would it take radioactive decay in a kilogram of
   granite to produce this many joules?

   _____

Questions to answer:
1. How many years would it take a thermally insulated 1-kg chunk
   of granite to undergo a 1000 K increase in temperature?

   _____

2. How many years would it take a thermally insulated one-
   million-kilogram chunk of granite to undergo a 1000 K
   increase in temperature?

   _____

3. Why are your answers to the above the same (or different)?

   _____

An electric toaster stays hot
while electric energy is supplied,
and doesn't cool until switched
off. Similarly, do you think the
energy source now keeping the
Earth hot will one day suddenly
switch off like a disconnected
toaster — or gradually decrease
over a long time?

Circle one:
4. [True]   [False]   The energy produced by Earth radioactivity
               ultimately becomes terrestrial radiation.

Name _____ Date _____

Chapter 18 Thermodynamics
Absolute Zero

A mass of air is contained so that the volume can change but the pressure
remains constant. Table I shows air volumes at various temperatures when
the air is warmed slowly.

1. Plot the data in Table I on the graph and connect the points.

TABLE I

TEMP. (°C)	VOLUME (mL)
0	50
25	55
50	60
75	65
100	70

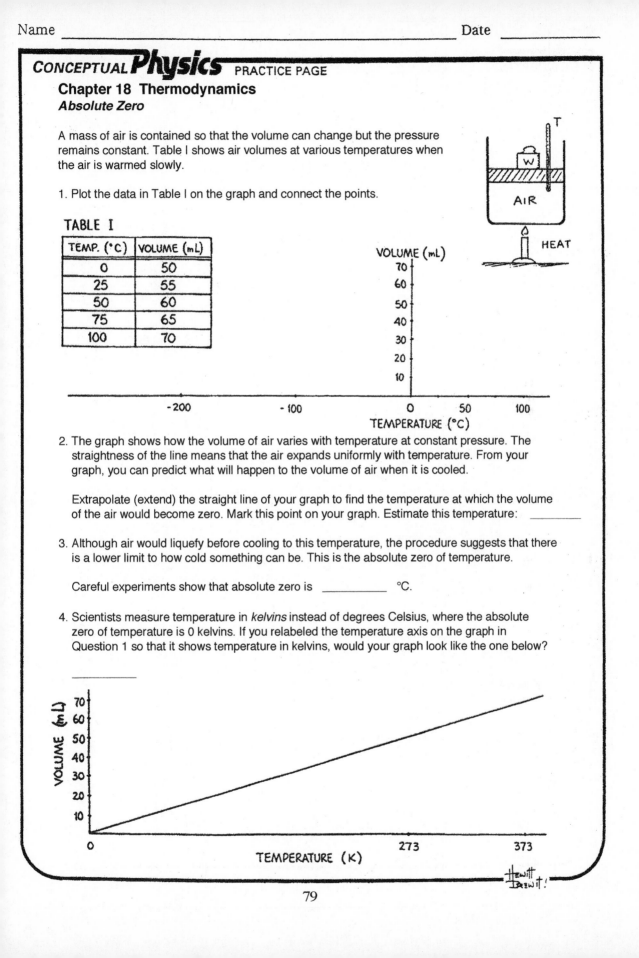

2. The graph shows how the volume of air varies with temperature at constant pressure. The
   straightness of the line means that the air expands uniformly with temperature. From your
   graph, you can predict what will happen to the volume of air when it is cooled.

   Extrapolate (extend) the straight line of your graph to find the temperature at which the volume
   of the air would become zero. Mark this point on your graph. Estimate this temperature: _____

3. Although air would liquefy before cooling to this temperature, the procedure suggests that there
   is a lower limit to how cold something can be. This is the absolute zero of temperature.

   Careful experiments show that absolute zero is _____ °C.

4. Scientists measure temperature in *kelvins* instead of degrees Celsius, where the absolute
   zero of temperature is 0 kelvins. If you relabeled the temperature axis on the graph in
   Question 1 so that it shows temperature in kelvins, would your graph look like the one below?

Name _____ Date _____

Chapter 19 Vibrations and Waves
Vibration and Wave Fundamentals

1. A sine curve that represents a transverse wave is drawn below. With a ruler, measure the wavelength and amplitude of the wave.

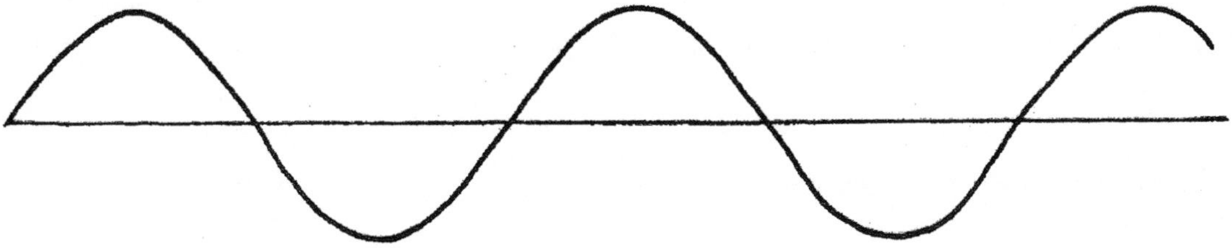

    a. Wavelength = _____

    b. Amplitude = _____

2. A kid on a playground swing makes a complete to-and-fro swing each 2 seconds. The frequency of swing is

    [0.5 hertz]   [1 hertz]   [2 hertz]

    and the period is

    [0.5 seconds]   [1 second]   [2 seconds].

3. *Complete the statements*:

THE PERIOD OF A 440-HERTZ SOUND WAVE IS _____ SECOND.

A MARINE WEATHER STATION REPORTS WAVES ALONG THE SHORE THAT ARE 8 SECONDS APART. THE FREQUENCY OF THE WAVES IS THEREFORE _____ HERTZ.

4. The annoying sound from a mosquito is produced when it beats its wings at the average rate of 600 wing beats per second.

    a. What is the frequency of the sound waves?

    _____

    b. What is the wavelength?
    (Assume the speed of sound is 340 m/s.)

    _____

Chapter 19 Vibrations and Waves
Vibration and Wave Fundamentals—continued

5. A machine gun fires 10 rounds per second. The speed of the bullets is 300 m/s.

    a. What is the distance in the air between the flying bullets? _____

    b. What happens to the distance between the bullets if the rate of fire is increased?

    _____

6. Consider a wave generator that produces 10 pulses per second. The speed of the waves is 300 cm/s.

    a. What is the wavelength of the waves? _____

    b. What happens to the wavelength if the frequency of pulses is increased?

    _____

7. The bird at the right watches the waves. If the portion of a wave between 2 crests passes the pole each second,

    a. what is the speed of the waves? _____

    b. what is the period of wave motion? _____

    c. If the distance between crests were 1.5 meters apart, and 2 crests pass the pole each second, what would be the speed of the wave?

    _____

    d. What would the period of wave motion be for 7.c ?

    _____

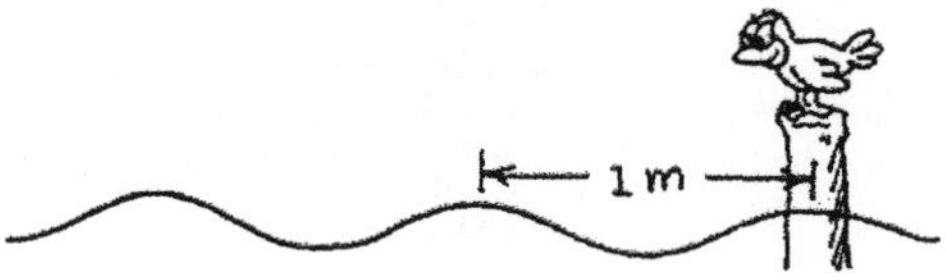

8. When an automobile moves toward a listener, the sound of its horn seems relatively

    [low pitched]   [high pitched]   [normal]

    and when moving away from the listener, its horn seems

    [low pitched]   [high pitched]   [normal].

9. The changed pitch of the Doppler effect is due to changes in wave

    [speed]   [frequency]   [both].

CONCEPTUAL **Physics** PRACTICE PAGE

Chapter 19 Vibrations and Waves
Shock Waves

The cone-shaped shock wave produced by a supersonic aircraft is actually the result of overlapping spherical waves of sound, as indicated by the overlapping circles in Figure 19.19 in your textbook. Sketches *a* through *e* below show the "animated" growth of only one of the many spherical sound waves (shown as an expanding circle in the two-dimensional drawing).

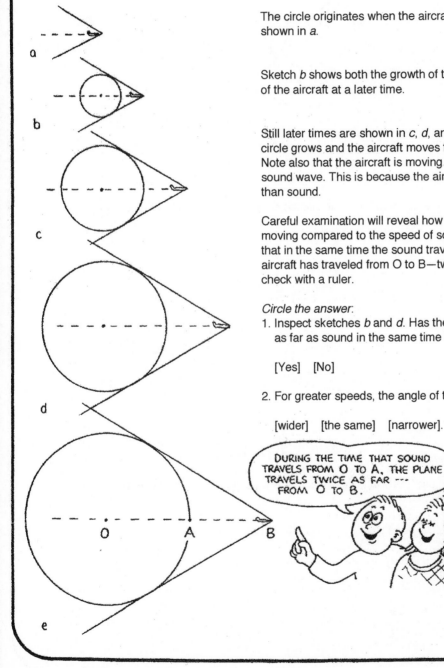

The circle originates when the aircraft is in the position shown in *a*.

Sketch *b* shows both the growth of the circle and position of the aircraft at a later time.

Still later times are shown in *c*, *d*, and *e*. Note that the circle grows and the aircraft moves farther to the right. Note also that the aircraft is moving farther than the sound wave. This is because the aircraft is moving faster than sound.

Careful examination will reveal how fast the aircraft is moving compared to the speed of sound. Sketch *e* shows that in the same time the sound travels from O to A, the aircraft has traveled from O to B—twice as far. You can check with a ruler.

Circle the answer:

1. Inspect sketches *b* and *d*. Has the aircraft traveled twice as far as sound in the same time in these positions also?

   [Yes]   [No]

2. For greater speeds, the angle of the shock wave would be

   [wider]   [the same]   [narrower].

DURING THE TIME THAT SOUND TRAVELS FROM O TO A, THE PLANE TRAVELS TWICE AS FAR --- FROM O TO B.

SO IT'S FLYING AT TWICE THE SPEED OF SOUND !

Chapter 19 Vibrations and Waves
Shock Waves—continued

3. Use a ruler to estimate the speeds of the aircraft that produce the shock waves in the two sketches below.

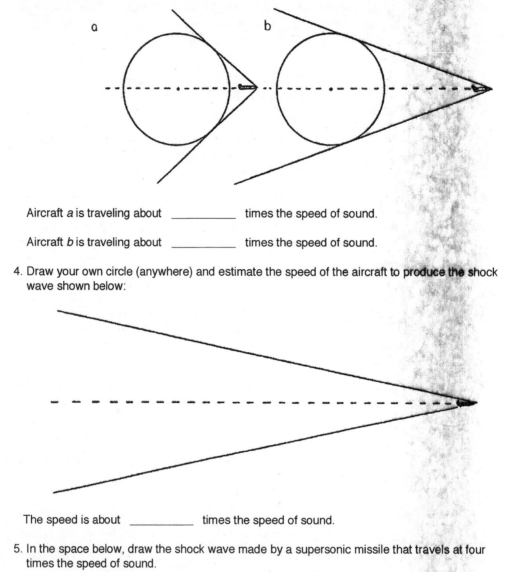

a

b

Aircraft *a* is traveling about _____ times the speed of sound.

Aircraft *b* is traveling about _____ times the speed of sound.

4. Draw your own circle (anywhere) and estimate the speed of the aircraft to produce the shock wave shown below:

The speed is about _____ times the speed of sound.

5. In the space below, draw the shock wave made by a supersonic missile that travels at four times the speed of sound.

CONCEPTUAL *Physics* PRACTICE PAGE

Chapter 20 Sound
Wave Superposition

A pair of pulses travel toward each at equal speeds. The composite waveforms, as they pass through each other and interfere, are shown at 1-second intervals. In the left column note how the pulses interfere to produce the composite waveform (solid line). Make a similar construction for the two wave pulses in the right column. Like the pulses in the first column, they each travel at 1 space per second.

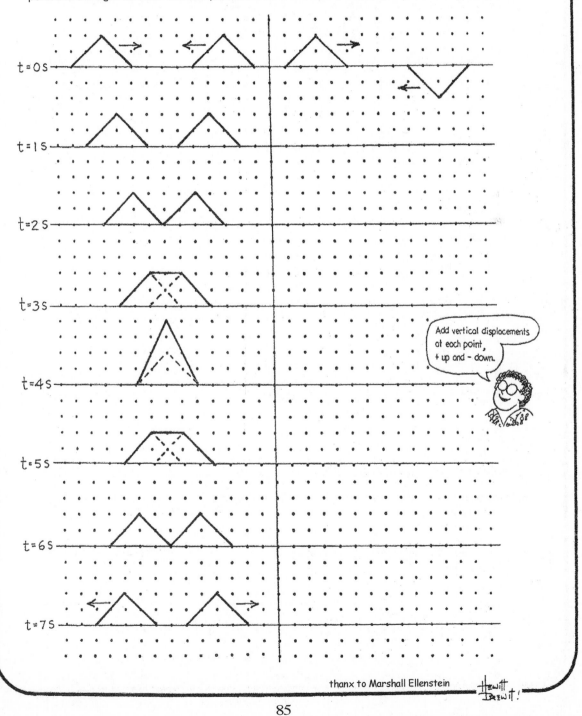

Add vertical displacements at each point, + up and − down.

thanx to Marshall Ellenstein

Chapter 20 Sound
Wave Superposition—continued

Construct the composite waveforms at 1-second intervals for the two waves traveling toward each other at equal speed.

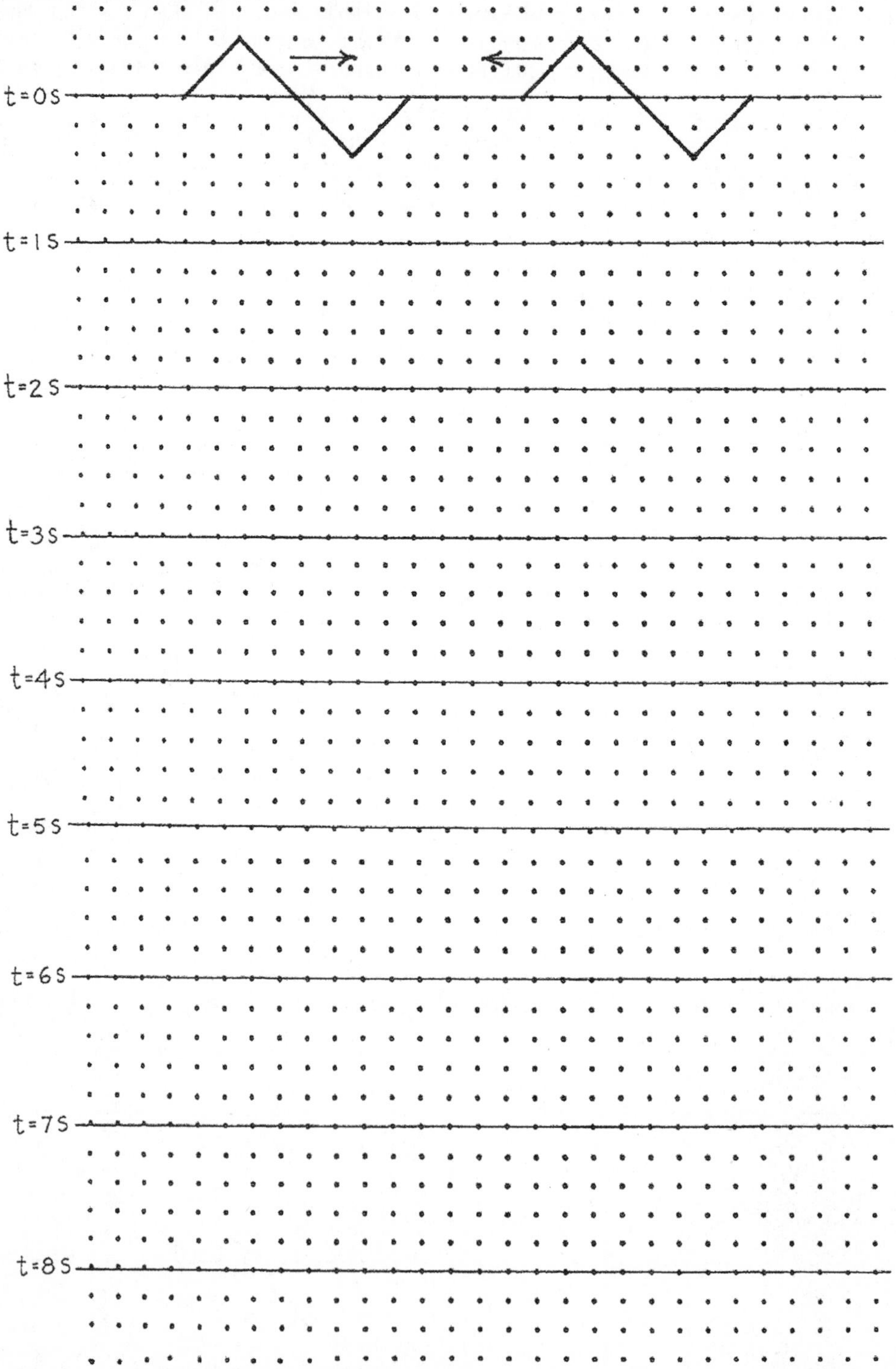

CONCEPTUAL **Physics** PRACTICE PAGE

Chapter 22 Electrostatics
Static Charge

1. Consider the diagram below.
   a. A pair of insulated metal spheres, A and B, touch each other, so in effect they form a single uncharged conductor.
   b. A positively charged rod is brought near A, but not touching, and electrons in the metal sphere are attracted toward the rod. Charges in the spheres have redistributed, and the negative charge is labeled. Draw the appropriate + signs that are repelled to the far side of B.
   c. Draw the signs of charge when the spheres are separated while the rod is still present, and
   d. after the rod has been removed. Your completed work should be similar to Figure 22.7 in the textbook. The spheres have been charged by *induction*.

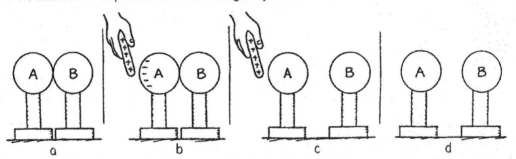

2. Consider below a single metal insulated sphere, (*a*) initially uncharged. When a negatively charged rod is nearby, (*b*), charges in the metal are separated. Electrons are repelled to the far side. When the sphere is touched with your finger, (*c*), electrons flow out of the sphere to Earth through your hand. The sphere is "grounded." Note the positive charge remaining (*d*) while the rod is still present and your finger removed, and (*e*) when the rod is removed. This is an example of *charge induction by grounding*. In this procedure the negative rod "gives" a positive charge to the sphere.

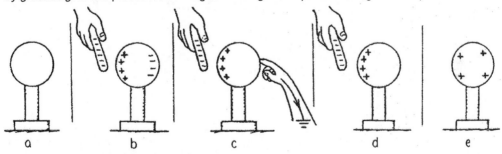

The diagrams below show a similar procedure with a positive rod. Draw the correct charges for *a* through *e*.

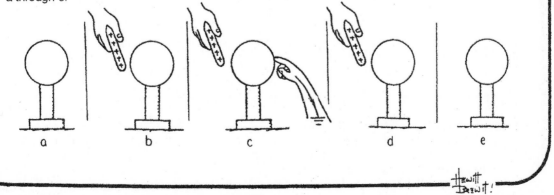

Chapter 22 Electrostatics
Electric Potential

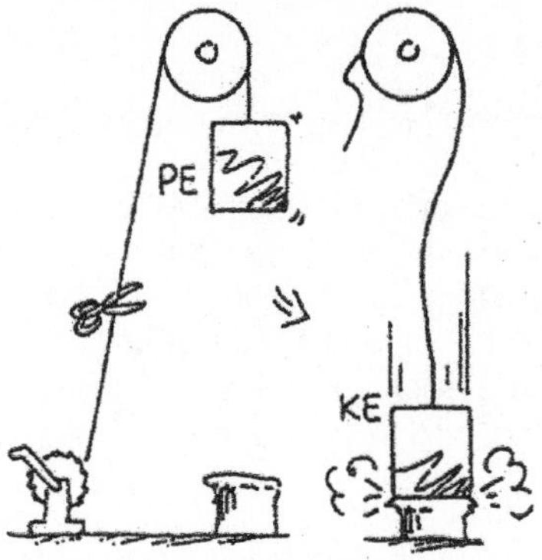

1. Just as PE (potential energy) transforms to KE (kinetic energy) for a mass lifted against the gravitational field (left), the electric PE of an electric charge transforms to other forms of energy when it changes location in an electric field (right). When released, how does the KE acquired by each compare to the decrease in PE?

_____

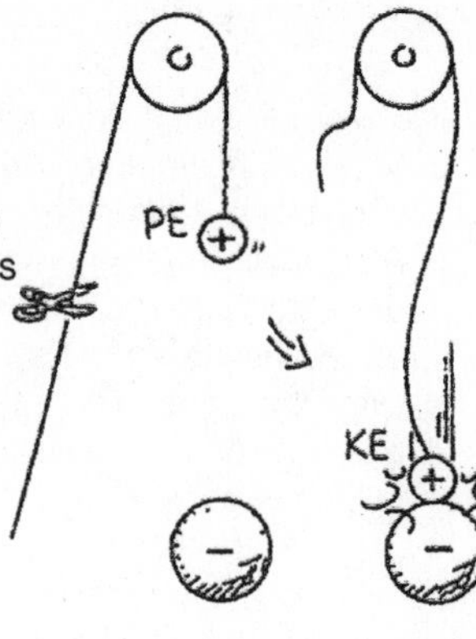

Complete the statements:

2. A force compresses the spring. The work done in compression is the product of the average force and the distance moved. *W = Fd*. This work increases the PE of the spring.

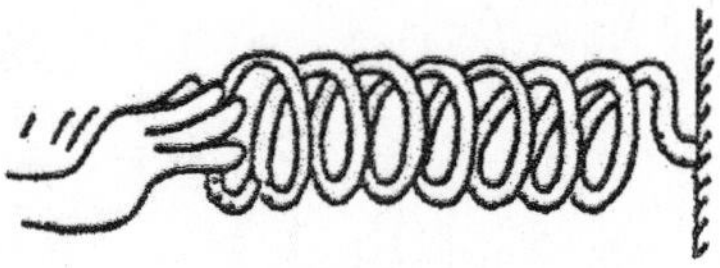

   Similarly, a force pushes the charge (call it a test charge) closer to the charged sphere. The work done in moving the test charge

   is the product of the average _____ and the _____

   moved. *W =* _____ . This work _____ the PE of the test charge.

   At any point, a greater quantity of test charge means a greater amount of PE, but not a greater amount of PE *per quantity* of charge. The quantities PE (measured in joules) and PE/charge (measured in volts) are different concepts.

   By definition: **Electric Potential** = $\dfrac{\textbf{PE}}{\textbf{charge}}$. 1 volt = 1 joule/coulomb.

3. Complete the statements:

   ELECTRIC PE/CHARGE HAS THE SPECIAL NAME *ELECTRIC* _____

   SINCE IT IS MEASURED IN *VOLTS* IT IS COMMONLY CALLED _____

4. If a conductor connected to the terminal of a battery has a potential of 12 volts, then each coulomb

   of charge on the conductor has a PE of _____ J.

5. Some people are confused between force and pressure. Recall that pressure is force *per area*. Similarly, some people get mixed up between electric PE and voltage. According to this chapter,

   voltage is electric PE per _____ .

CONCEPTUAL Physics PRACTICE PAGE

Chapter 23 Electric Current
Flow of Charge

1. Water doesn't flow in the pipe when both ends (*a*) are at the same level. Another way of saying this is that water will not flow in the pipe when both ends have the same potential energy (PE). Similarly, charge will not flow in a conductor if both ends of the conductor are the same electric potential. But tip the water pipe, as in (*b*), and water will flow. Similarly, charge will flow when you increase the electric potential of an electric conductor so there is a potential difference across the ends.

a. The unit of electric potential difference is

   [volt]   [ampere]   [ohm]   [watt].

b. It is common to call electric potential difference

   [voltage]   [amperage]   [wattage].

c. The flow of electric charge is called electric

   [voltage]   [current]   [power]

   and is measured in

   [volts]   [amperes]   [ohms]   [watts].

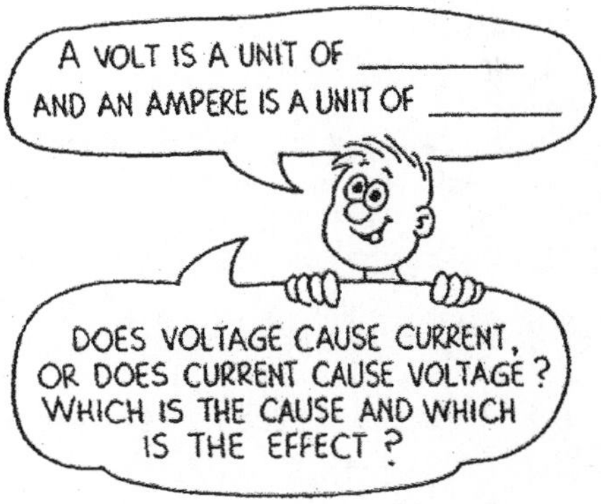

A VOLT IS A UNIT OF _____
AND AN AMPERE IS A UNIT OF _____

DOES VOLTAGE CAUSE CURRENT, OR DOES CURRENT CAUSE VOLTAGE? WHICH IS THE CAUSE AND WHICH IS THE EFFECT?

Complete the statements:

2. a. A current of 1 ampere is a flow of charge at the rate of _____ coulomb per second.

   b. When a charge of 15 C flows through any area in a circuit each second, the current is _____ A.

   c. One volt is the potential difference between two points if 1 joule of energy is needed to move

      _____ coulomb of charge between the two points.

   d. When a lamp is plugged into a 120-V socket, each coulomb of charge that flows in the circuit is raised to a potential energy of _____ joules.

   e. Which offers more resistance to water flow, a wide pipe or a narrow pipe? _____

      Similarly, which offers more resistance to the flow of charge, a thick wire or a thin wire?

      _____

Chapter 23 Electric Current
Ohm's Law

1. How much current flows in a 1000-ohm resistor when 1.5 volts are impressed across it?

   _____

2. If the filament resistance in an automobile headlamp is 3 ohms, how many amps does it draw when connected to a 12-volt battery?

   _____

3. The resistance of the side lights on an automobile are 10 ohms. How much current flows in them when connected to 12 volts?

   _____

4. What is the current in the 30-ohm heating coil of a coffee maker that operates on a 120-volt circuit?

   _____

CURRENT = $\frac{VOLTAGE}{RESISTANCE}$ OR $I = \frac{V}{R}$

USE OHM'S LAW IN THE TRIANGLE TO FIND THE QUANTITY YOU WANT. COVER THE LETTER WITH YOUR FINGER AND THE REMAINING TWO SHOW YOU THE FORMULA!

$\frac{V}{I \times R}$

CONDUCTORS AND RESISTORS HAVE RESISTANCE TO THE CURRENT IN THEM.

5. During a lie detector test, a voltage of 6 V is impressed across two fingers. When a certain question is asked, the resistance between the fingers drops from 400,000 ohms to 200,000 ohms.

   a. What is the current initially through the fingers? _____

   b. What is the current through the fingers when the resistance between them drops? _____

6. How much resistance allows an impressed voltage of 6 V to produce a current of 0.006 A?

   _____

7. What is the resistance of a clothes iron that draws a current of 12 A at 120 V?

   _____

8. What is the voltage across a 100-ohm circuit element that draws a current of 1 A?

   _____

OHM MY GOODNESS!

9. What voltage will produce 3 A through a 15-ohm resistor?

   _____

10. The current in an incandescent lamp is 0.5 A when connected to a 120-V circuit, and 0.2 A when connected to a 10-V source. Does the resistance of the lamp change in these cases? Explain your answer and defend it with numerical values.

   _____

   _____

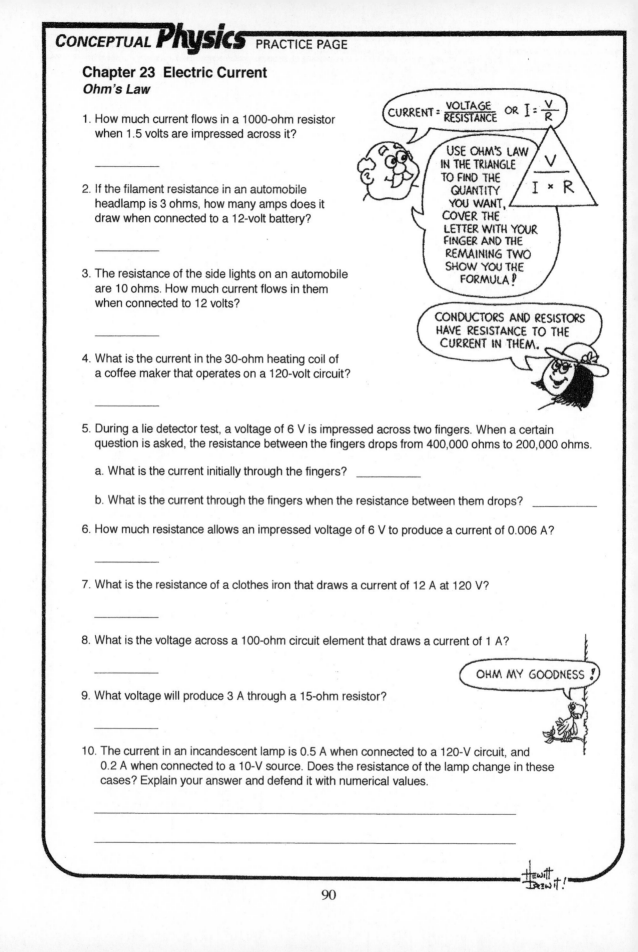

CONCEPTUAL *Physics* PRACTICE PAGE

Chapter 23 Electric Current
Electric Power

Recall that the rate at which energy is converted from one form to another is *power*.

$$\text{Power} = \frac{\text{energy converted}}{\text{time}} = \frac{\text{voltage} \times \text{charge}}{\text{time}} = \text{voltage} \times \frac{\text{charge}}{\text{time}} = \text{voltage} \times \text{current}$$

The unit of power is the *watt* (or *kilowatt*), so in units form,

Electric power (*watts*) = current (*amperes*) × voltage (*volts*), where 1 *watt* = 1 *ampere* × 1 *volt*.

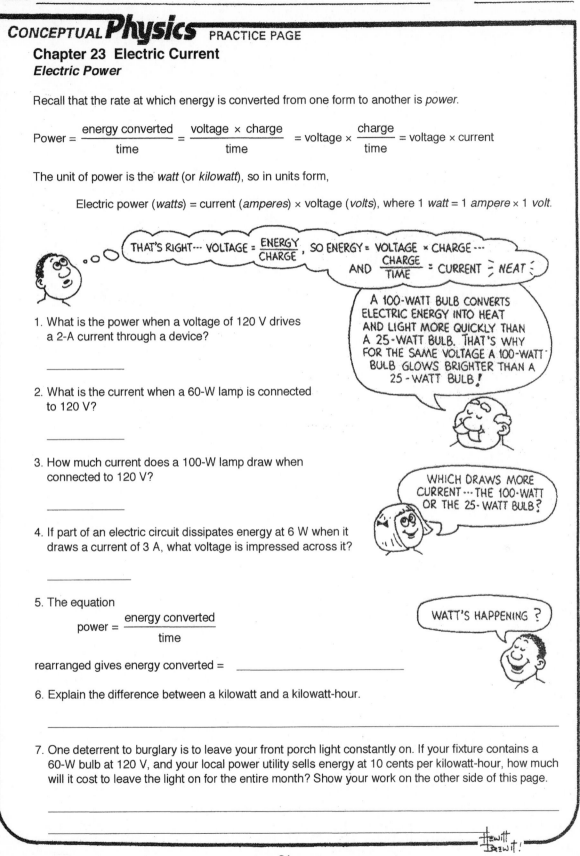

THAT'S RIGHT··· VOLTAGE = $\frac{ENERGY}{CHARGE}$, SO ENERGY = VOLTAGE × CHARGE ··· AND $\frac{CHARGE}{TIME}$ = CURRENT ¿ NEAT ¿

A 100-WATT BULB CONVERTS ELECTRIC ENERGY INTO HEAT AND LIGHT MORE QUICKLY THAN A 25-WATT BULB. THAT'S WHY FOR THE SAME VOLTAGE A 100-WATT BULB GLOWS BRIGHTER THAN A 25-WATT BULB!

1. What is the power when a voltage of 120 V drives a 2-A current through a device?

   _____

2. What is the current when a 60-W lamp is connected to 120 V?

   _____

3. How much current does a 100-W lamp draw when connected to 120 V?

   _____

WHICH DRAWS MORE CURRENT ··· THE 100-WATT OR THE 25-WATT BULB?

4. If part of an electric circuit dissipates energy at 6 W when it draws a current of 3 A, what voltage is impressed across it?

   _____

5. The equation

   $$\text{power} = \frac{\text{energy converted}}{\text{time}}$$

WATT'S HAPPENING ?

rearranged gives energy converted = _____

6. Explain the difference between a kilowatt and a kilowatt-hour.

   _____

7. One deterrent to burglary is to leave your front porch light constantly on. If your fixture contains a 60-W bulb at 120 V, and your local power utility sells energy at 10 cents per kilowatt-hour, how much will it cost to leave the light on for the entire month? Show your work on the other side of this page.

   _____

   _____

CONCEPTUAL **Physics** PRACTICE PAGE

Chapter 23 Electric Current
Series Circuits

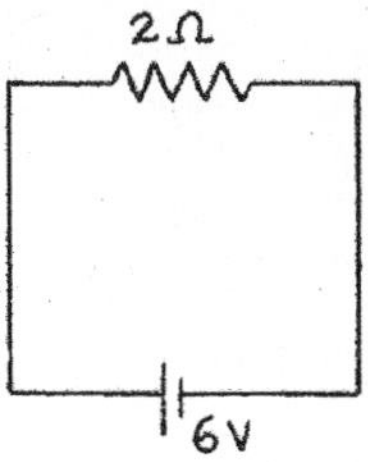

2 Ω

THE EQUIVALENT RESISTANCE OF RESISTORS IN SERIES IS SIMPLY THEIR SUM!

1. In the circuit shown at the right, a voltage of 6 V pushes charge through a single resistor of 2 Ω. According to Ohm's law, the current in the resistor (and therefore in the whole circuit) is

   _____ A.

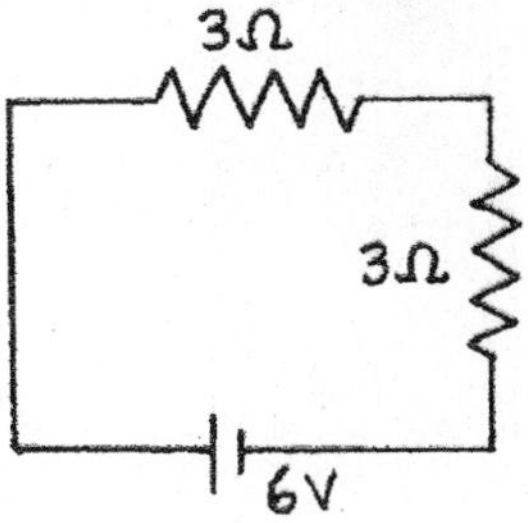

   6 V

2. Two 3-Ω resistors and a 6-V battery comprise the circuit on

   the right. The total resistance of the circuit is _____ Ω.

   The current in the circuit is then _____ A.

   3 Ω

   3 Ω

3. The equivalent resistance of three 4-Ω resistors in series would be

   _____ Ω.

   6 V

4. Does current flow *through* a resistor, or *across* a resistor? _____

   Is voltage established *through* a resistor, or *across* a resistor? _____

5. Does current in the lamps of a circuit occur simultaneously, or does charge flow first through one lamp, then the other, and finally the last in turn?

   _____

6. Circuits *a* and *b* below are identical with all bulbs rated at equal wattage (therefore equal resistance). The only difference between the circuits is that Bulb 5 has a short circuit, as shown.

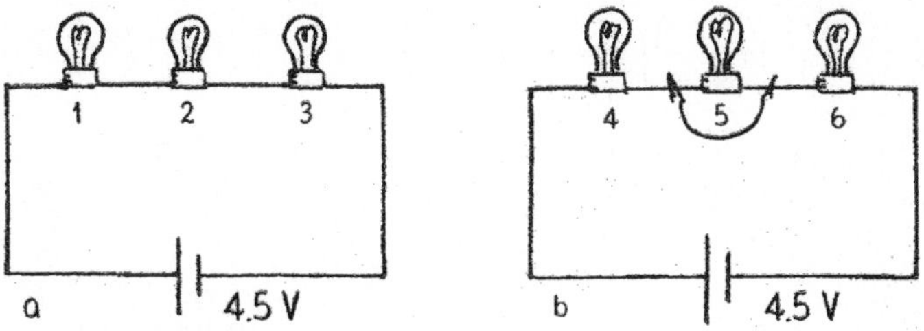

   1   2   3

   a   4.5 V

   4   5   6

   b   4.5 V

   a. In which circuit is the current greater? _____

   b. In which circuit are all three bulbs equally bright? _____

   c. Which bulbs are the brightest? _____

   d. Which bulb is the dimmest? _____

   e. Which bulbs have the largest voltage drops across them? _____

   f. Which circuit dissipates more power? _____

   g. Which circuit produces more light? _____

Chapter 23 Electric Current
Parallel Circuits

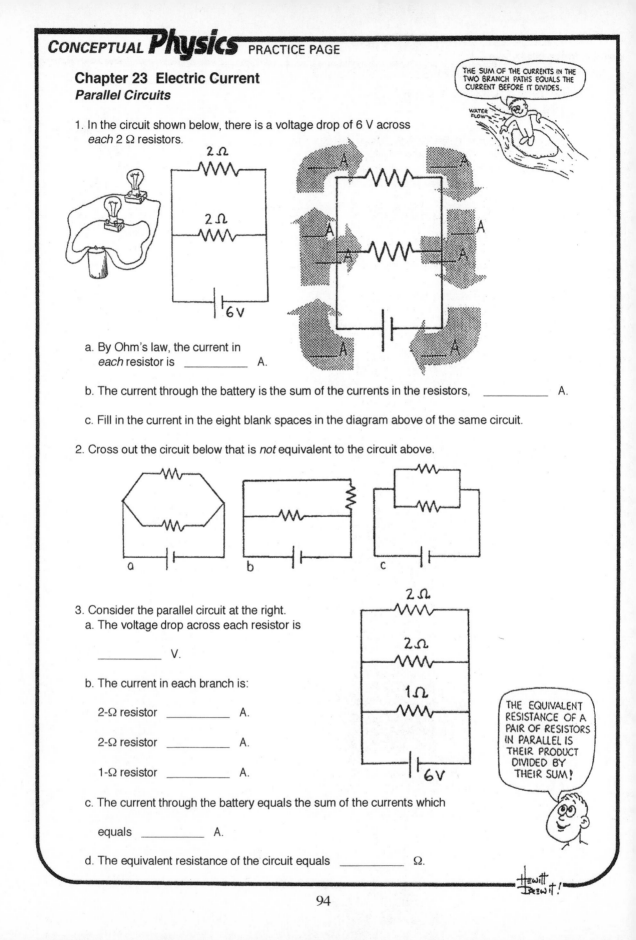

THE SUM OF THE CURRENTS IN THE TWO BRANCH PATHS EQUALS THE CURRENT BEFORE IT DIVIDES.

WATER FLOW

1. In the circuit shown below, there is a voltage drop of 6 V across *each* 2 Ω resistors.

2 Ω

2 Ω

6 V

A   A

A   A

A   A

A   A

a. By Ohm's law, the current in *each* resistor is _____ A.

b. The current through the battery is the sum of the currents in the resistors, _____ A.

c. Fill in the current in the eight blank spaces in the diagram above of the same circuit.

2. Cross out the circuit below that is *not* equivalent to the circuit above.

a   b   c

3. Consider the parallel circuit at the right.
   a. The voltage drop across each resistor is

   _____ V.

   b. The current in each branch is:

   2-Ω resistor _____ A.

   2-Ω resistor _____ A.

   1-Ω resistor _____ A.

   c. The current through the battery equals the sum of the currents which

   equals _____ A.

   d. The equivalent resistance of the circuit equals _____ Ω.

2 Ω

2 Ω

1 Ω

6 V

THE EQUIVALENT RESISTANCE OF A PAIR OF RESISTORS IN PARALLEL IS THEIR PRODUCT DIVIDED BY THEIR SUM!

Name _____   Date _____

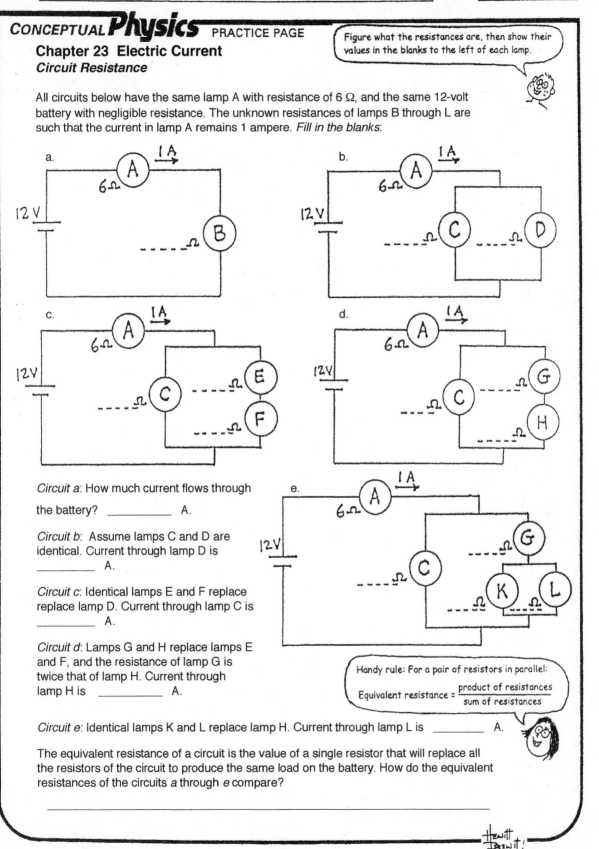

CONCEPTUAL **Physics** PRACTICE PAGE

Chapter 23 Electric Current
Circuit Resistance

Figure what the resistances are, then show their values in the blanks to the left of each lamp.

All circuits below have the same lamp A with resistance of 6 Ω, and the same 12-volt battery with negligible resistance. The unknown resistances of lamps B through L are such that the current in lamp A remains 1 ampere. *Fill in the blanks*:

a.

b.

c.

d.

e.

Circuit a: How much current flows through the battery? _____ A.

Circuit b: Assume lamps C and D are identical. Current through lamp D is _____ A.

Circuit c: Identical lamps E and F replace replace lamp D. Current through lamp C is _____ A.

Circuit d: Lamps G and H replace lamps E and F, and the resistance of lamp G is twice that of lamp H. Current through lamp H is _____ A.

Handy rule: For a pair of resistors in parallel:

$$\text{Equivalent resistance} = \frac{\text{product of resistances}}{\text{sum of resistances}}$$

Circuit e: Identical lamps K and L replace lamp H. Current through lamp L is _____ A.

The equivalent resistance of a circuit is the value of a single resistor that will replace all the resistors of the circuit to produce the same load on the battery. How do the equivalent resistances of the circuits *a* through *e* compare?

_____

_____

95

Chapter 23 Electric Current
Electric Power in Circuits

The table beside circuit *a* below shows the current through each resistor, the voltage across each resistor, and the power dissipated as heat in each resistor. Find the similar correct values for circuits *b* through *d*, and *write* your answers in the tables shown.

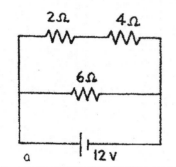

a 12 V

RESISTANCE	CURRENT ×	VOLTAGE =	POWER
2 Ω	2 A	4 V	8 W
4 Ω	2 A	8 V	16 W
6 Ω	2 A	12 V	2A W

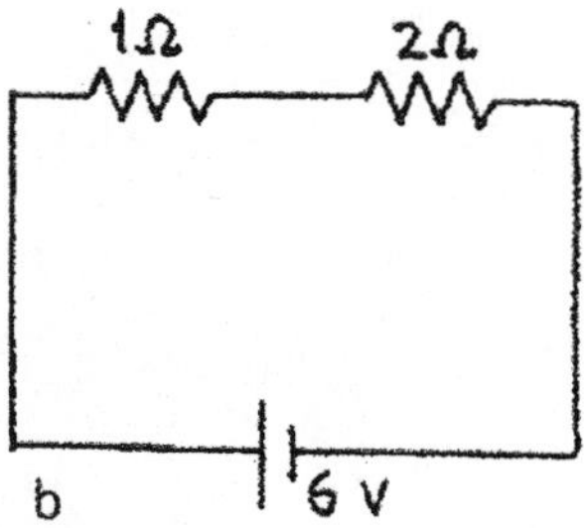

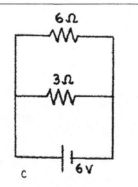

b 6 V

RESISTANCE	CURRENT ×	VOLTAGE =	POWER
1 Ω			
2 Ω			

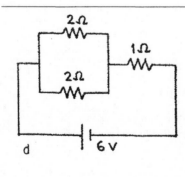

c 6 V

RESISTANCE	CURRENT ×	VOLTAGE =	POWER
6 Ω			
3 Ω			

d 6 V

RESISTANCE	CURRENT ×	VOLTAGE =	POWER
2 Ω			
2 Ω			
1 Ω			

CONCEPTUAL *Physics* PRACTICE PAGE

Chapter 24 Magnetism
Magnetic Fundamentals

Fill in the blanks:

1. Attraction or repulsion of charges depends on their *signs*, positives or negatives. Attraction or repulsion of magnets depends on their magnetic _____:
_____ or _____.

2. Opposite poles attract; like poles _____.

3. A magnetic field is produced by the _____ of electric charge.

4. Clusters of magnetically aligned atoms are magnetic _____.

5. A magnetic _____ surrounds a current-carrying wire.

6. When a current-carrying wire is made to form a coil around a piece of iron, the result is an

_____

7. A charged particle moving in a magnetic field experiences a deflecting _____

that is maximum when the charge moves _____ to the field.

8. A current-carrying wire experiences a deflecting _____ that is maximum when the wire

and magnetic field are _____ to one another.

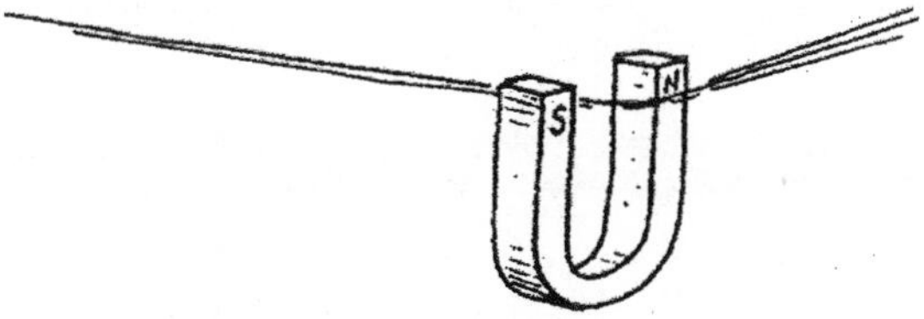

9. A simple instrument designed to detect electric current is the _____ ; when

calibrated to measure current, it is an _____ ; when calibrated to measure voltage,

it is a _____

10. The largest size magnet in the world is the _____ itself.

Chapter 24 Magnetism
Magnetic Fundamentals—continued

11. The illustration below is similar to Figure 24.2 in your textbook. Iron filings trace out patterns of magnetic field lines about a bar magnet. In the field are some magnetic compasses. The compass needle in only one compass is shown. Draw in the needles with proper orientation in the other compasses.

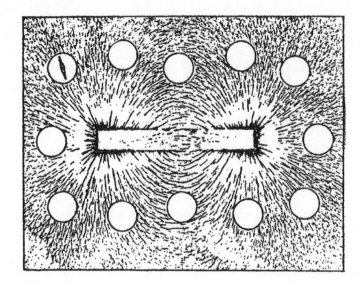

12. The illustration below is similar to Figure 24.10b in your textbook. Iron filings trace out magnetic field pattern about the loop of current-carrying wire. Draw in the compass needle orientations for all the compasses.

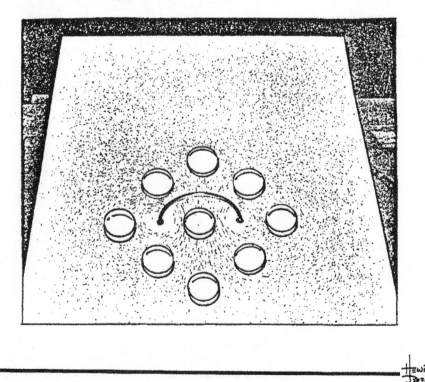

CONCEPTUAL **Physics** PRACTICE PAGE

Chapter 25 Electromagnetic Induction
Faraday's Law

Circle the correct answers:

1. Hans Christian Oersted discovered that magnetism and
   and electricity are

   [related]   [independent of each other].

   Magnetism is produced by

   [batteries]   [motion of electric charges].

Faraday and Henry discovered that electric current can be
produced by

   [batteries]   [motion of a magnet].

More specifically, voltage is induced in a loop of wire
if there is a change in

   [batteries]   [magnetic field in the loop].

This phenomenon is called

   [electromagnetism]   [electromagnetic induction].

2. When a magnet is plunged in and out of a coil of wire, voltage is induced in the coil. If the rate of
   the in-and-out motion of the magnet is doubled, the induced voltage

   [doubles]   [halves]   [remains the same].

   If instead the number of loops in the coil is doubled, the induced voltage

   [doubles]   [halves]   [remains the same].

3. A rapidly changing magnetic field in any region of space induces a rapidly changing

   [electric field]   [magnetic field]   [gravitational field]

   which in turn induces a rapidly changing

   [magnetic field]   [electric field]   [baseball field].

   This generation and regeneration of electric and magnetic fields make up

   [electromagnetic waves]   [sound waves]   [both of these].

Chapter 25 Electromagnet Induction
Transformers

Consider a simple transformer that has a 100-turn primary coil and a 1000-turn secondary coil. The primary is connected to a 120-V AC source and the secondary is connected to an electrical device with a resistance of 1000 ohms.

1. What will be the voltage output of the secondary?

   _____ V.

2. What current flows in the secondary circuit?

   _____ A.

3. Now that you know the voltage and the current, what is the power in the secondary coil?

   _____ W.

4. Neglecting small heating losses, and knowing that energy is conserved, what is the power in the primary coil?

   _____ W.

5. Now that you know the power and the voltage across the primary coil, what is the current drawn by the primary coil?

   _____ A.

Circle the answers:

6. The results show voltage is stepped [up] [down] from primary to secondary, and that

   current is correspondingly stepped [up] [down].

7. For a step-up transformer, there are [more] [fewer] turns in the secondary coil than in the primary.

   For such a transformer, there is [more] [less] current in the secondary than in the primary.

8. A transformer can step up [voltage] [energy and power] , but in no way can it step up

   [voltage] [energy and power].

9. If 120 V is used to power a toy electric train that operates on 6 V, then a [step up] [step down]

   transformer should be used that has a primary to secondary turns ratio of [1/20] [20/1].

10. A transformer operates on [dc] [ac]

   because the magnetic field within the iron core

   must [continually change] [remain steady].

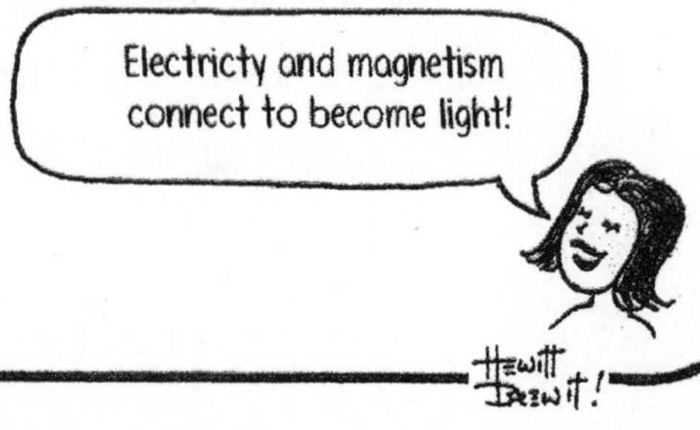

Electricty and magnetism connect to become light!

Name _____   Date _____

CONCEPTUAL **Physics** PRACTICE PAGE

Chapter 26 Properties of Light
Speed, Wavelength, and Frequency

1. The first investigation that led to a determination of the speed of light was performed in about 1675 by the Danish astronomer Olaus Roemer. He made careful measurements of the period of Io, a moon about the planet Jupiter, and was surprised to find an irregularity in Io's observed period. While Earth was moving away from Jupiter, the measured periods were slightly longer than average. While Earth approached Jupiter, they were shorter than average. Roemer estimated that the cumulative discrepancy amounted to about 16.5 minutes. Later interpretations showed that what occurs is that light takes about 16.5 minutes to travel the extra 300,000,000-km distance across Earth's orbit. Aha! We have enough information to calculate the speed of light!

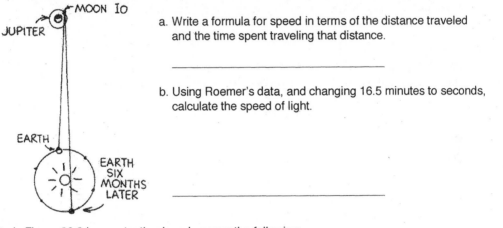

a. Write a formula for speed in terms of the distance traveled and the time spent traveling that distance.

_____

b. Using Roemer's data, and changing 16.5 minutes to seconds, calculate the speed of light.

_____

_____

Study Figure 26.3 in your textbook and answer the following:

2. a. Which has the longer *wavelengths*? [radio waves]   [light waves].

   b. Which has the longer *wavelengths*? [light waves]   [gamma waves].

   c. Which has the higher *frequencies*? [ultraviolet waves]   [infrared waves].

   d. Which has the higher *frequencies*? [ultraviolet waves]   [gamma rays].

Carefully study the section "Transparent Materials" in your textbook and answer the following:

3. a. Exactly what do vibrating electrons emit?

_____

   b. When ultraviolet light shines on glass, what does it do to electrons in the glass structure?

_____

   c. When energetic electrons in the glass structure vibrate against neighboring atoms, what happens to the energy of vibration?

_____

   d. What happens to the energy of a vibrating electron that does not collide with neighboring atoms?

_____

Chapter 26 Properties of Light
Speed, Wavelength, and Frequency—continued

e. Light in which range of frequencies is absorbed in glass?   [visible]   [ultraviolet].

f. Light in which range of frequencies is transmitted through glass?   [visible]   [ultraviolet].

g. How is the speed of light in glass affected by the succession of time delays that accompany the absorption and re-emission of light from atom to atom in the glass?

_____

h. How does the speed of light compare in water, glass, and diamond?

_____

4. The Sun normally shines on both Earth and Moon. Both cast shadows. Sometimes the Moon's shadow falls on Earth, and at other times Earth's shadow falls on the Moon.

a. The sketch shows the Sun and Earth. Draw the Moon at a position for a solar eclipse.

b. This sketch also shows the Sun and Earth. Draw the Moon at a position for a lunar eclipse.

5. The diagram shows the limits of light rays when a large lamp makes a shadow of a small object on a screen. Make a sketch of the shadow on the screen, shading the umbra darker than the penumbra. In what part of the shadow could an ant on the screen see part of the lamp?

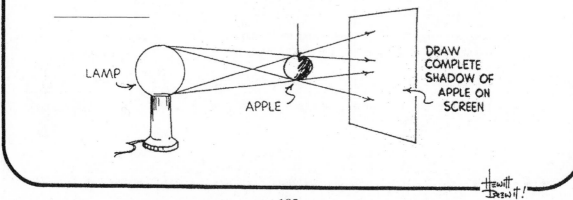

CONCEPTUAL *Physics* PRACTICE PAGE

Chapter 27 Color
Color Addition

The sketch to the right shows the shadow
of an instructor in front of a white screen
in a dark room. The light source is red,
so the screen looks red and the shadow
looks black. Color the sketch, or label
the colors with pen or pencil.

A green lamp is added and makes a
second shadow. The shadow cast by
the red lamp is no longer black, but is
illuminated by green light. So it is green.
Color or mark it green. The shadow
cast by the green lamp is not black
because it is illuminated by the red lamp.
Indicate its color. Do the same for the
background, which receives a mixture
of red and green light.

A blue lamp is added and three shadows
appear. Indicate the appropriate colors
of the shadows and the background.

The lamps are placed closer together
so the shadows overlap. Indicate the
colors of all screen areas.

Chapter 27 Color
Color Addition—continued

If you have colored markers or pencils, have a try at these.

CONCEPTUAL *Physics* PRACTICE PAGE

Chapter 28 Reflection and Refraction
Pool Room Optics

The law of reflection for optics is useful in playing pool. A ball bouncing off the bank of a pool table behaves like a photon reflecting off a mirror. As the sketch shows, angles become straight lines with the help of mirrors. The diagram shows a top view of this, with a flattened "mirrored" region. Note that the angled path on the table appears as a straight line (dashed) in the mirrored region.

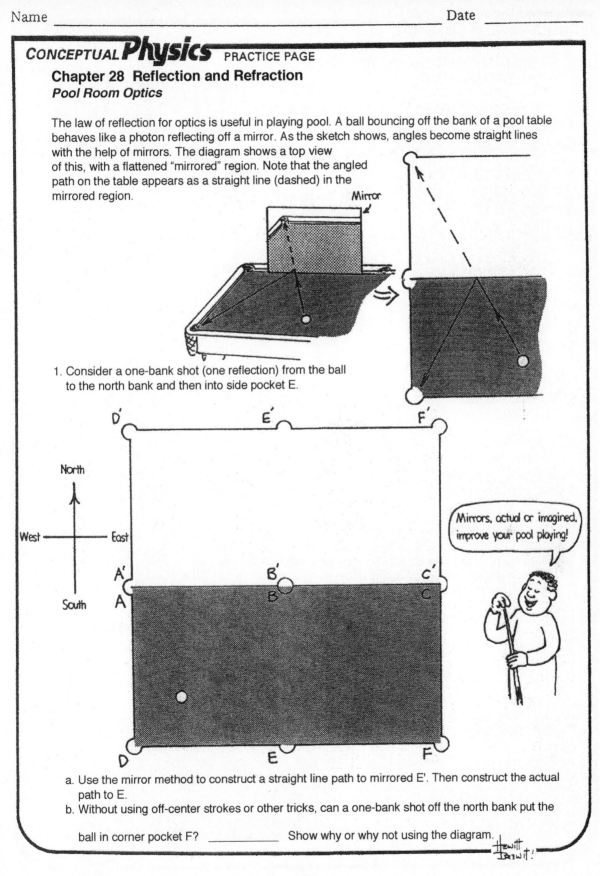

1. Consider a one-bank shot (one reflection) from the ball to the north bank and then into side pocket E.

North

West —— East

South

Mirrors, actual or imagined, improve your pool playing!

a. Use the mirror method to construct a straight line path to mirrored E'. Then construct the actual path to E.

b. Without using off-center strokes or other tricks, can a one-bank shot off the north bank put the

ball in corner pocket F? _____ Show why or why not using the diagram.

Chapter 28 Reflection and Refraction
Pool Room Optics—continued

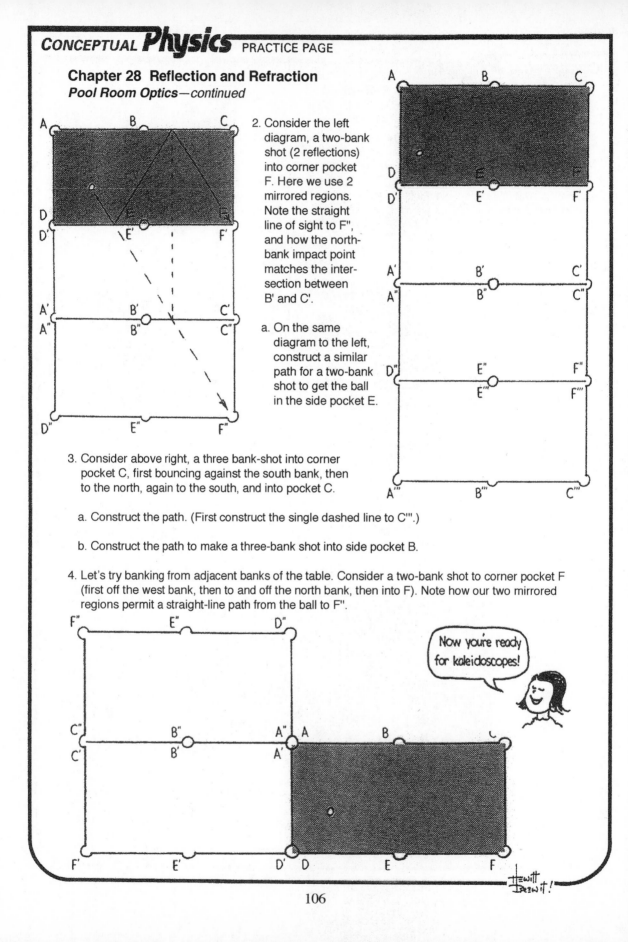

2. Consider the left diagram, a two-bank shot (2 reflections) into corner pocket F. Here we use 2 mirrored regions. Note the straight line of sight to F", and how the north-bank impact point matches the inter-section between B' and C'.

a. On the same diagram to the left, construct a similar path for a two-bank shot to get the ball in the side pocket E.

3. Consider above right, a three bank-shot into corner pocket C, first bouncing against the south bank, then to the north, again to the south, and into pocket C.

   a. Construct the path. (First construct the single dashed line to C'''.)

   b. Construct the path to make a three-bank shot into side pocket B.

4. Let's try banking from adjacent banks of the table. Consider a two-bank shot to corner pocket F (first off the west bank, then to and off the north bank, then into F). Note how our two mirrored regions permit a straight-line path from the ball to F".

Now you're ready for kaleidoscopes!

CONCEPTUAL **Physics** PRACTICE PAGE

Chapter 28 Reflection and Refraction
Reflection

Abe and Bev both look in a plane mirror directly in front of Abe (left view). Abe can see himself while Bev cannot see herself—but can Abe see Bev, and can Bev see Abe?

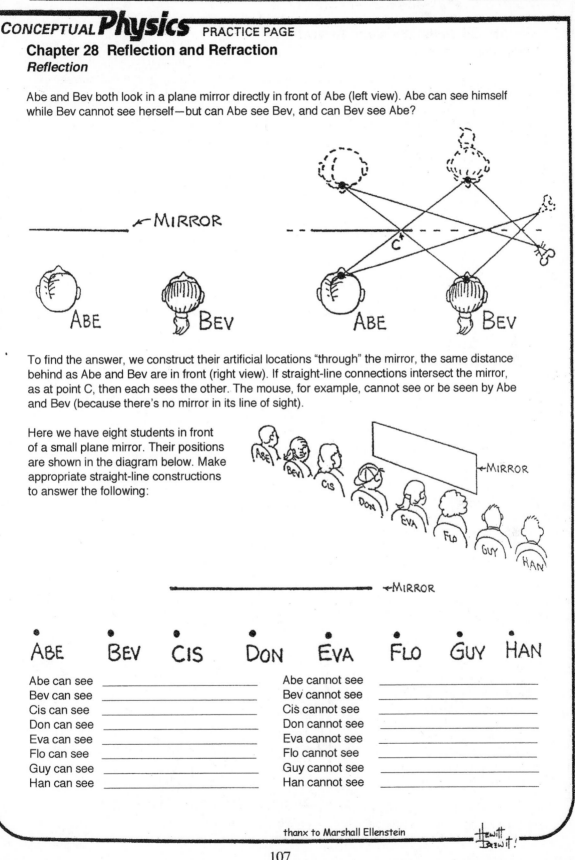

To find the answer, we construct their artificial locations "through" the mirror, the same distance behind as Abe and Bev are in front (right view). If straight-line connections intersect the mirror, as at point C, then each sees the other. The mouse, for example, cannot see or be seen by Abe and Bev (because there's no mirror in its line of sight).

Here we have eight students in front of a small plane mirror. Their positions are shown in the diagram below. Make appropriate straight-line constructions to answer the following:

Abe can see _____	Abe cannot see _____
Bev can see _____	Bev cannot see _____
Cis can see _____	Cis cannot see _____
Don can see _____	Don cannot see _____
Eva can see _____	Eva cannot see _____
Flo can see _____	Flo cannot see _____
Guy can see _____	Guy cannot see _____
Han can see _____	Han cannot see _____

thanx to Marshall Ellenstein

Chapter 28 Reflections and Refractions
Reflection—continued

Six of our group are now arranged differently in front of the same plane mirror. Their positions are shown below. Make appropriate constructions for this interesting arrangement, and answer the questions provided below:

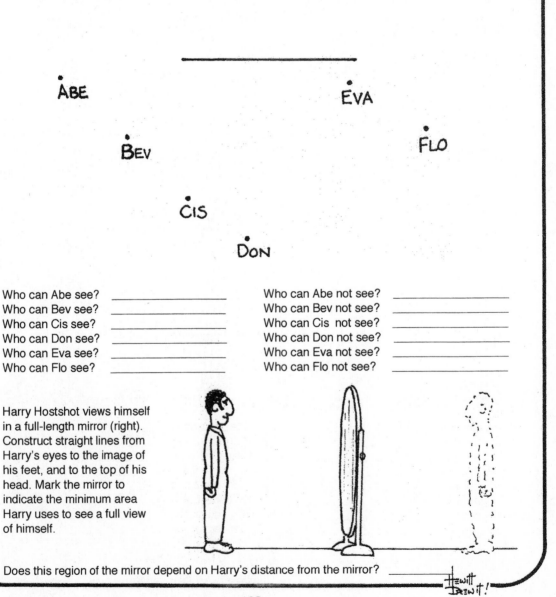

Who can Abe see? _____
Who can Bev see? _____
Who can Cis see? _____
Who can Don see? _____
Who can Eva see? _____
Who can Flo see? _____

Who can Abe not see? _____
Who can Bev not see? _____
Who can Cis not see? _____
Who can Don not see? _____
Who can Eva not see? _____
Who can Flo not see? _____

Harry Hostshot views himself in a full-length mirror (right). Construct straight lines from Harry's eyes to the image of his feet, and to the top of his head. Mark the mirror to indicate the minimum area Harry uses to see a full view of himself.

Does this region of the mirror depend on Harry's distance from the mirror? _____

Chapter 28 Reflection and Refraction
Reflected Views

1. The ray diagram below shows the extension of one of the reflected rays from the plane mirror.

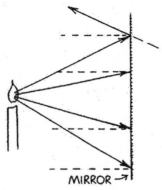

MIRROR ⟶

Complete the above diagram:
a. Carefully draw the three other reflected rays.
b. Extend your drawn rays behind the mirror to locate the image of the flame.
   (Assume the candle and image are viewed by an observer on the left.)

2. A girl takes a photograph of the bridge as shown. Which of the two sketches below correctly shows the reflected view of the bridge? Defend your answer.

_____

_____

Chapter 28 Reflection and Refraction
More Reflection

1. Light from a flashlight shines on a mirror and illuminates one of the cards. Draw the reflected beam to indicate the illuminated card.

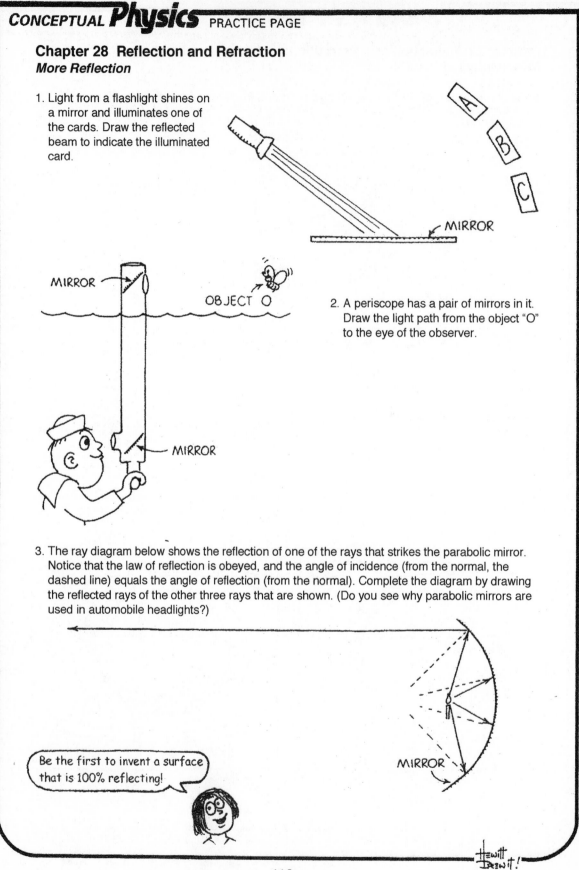

2. A periscope has a pair of mirrors in it. Draw the light path from the object "O" to the eye of the observer.

3. The ray diagram below shows the reflection of one of the rays that strikes the parabolic mirror. Notice that the law of reflection is obeyed, and the angle of incidence (from the normal, the dashed line) equals the angle of reflection (from the normal). Complete the diagram by drawing the reflected rays of the other three rays that are shown. (Do you see why parabolic mirrors are used in automobile headlights?)

Be the first to invent a surface that is 100% reflecting!

CONCEPTUAL **Physics** PRACTICE PAGE

Chapter 28 Reflection and Refraction
Refraction

1. A pair of toy cart wheels are rolled obliquely from a smooth surface onto two plots of grass—a rectangular plot on the left, and a triangular plot on the right. The ground is on a slight incline so that after slowing down in the grass, the wheels speed up again when emerging on the smooth surface. Finish each sketch and show some positions of the wheels inside the plots and on the other side. Clearly indicate their paths and directions of travel.

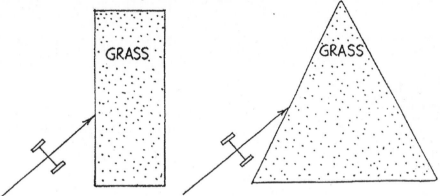

2. Red, green, and blue rays of light are incident upon a glass prism as shown below. The average speed of red light in the glass is less than in air, so the red ray is refracted. When it emerges into the air it regains its original speed and travels in the direction shown. Green light takes longer to get through the glass. Because of its slower speed it is refracted as shown. Blue light travels even slower in glass. Complete the diagram by estimating the path of the blue ray.

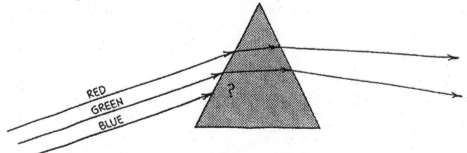

3. Below we consider a prism-shaped hole in a piece of glass—that is, an "air prism." Complete the diagram, showing likely paths of the beams of red, green, and blue light as they pass through this "prism" and then into glass.

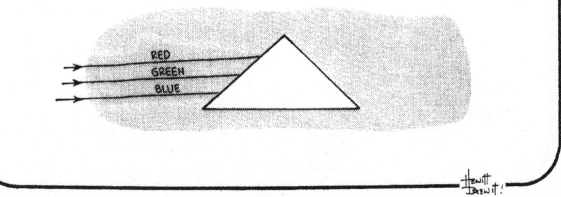

Chapter 28 Reflection and Refraction
Refraction—continued

4. Light of different colors diverges when emerging from a prism. Newton showed that with a second prism he could make the diverging beams become parallel again. Which placement of the second prism will do this?

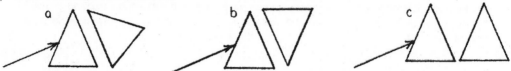

a   b   c

5. The sketch shows that due to refraction, the man sees the fish closer to the water surface than it actually is.

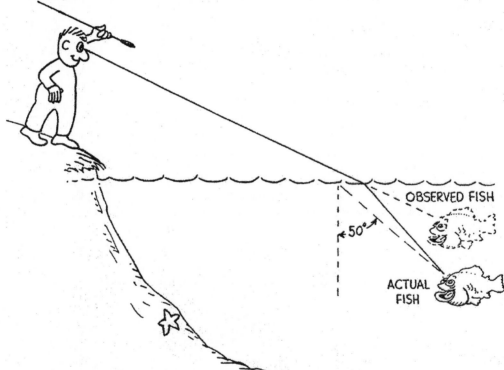

OBSERVED FISH

50°

ACTUAL FISH

a. Draw a ray beginning at the fish's eye to show the line of sight of the fish when it looks upward at 50° to the normal at the water surface. Draw the direction of the ray after it meets the surface of water.

b. At the 50° angle, does the fish see the man, or does it see the reflected view of the starfish at the bottom of the pond? Explain.

_____

c. To see the man, should the fish look higher or lower than the 50° path? _____

d. If the fish's eye were barely above the water surface, it would see the world above in a 180° view, horizon to horizon. The fisheye view of the world above as seen beneath the water, however, is very different. Due to the 48° critical angle of water, the fish sees a normally 180°

horizon-to-horizon view compressed within an angle of _____.

Name ______________________________ Date ____________

CONCEPTUAL **Physics** PRACTICE PAGE

Chapter 28 Reflection and Refraction

More Refraction

1. The sketch to the right shows a light ray moving from air into water, at 45° to the normal. Which of the three rays indicated with capital letters is most likely the light ray that continues inside the water?

____

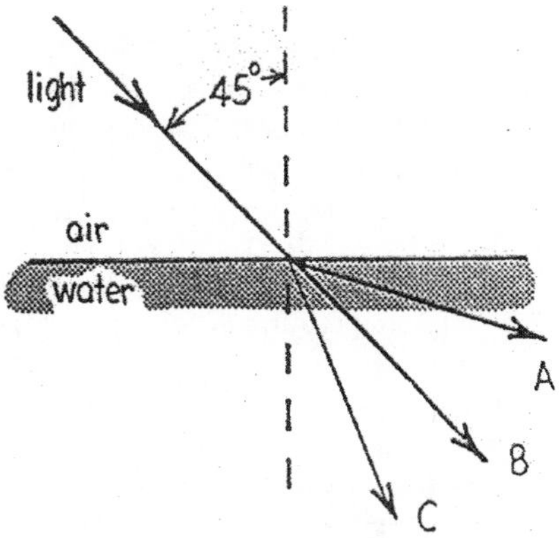

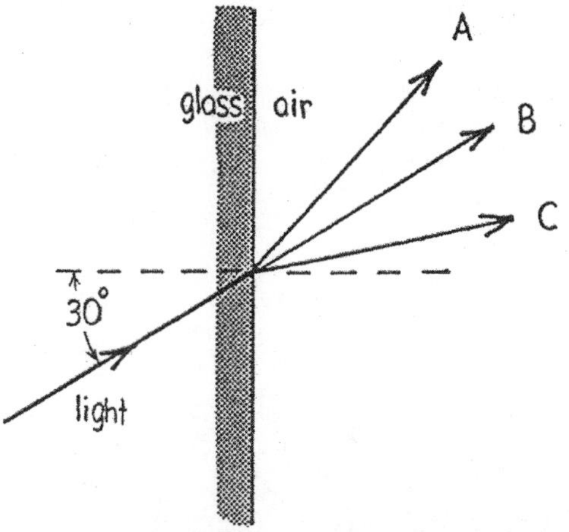

2. The sketch on the left shows a light ray moving from glass into air, at 30° to the normal. Which of the three is most likely the light ray that continues in the air?

____

3. To the right, a light ray is shown moving from air into a glass block, at 40° to the normal. Which of the three rays is most likely the light ray that travels in the air after emerging from the opposite side of the block? (Sketch the path the light would take inside the glass.)

____

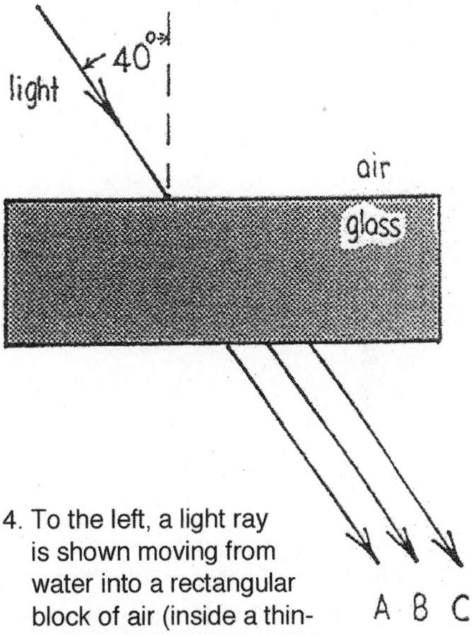

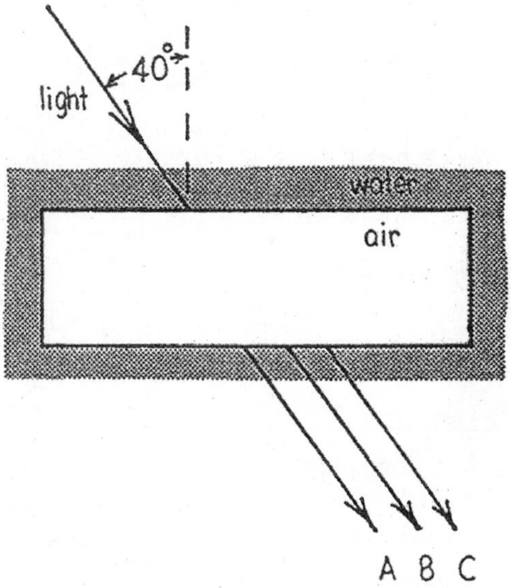

4. To the left, a light ray is shown moving from water into a rectangular block of air (inside a thin-walled plastic box), at 40° to the normal. Which of the rays is most likely the light ray that continues into the water on the opposite side of the block?

____

Sketch the path the light would take inside the air.

thanx to Clarence Bakken

Chapter 28 Reflection and Refraction
More Refraction—continued

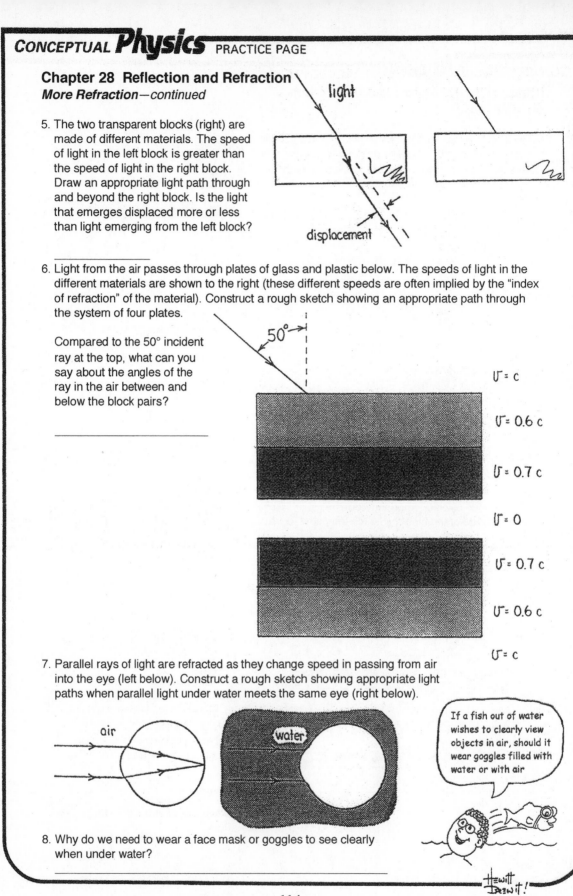

5. The two transparent blocks (right) are made of different materials. The speed of light in the left block is greater than the speed of light in the right block. Draw an appropriate light path through and beyond the right block. Is the light that emerges displaced more or less than light emerging from the left block?

———————————

6. Light from the air passes through plates of glass and plastic below. The speeds of light in the different materials are shown to the right (these different speeds are often implied by the "index of refraction" of the material). Construct a rough sketch showing an appropriate path through the system of four plates.

Compared to the 50° incident ray at the top, what can you say about the angles of the ray in the air between and below the block pairs?

———————————————————

$U = c$

$U = 0.6\ c$

$U = 0.7\ c$

$U = 0$

$U = 0.7\ c$

$U = 0.6\ c$

$U = c$

7. Parallel rays of light are refracted as they change speed in passing from air into the eye (left below). Construct a rough sketch showing appropriate light paths when parallel light under water meets the same eye (right below).

air

water

If a fish out of water wishes to clearly view objects in air, should it wear goggles filled with water or with air

8. Why do we need to wear a face mask or goggles to see clearly when under water?

———————————————————————————————

CONCEPTUAL *Physics* PRACTICE PAGE

Chapter 28 Reflection and Refraction
Lenses

Rays of light bend as shown when passing through the glass blocks.

1. Show how light rays bend when they pass through the arrangement of glass blocks below.

2. Show how light rays bend when they pass through the lens below. Is the lens a converging or a diverging lens? What is your evidence?

3. Show how light rays bend when they pass through the arrangement of glass blocks below.

4. Show how light rays bend when they pass through the lens shown below. Is the lens a converging or diverging lens? What is your evidence?

Chapter 28 Reflection and Refraction
Lenses—continued

5. Which type of lens is used to corrected farsightedness? _____
   Nearsightedness? _____

6. Construct rays to find the location and relative size of the arrow's image for each of the lenses. Rays that pass through the middle of a lens continue undeviated. In a converging lens, rays from the tip of the arrow that are parallel to the optic axis extend through the far focal point after going through the lens. Rays that go through the near focal point travel parallel to the axis after going through the lens. In a diverging lens, rays parallel to the axis diverge and appear to originate from the near focal point after passing through the lens. Have fun!

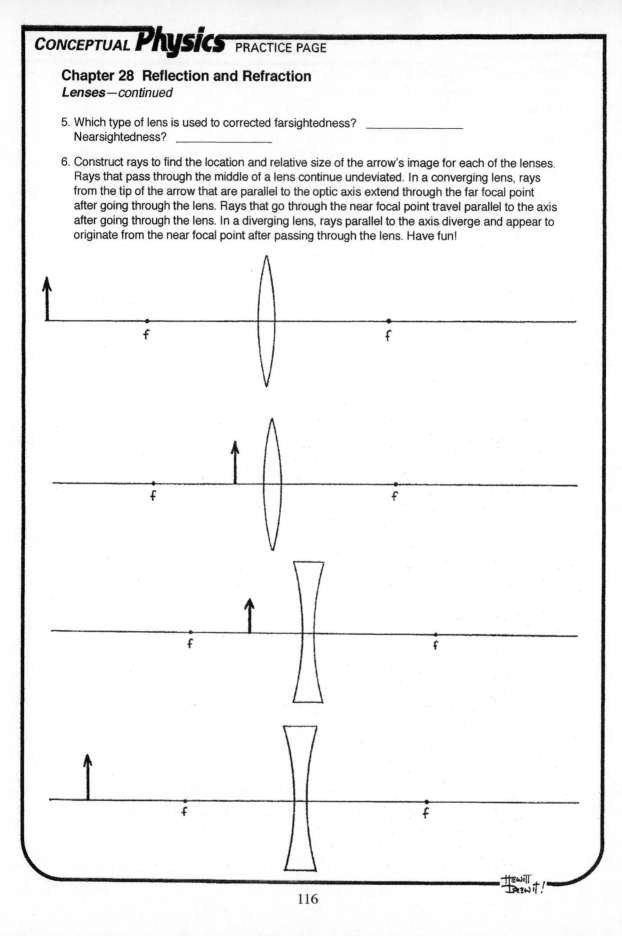

CONCEPTUAL *Physics* PRACTICE PAGE

Chapter 29 Light Waves
Diffraction and Interference

1. Shown are concentric solid and dashed circles, each different in radius by 1 cm. Consider the circular pattern a top view of water waves, where the solid circles are crests and the dashed circles are troughs.

   a. Draw another set of the same concentric circles with a compass. Choose any part of the paper for your center (except the present central point). Let the circles run off the edge of the paper.

   b. Find where a dashed line crosses a solid line and draw a large dot at the intersection. Do this for ALL places where a solid and dashed line intersect.

   c. With a wide felt marker, connect the dots with the solid lines. These *nodal lines* lie in regions where the waves have cancelled—where the crest of one wave overlaps the trough of another (see Figures 29.15 and 29.16 in your textbook).

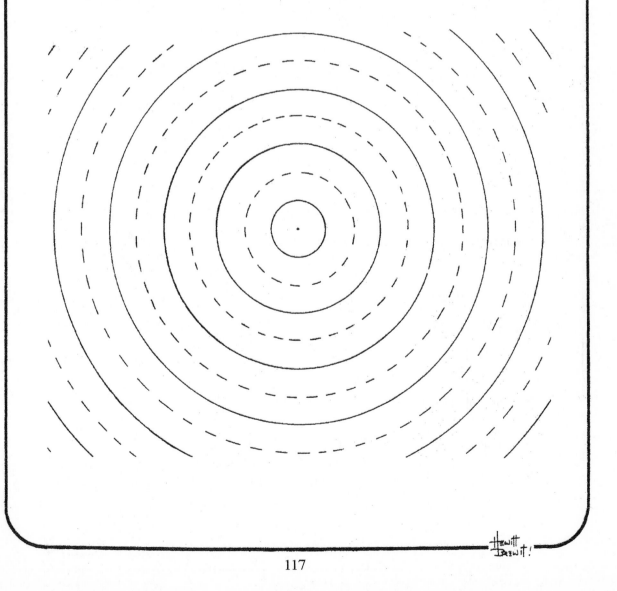

Chapter 29 Light Waves
Diffraction and Interference—continued

2. Look at the construction of overlapping circles on your classmates' papers. Some will have more nodal lines than others, due to different starting points. How does the number of nodal lines in a pattern relate to the distance between centers of circles, (or sources of waves)?

_____

_____

3. Figure 29.19 from your textbook is repeated below. Carefully count the number of wavelengths (same as the number of wave crests) along the following paths between the slits and the screen.

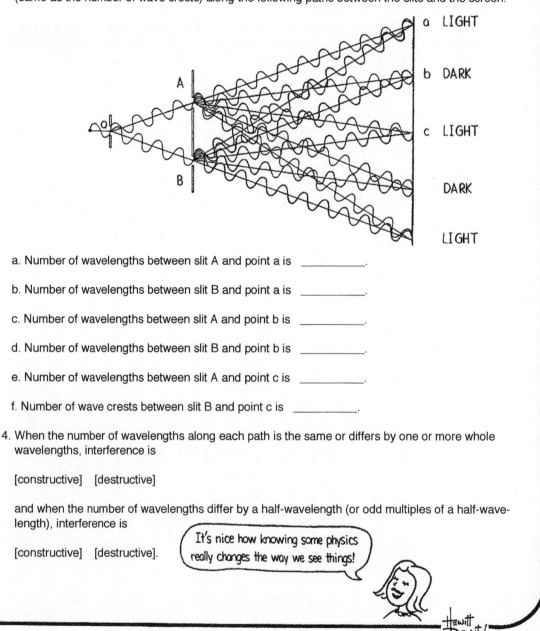

a. Number of wavelengths between slit A and point a is _____.

b. Number of wavelengths between slit B and point a is _____.

c. Number of wavelengths between slit A and point b is _____.

d. Number of wavelengths between slit B and point b is _____.

e. Number of wavelengths between slit A and point c is _____.

f. Number of wave crests between slit B and point c is _____.

4. When the number of wavelengths along each path is the same or differs by one or more whole wavelengths, interference is

[constructive]   [destructive]

and when the number of wavelengths differ by a half-wavelength (or odd multiples of a half-wavelength), interference is

[constructive]   [destructive].

It's nice how knowing some physics really changes the way we see things!

Chapter 29 Light Waves
Polarization

The amplitude of a light wave has magnitude and direction, and can be represented by a vector. Polarized light that vibrates in a single direction is represented by a single vector. To the left the single vector represents vertically polarized light. The pair of perpendicular vectors to the right represents nonpolarized light. The vibrations of nonpolarized light are equal in all directions, with as many vertical components as horizontal components.

1. In the sketch below, nonpolarized light from a flashlight strikes a pair of Polaroid filters.

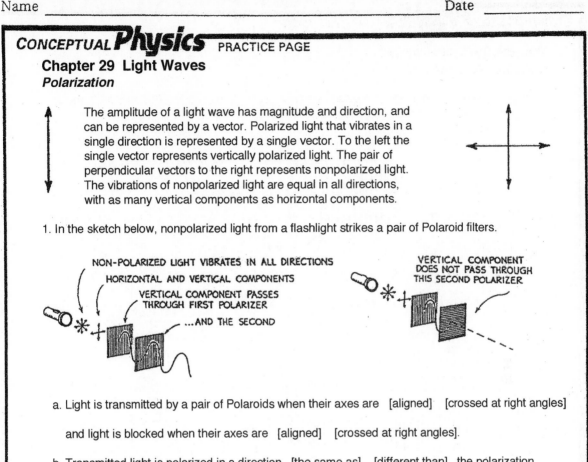

a. Light is transmitted by a pair of Polaroids when their axes are   [aligned]   [crossed at right angles]

   and light is blocked when their axes are   [aligned]   [crossed at right angles].

b. Transmitted light is polarized in a direction   [the same as]   [different than]   the polarization axis of the filter.

2. Consider the transmission of light through a pair of Polaroids with polarization axes at 45° to each other. Although in practice the Polaroids are one atop the other, we show them spread out side by side below. From left to right:
   (a) Nonpolarized light is represented by its horizontal and vertical components.
   (b) These components strike filter A.
   (c) The vertical component is transmitted, and
   (d) falls upon filter B. This vertical component is not aligned with the polarization axis of filter B, but it has a component that is aligned—component *t*,
   (e) which is transmitted.

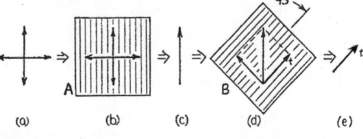

a. The amount of light that gets through Filter B, compared to the amount that gets through

   Filter A is   [more]   [less]   [the same].

b. The component perpendicular to *t* that falls on Filter B is   [also transmitted]   [absorbed].

Chapter 29 Light Waves
Polarization—continued

3. Below are a pair of Polaroids with polarization axes at 30° to each other. Carefully draw vectors and appropriate components (as in Question 2) to show the vector that emerges at *e*.

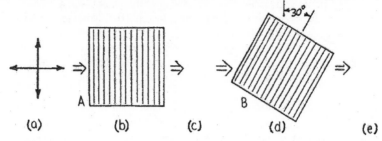

(a)   (b)   (c)   (d)   (e)

a. The amount of light that gets through the Polaroids at 30°, compared to the amount that gets

through the 45° Polaroids is   [less]   [more]   [the same].

4. Figure 29.35 in your textbook shows the smile of Ludmila Hewitt emerging through three Polaroids. Use vector diagrams to complete steps *b* through *g* below to show how light gets through the three-Polaroid system.

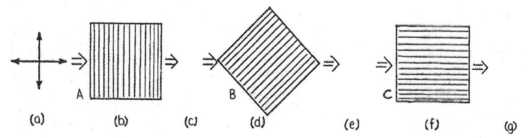

(a)   (b)   (c)   (d)   (e)   (f)   (g)

5. A novel use of polarization is shown below. How do the polarized side windows in these next-to-each-other houses provide privacy for the occupants? (Who can see what?)

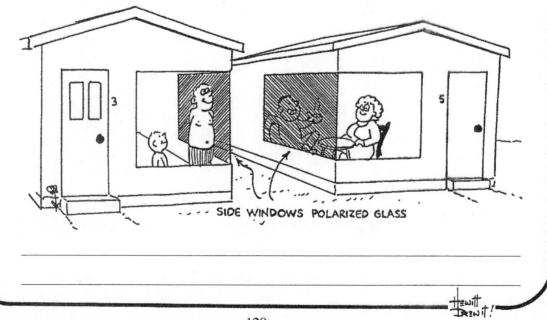

SIDE WINDOWS POLARIZED GLASS

CONCEPTUAL *Physics* PRACTICE PAGE

Chapters 31 and 32 Light Quanta and The Atom and The Quantum
Light Quanta

1. To say that light is quantized means that light is made up of

   [elemental units]   [waves].

2. Compared to photons of low-frequency light, photons of higher-frequency light have more

   [energy]   [speed]   [quanta].

3. The photoelectric effect supports the

   [wave model of light]   [particle model of light].

4. The photoelectric effect is evident when light shone on certain

   photosensitive materials ejects [photon]   [electrons].

5. The photoelectric effect is more effective with violet light than with red light because the photons

   [resonate with the atoms in the material]

   [deliver more energy to the material]

   [are more numerous].

6. According to De Broglie's wave model of matter, a beam of light

   and a beam of electrons [are fundamentally different]   [are similar].

7. According to De Broglie, the greater the speed of an electron beam, the

   [longer is its wavelength]   [shorter is its wavelength].

8. The discreteness of the energy levels of electrons about the atomic nucleus is best understood

   by considering the electron to be a [wave]   [particle].

9. Heavier atoms are not appreciably larger in size than lighter atoms. The main reason for this is that the greater nuclear charge

   [pulls surrounding electrons into tighter orbits]

   [holds more electrons about the atomic nucleus]

   [produces a denser atomic structure].

10. Whereas in the everyday macroworld the study of motion is called *mechanics* in the microworld the study of quanta is called

   [Newtonian mechanics]   [quantum mechanics].

A QUANTUM MECHANIC!

CONCEPTUAL **Physics** PRACTICE PAGE

Chapter 33 Atomic Nucleus and Radioactivity
Radioactivity

Complete the following statements:

1.a. A lone neutron spontaneously decays into a proton plus an _____ .

 b. Alpha and beta rays are made of streams of particles, whereas gamma rays are streams of

   _____ .

 c. An electrically charged atom is called an _____ .

 d. Different _____ of an element are chemically
    identical but differ in the number of neutrons in the nucleus.

 e. Transuranic elements are those beyond atomic number _____ .

 f. If the amount of a certain radioactive sample decreases by half in four weeks,

    in four more weeks the amount remaining should be _____
    the original amount.

 g. Water from a natural hot spring is warmed by _____ inside Earth.

2. The gas in the little girl's balloon is made up of former alpha and beta particles produced by
   radioactive decay.

 a. If the mixture is electrically neutral, how many more
    beta particles than alpha particles are in the balloon?

    _____

    _____

 b. Why is your answer to the above not the "same"?

    _____

    _____

 c. Why are the alpha and beta particles no longer harmful
    to the child?

    _____

    _____

    _____

 d. What element does this mixture make?

    _____

Chapter 33 Atomic Nucleus and Radioactivity
Nuclear Reactions

Complete these nuclear reactions:

1. $^{238}_{92}U \rightarrow {}^{234}_{90}Th + {}^{4}_{2}\underline{\quad}$

THORIUM LATE, I OVERTHLEPT!

2. $^{234}_{90}Th \rightarrow {}^{234}_{91}Pa + {}^{0}_{-1}\underline{\quad}$

3. $^{234}_{91}Pa \rightarrow \underline{\quad} + {}^{4}_{2}He$

4. $^{220}_{86}Rn \rightarrow \underline{\quad} + {}^{4}_{2}He$

5. $^{216}_{84}Po \rightarrow \underline{\quad} + {}^{0}_{-1}e$

6. $^{216}_{84}Po \rightarrow \underline{\quad} + {}^{4}_{2}He$

7. $^{210}_{83}Bi \rightarrow \underline{\quad} + {}^{0}_{-1}e$

NUCLEAR PHYSICS --- IT'S THE SAME TO ME WITH THE FIRST TWO LETTERS INTERCHANGED!

8. $^{1}_{0}n + {}^{10}_{5}B \rightarrow \underline{\quad} + {}^{4}_{2}He$

CONCEPTUAL *Physics* PRACTICE PAGE

Chapter 33 Atomic Nucleus and Radioactivity
Natural Transmutation

Fill in the decay-scheme diagram below, similar to that shown in Figure 33.14 in your textbook, but beginning with U-235 and ending with an isotope of lead. Use the table at the left, and identify each element in the series with its chemical symbol.

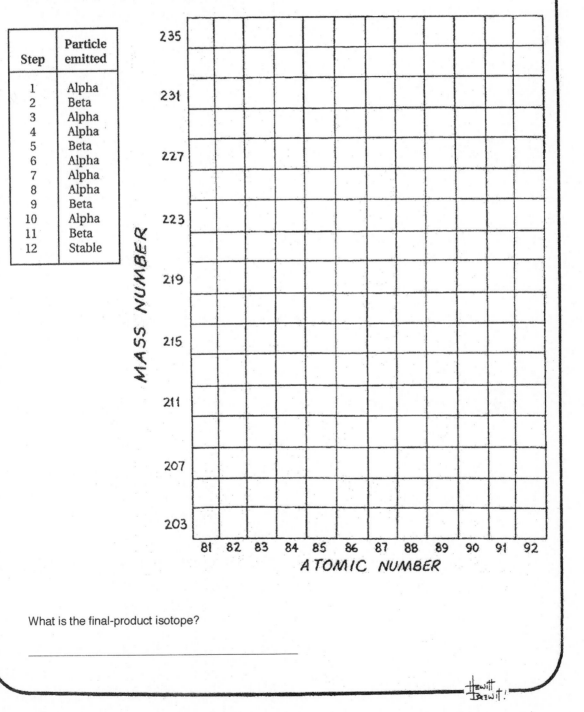

Step	Particle emitted
1	Alpha
2	Beta
3	Alpha
4	Alpha
5	Beta
6	Alpha
7	Alpha
8	Alpha
9	Beta
10	Alpha
11	Beta
12	Stable

What is the final-product isotope?

_____

Name _____   Date _____

Chapter 34 Nuclear Fission and Fusion
Nuclear Reactions

1. Complete the table for a chain reaction in which two neutrons from each step individually cause a new reaction.

EVENT	1	2	3	4	5	6	7
NO. OF REACTIONS	1	2	4				

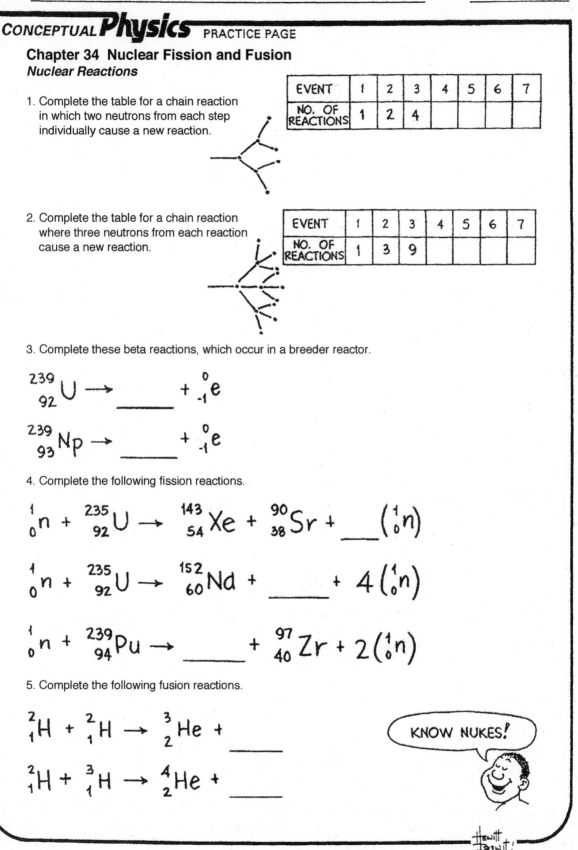

2. Complete the table for a chain reaction where three neutrons from each reaction cause a new reaction.

EVENT	1	2	3	4	5	6	7
NO. OF REACTIONS	1	3	9				

3. Complete these beta reactions, which occur in a breeder reactor.

$$^{239}_{92}U \rightarrow \underline{\quad\quad} + \,^{0}_{-1}e$$

$$^{239}_{93}Np \rightarrow \underline{\quad\quad} + \,^{0}_{-1}e$$

4. Complete the following fission reactions.

$$^{1}_{0}n + \,^{235}_{92}U \rightarrow \,^{143}_{54}Xe + \,^{90}_{38}Sr + \underline{\quad}(\,^{1}_{0}n)$$

$$^{1}_{0}n + \,^{235}_{92}U \rightarrow \,^{152}_{60}Nd + \underline{\quad\quad} + 4(\,^{1}_{0}n)$$

$$^{1}_{0}n + \,^{239}_{94}Pu \rightarrow \underline{\quad\quad} + \,^{97}_{40}Zr + 2(\,^{1}_{0}n)$$

5. Complete the following fusion reactions.

$$^{2}_{1}H + \,^{2}_{1}H \rightarrow \,^{3}_{2}He + \underline{\quad\quad}$$

$$^{2}_{1}H + \,^{3}_{1}H \rightarrow \,^{4}_{2}He + \underline{\quad\quad}$$

KNOW NUKES!

127

Name _____ Date _____

Chapter 35 Special Theory of Relativity
Time Dilation

Chapter 35 in your textbook discusses *The Twin Trip*, in which a traveling twin takes a 2-hour journey while a stay-at-home brother records the passage of 2 ½ hours. Quite remarkable! Times in both frames of reference are indicated by flashes of light, sent each 6 minutes from the spaceship, and received on Earth at 12-minute intervals for the spaceship leaving, and 3-minute intervals for the spaceship returning. Read this section in the book carefully, and fill in the clock readings aboard the spaceship when each flash is emitted, and on Earth when each flash is received.

FLASH	SHIP LEAVING EARTH TIME ON SHIP WHEN FLASH SENT	TIME ON EARTH WHEN FLASH SEEN	FLASH	SHIP APPROACHING EARTH TIME ON SHIP WHEN FLASH SEEN	TIME ON EARTH WHEN FLASH SEEN
0	12:00	12:00	11		
1	12:06		12		
2			13		
3			14		
4			15		
5			16		
6			17		
7			18		
8			19		
9			20		
10					

THIS CHECKS: FOR $v = 0.6c$

$$t = \frac{t_0}{\sqrt{1 - \left(\frac{v}{c}\right)^2}} = \frac{2 \text{ HR}}{\sqrt{1 - \left(\frac{0.6c}{c}\right)^2}} = 2.5 \text{ HR}$$

Hewitt Drewit!

ANSWERS TO THE PRACTICE PAGES

Compare your responses to the previous pages with my responses in the reduced ones that follow. You have the choice of taking a shortcut and looking at my responses first—or you can be nice to yourself and first work out your own—before looking. In working through the practice pages on your own or with friends, check your answers only *after* you've given them a good college try. Then you may experience the exhilaration that comes with doing a good thing well.

Learning can be enjoyable!

CONCEPTUAL *Physics* PRACTICE PAGE

Chapter 1 About Science
Making Hypotheses

The word science comes from Latin, meaning "to know."
The word *hypothesis* comes from Greek, "under an idea."
A hypothesis (an educated guess) often leads to new
knowledge and may help to establish a theory.

Examples:

1. It is well known that objects generally expand when
heated. An iron plate gets slightly bigger, for example,
when placed in an oven. But what of a hole in the middle
of the plate? One friend may say the size of the hole will
increase, and another may say it will decrease.

WHICH IS AN EDUCATED GUESS...
A HYPOTHESIS OR A THEORY?

WHICH RESULTS
FROM A LARGE
BODY OF
KNOWLEDGE?

a. What is your hypothesis about hole size, and if you
are wrong, is there a test for finding out?

HYP 1: HOLE GETS BIGGER, HYP 2: SMALLER, HYP 3: NO CHANGE

TEST: HEAT IT IN AN OVEN, THEN MEASURE! (HYP 1 IS CORRECT.)

I CUT A DISK FROM THIS
IRON PLATE. WHEN I HEAT
THE PLATE, WILL THE HOLE
GET BIGGER, OR SMALLER?

b. There are often several ways to test a hypothesis. For example, you can perform
a physical experiment and witness the results yourself, or you can use the library
or internet to find the reported results of other investigators. Which of these two
methods do you favor, and why?

(IT DEPENDS ON THE SITUATION—MOST RESEARCH INVOLVES BOTH.)

WHAT HAPPENS
IF HE PLUGS
THE DISK BACK
INTO THE HOLE
BEFORE HEATING
EVERYTHING?

2. Before the time of the printing press, books were hand-copied by scribes,
many of whom were monks in monasteries. There is the story of the scribe
who was frustrated to find a smudge on an important page he was copying.
The smudge blotted out part of the sentence that reported the number of
teeth in the head of a donkey. The scribe was very upset and didn't know
what to do. He consulted with other scribes to see if any of their books
stated the number of teeth in the head of a donkey. After many hours of
fruitless searching through the library, it was agreed that the best thing to
do was to send a messenger by donkey to the next monastery and continue
the search there. What would be your advice?

ACTUALLY LOOK IN THE DONKEY'S MOUTH AND COUNT!

Making Distinctions

Many people don't seem to see the difference between a thing and
the abuse of the thing. For example, a city council that bans skateboarding may not distinguish between skateboarding and reckless
skateboarding. A person who advocates that a particular technology
be banned may not distinguish between that technology and the
abuses of that technology. There's a difference between a thing and
the abuse of the thing.

On a separate sheet of paper, list other examples where use and abuse are often not distinguished.
Compare your list with others in your class.

CONCEPTUAL *Physics* PRACTICE PAGE

Chapter 1 About Science
Pinhole Formation

Look carefully on the round spots of light on the shady ground beneath trees. These are *sunballs*,
which are images of the sun. They are cast by openings between leaves in the trees that act as
pinholes. (Did you make a pinhole "camera" back in middle school?) Large sunballs, several
centimeters in diameter or so, are cast by openings that are relatively high above the ground,
while small ones are produced by
closer "pinholes." The interesting
point is that the ratio of the
diameter of the sunball to its
distance from the pinhole is the
same ratio of the Sun's diameter
to its distance from the pinhole.
We know the Sun is approximately
150,000,000 km from the pinhole, so careful measurements of
the ratio of diameter/distance
for a sunball leads you to the
diameter of the Sun. That's what
this page is about. Instead of
measuring sunballs under the
shade of trees on a sunny day,
make your own easier-to-
measure sunball.

150,000,000 km

1. Poke a small hole in a piece of card. Perhaps an index card will do, and
poke the hole with a sharp pencil or pen. Hold the card in the sunlight
and note the circular image that is cast. This is an image of the Sun.
Note that its size doesn't depend on the size of the hole in the card, but
only on its distance. The image is a circle when cast on a surface
perpendicular to the rays—otherwise it's "stretched out" as an ellipse.

2. Try holes of various shapes: say a square hole, or a triangular hole. What is the shape of the
image when its distance from the card is large compared with the size of the hole? Does the
shape of the pinhole make a difference?

IMAGE IS ALWAYS A CIRCLE. SHAPE OF PINHOLE IS *NOT* THE SHAPE OF THE

IMAGE CAST THROUGH IT (EXCEPT WHEN VERY CLOSE).

3. Measure the diameter of a small coin. Then place the coin on a viewing area that is perpendicular
to the Sun's rays. Position the card so the image of the sunball exactly covers the coin. Carefully
measure the distance between the coin and the small hole in the card. Complete the following:

$$\frac{\text{Diameter of sunball}}{\text{Distance of pinhole}} = \frac{d}{h} = \frac{1}{110} \quad \text{(SO SUN'S DIAMETER} = \frac{1}{110} \times 150,000,000 \text{ km)}.$$

With this ratio, estimate the diameter of the Sun. Show your work on
a separate piece of paper.

4. If you did this on a day when the Sun is partially eclipsed, what shape
of image would you expect to see?

WHAT SHAPE DO SUNBALLS
HAVE DURING A PARTIAL
ECLIPSE OF THE SUN?

UPSIDE-DOWN CRESCENT. IMAGE OF THE PARTIALLY-ECLIPSED SUN.

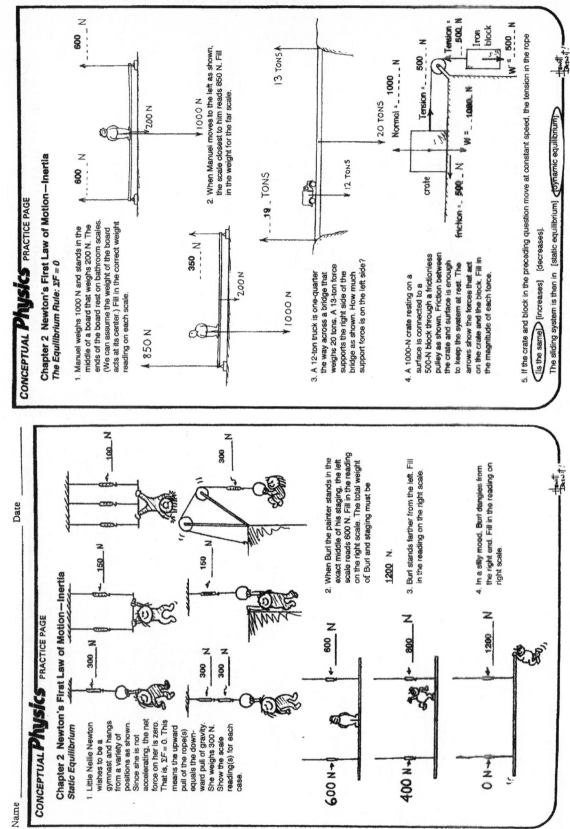

CONCEPTUAL Physics PRACTICE PAGE

Chapter 2 Newton's First Law of Motion—Inertia
Static Equilibrium

1. Little Nellie Newton wishes to be a gymnast and hangs from a variety of positions as shown. Since she is not accelerating, the net force on her is zero. That is, $\Sigma F = 0$. This means the upward pull of the rope(s) equals the downward pull of gravity. She weighs 300 N. Show the scale reading(s) for each case.

100 N   150 N   300 N

300 N   300 N

300 N

150 N

2. When Burl the painter stands in the exact middle of his staging, the left scale reads 600 N. Fill in the reading on the right scale. The total weight of Burl and staging must be 1200 N.

600 N→   600 N

3. Burl stands farther from the left. Fill in the reading on the right scale.

400 N→   800 N

4. In a silly mood, Burl dangles from the right end. Fill in the reading on right scale.

0 N→   1200 N

3

CONCEPTUAL Physics PRACTICE PAGE

Chapter 2 Newton's First Law of Motion—Inertia
The Equilibrium Rule: ΣF = 0

1. Manuel weighs 1000 N and stands in the middle of a board that weighs 200 N. The ends of the board rest on bathroom scales. (We can assume the weight of the board acts at its center.) Fill in the correct weight reading on each scale.

600 N   600 N
200 N
1000 N

2. When Manuel moves to the left as shown, the scale closest to him reads 850 N. Fill in the weight for the far scale.

850 N   350 N
200 N
1000 N

3. A 12-ton truck is one-quarter the way across a bridge that weighs 20 tons. A 13-ton force supports the right side of the bridge as shown. How much support force is on the left side?

13 TONS
19 TONS
12 TONS
20 TONS

4. A 1000-N crate resting on a surface is connected to a 500-N block through a frictionless pulley as shown. Friction between the crate and surface is enough to keep the system at rest. The arrows show the forces that act on the crate and the block. Fill in the magnitude of each force.

Tension = 500 N
Normal = 1000 N
Tension = 500 N
W = 1000 N
crate
friction = 500 N
Iron block
W = 500 N

5. If the crate and block in the preceding question move at constant speed, the tension in the rope [is the same] [increases] [decreases].

The sliding system is then in [static equilibrium] (dynamic equilibrium).

4

CONCEPTUAL *Physics* PRACTICE PAGE

Chapter 2 Newton's First Law of Motion—Inertia
Vectors and Equilibrium

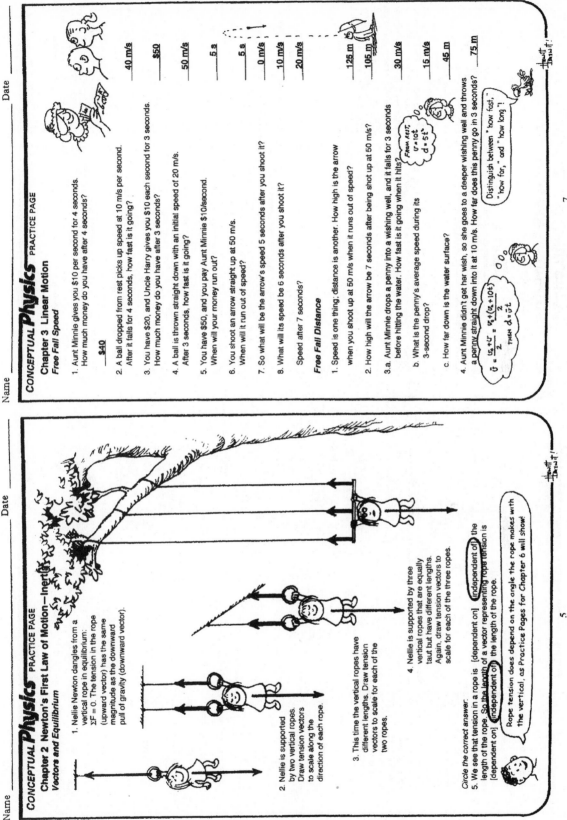

1. Nellie Newton dangles from a vertical rope in equilibrium: $\Sigma F = 0$. The tension in the rope (upward vector) has the same magnitude as the downward pull of gravity (downward vector).

2. Nellie is supported by two vertical ropes. Draw tension vectors to scale along the direction of each rope.

3. This time the vertical ropes have different lengths. Draw tension vectors to scale for each of the two ropes.

4. Nellie is supported by three vertical ropes that are equally taut but have different lengths. Again, draw tension vectors to scale for each of the three ropes.

Circle the correct answer.

5. We see that tension in a rope is [dependent on] (independent of) the length of the rope. So the length of a vector representing rope tension is [dependent on] (independent of) the length of the rope.

Rope tension does depend on the angle the rope makes with the vertical, as Practice Pages for Chapter 6 will show!

5

CONCEPTUAL *Physics* PRACTICE PAGE

Chapter 3 Linear Motion
Free Fall Speed

1. Aunt Minnie gives you $10 per second for 4 seconds. How much money do you have after 4 seconds?

___$40___

2. A ball dropped from rest picks up speed at 10 m/s per second. After it falls for 4 seconds, how fast is it going?

___40 m/s___

3. You have $20, and Uncle Harry gives you $10 each second for 3 seconds. How much money do you have after 3 seconds?

___$50___

4. A ball is thrown straight down with an initial speed of 20 m/s. After 3 seconds, how fast is it going?

___50 m/s___

5. You have $50, and you pay Aunt Minnie $10/second. When will your money run out?

___5 s___

6. You shoot an arrow straight up at 50 m/s. When will it run out of speed?

___5 s___

7. So what will be the arrow's speed 5 seconds after you shoot it?

___0 m/s___

8. What will its speed be 6 seconds after you shoot it?

___10 m/s___

Speed after 7 seconds?

___20 m/s___

Free Fall Distance

1. Speed is one thing; distance is another. How high is the arrow when you shoot up at 50 m/s when it runs out of speed?

___125 m___

2. How high will the arrow be 7 seconds after being shot up at 50 m/s?

___105 m___

3. a. Aunt Minnie drops a penny into a wishing well, and it falls for 3 seconds before hitting the water. How fast is it going when it hits?

From rest,
$v = at$
$d = 5t^2$

___30 m/s___

b. What is the penny's average speed during its 3-second drop?

___15 m/s___

c. How far down is the water surface?

___45 m___

4. Aunt Minnie didn't get her wish, so she goes to a deeper wishing well and throws a penny straight down into it at 10 m/s. How far does this penny go in 3 seconds?

___75 m___

$$\bar{v} = \frac{v_0 + v}{2} = \frac{v_0 + (v_0 + 10t)}{2}$$
THEN $d = \bar{v} \cdot t$

Distinguish between "how fast," "how far," and "how long"!

7

CONCEPTUAL Physics PRACTICE PAGE

Chapter 3 Linear Motion
Acceleration of Free Fall

A rock dropped from the top of a cliff picks up speed as it falls. Pretend that a speedometer and odometer are attached to the rock to indicate readings of speed and distance at 1-second intervals. Both speed and distance are zero at time = zero (see sketch). Note that after falling 1 second, the speed reading is 10 m/s and the distance fallen is 5 m. The readings of succeeding seconds of fall are not shown and are left for you to complete. So draw the position of the speedometer pointer and write in the correct odometer reading for each time. Use $g = 10$ m/s^2 and neglect air resistance.

YOU NEED TO KNOW:
Instantaneous speed of fall from rest:
$$v = gt$$
Distance fallen from rest:
$$d = v_{average}t$$
or
$$d = \tfrac{1}{2}gt^2$$

1. The speedometer reading increases the same amount, __10__ m/s, each second.
This increase in speed per second is called __ACCELERATION__.

2. The distance fallen increases as the square of the __TIME__.

3. If it takes 7 seconds to reach the ground, then its speed at impact is __70__ m/s, the total distance fallen is __245__ m, and its acceleration of fall just before impact is __10__ m/s^2.

t = 0 s
t = 1 s
t = 2 s
t = 3 s
t = 4 s
t = 5 s
t = 6 s

CONCEPTUAL Physics PRACTICE PAGE

Chapter 3 Linear Motion
Hang Time

Some athletes and dancers have great jumping ability. When leaping, they seem to momentarily "hang in the air" and defy gravity. The time that a jumper is airborne with feet off the ground is called hang time. Ask your friends to estimate the hang time of the great jumpers. They may say two or three seconds. But surprisingly, the hang time of the greatest jumpers is most always less than 1 second! A longer time is one of many illusions we have about nature.

To better understand this, find the answers to the following questions:

1. If you step off a table and it takes one-half second to reach the floor, what will be the speed when you meet the floor?

Speed of free fall = acceleration × time
= 10 m/s^2 × number of seconds
= 10t m.

$$v = gt = 10 \text{ m/s}^2 \times \tfrac{1}{2} = 5 \text{ m/s}$$

2. What will be your average speed of fall?

Average speed = $\dfrac{\text{initial speed} + \text{final speed}}{2}$

$$v = \frac{0 + 5 \text{ m/s}}{2} = 2.5 \text{ m/s}$$

3. What will be the distance of fall?

Distance = average speed × time.

$$d = vt = 2.5 \text{ m/s} \times \tfrac{1}{2}\text{ s} = 1.25 \text{ m}$$

4. So how high is the surface of the table above the floor? ___1.25 m___

Jumping ability is best measured by a standing vertical jump. Stand facing a wall with feet flat on the floor and arms extended upward. Make a mark on the wall at the top of your reach. Then make your jump and at the peak make another mark. The distance between these two marks measures your vertical leap. If it's more than 0.6 meters (2 feet), you're exceptional.

5. What is your vertical jumping distance?

6. Calculate your personal hang time using the formula $d = 1/2\, gt^2$. (Remember that hang time is the time that you move upward + the time you return downward.)

___(VARIES)___

Almost anybody can safely step off a 1.25-m (4-feet) high table. Can anybody in your school jump from the floor up onto the same table? ___No way!___

There's a big difference in how high you can reach and how high you raise your "center of gravity" when you jump. Even basketball star Michael Jordan in his prime couldn't quite raise his body 1.25 meters high, although he could easily reach higher than the more-than-3-meter high basket.

Here we're talking about vertical motion. How about running jumps? We'll see in Chapter 10 that the height of a jump depends only on the jumper's vertical speed at launch. While airborne, the jumper's horizontal speed remains constant while the vertical speed undergoes acceleration due to gravity. While airborne, no amount of leg or arm pumping or other bodily motions can change your hang time.

CONCEPTUAL *Physics* PRACTICE PAGE

Chapter 3 Linear Motion
Non-Accelerated Motion

1. The sketch shows a ball rolling at constant velocity along a level floor. The ball rolls from the first position shown to the second in 1 second. The two positions are 1 meter apart. Sketch the ball at successive 1-second intervals all the way to the wall (neglect resistance).

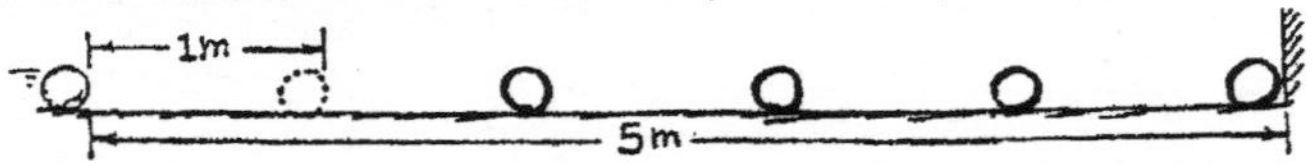

a. Did you draw successive ball positions evenly spaced, farther apart, or closer together? Why?
EVENLY SPACED—EQUAL DISTANCE IN EQUAL TIME —> CONSTANT v

b. The ball reaches the wall with a speed of __1__ m/s and takes a time of __5__ seconds.

2. Table I shows data of sprinting speeds of some animals. Make whatever computations necessary to complete the table.

TABLE I

ANIMAL	DISTANCE	TIME	SPEED
CHEETAH	75 m	3 s	25 m/s
GREYHOUND	160 m	10 s	16 m/s
GAZELLE	1 km	0.01 h	100 km/h
TURTLE	30 cm	30 s	1 cm/s

Accelerated Motion

3. An object starting from rest gains a speed $v = at$ when it undergoes uniform acceleration. The distance it covers is $d = 1/2\ at^2$. Uniform acceleration occurs for a ball rolling down an inclined plane. The plane below is tilted so a ball picks up a speed of 2 m/s each second; then its acceleration $a = 2$ m/s². The positions of the ball are shown at 1-second intervals. Complete the six blank spaces for distance covered and the four blank spaces for speeds.

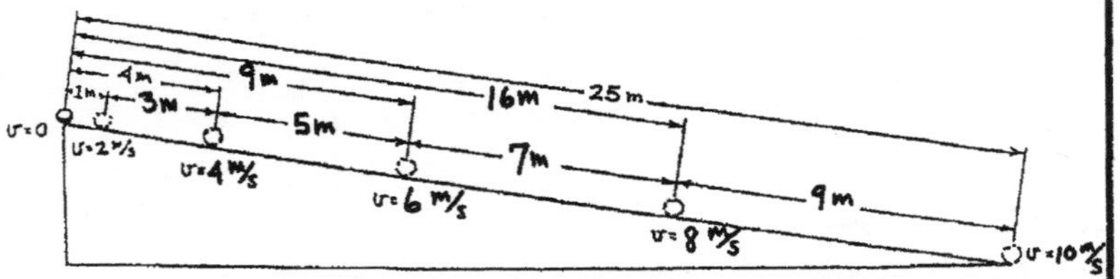

a. Do you see that the total distance from the starting point increases as the square of the time? This was discovered by Galileo. If the incline were to continue, predict the ball's distance from the starting point for the next 3 seconds.
YES: DISTANCE INCREASES AS SQUARE OF TIME: 36 m, 49 m, 64 m.

b. Note the increase of distance between ball positions with time. Do you see an odd-integer pattern (also discovered by Galileo) for this increase? If the incline were to continue, predict the successive distances between ball positions for the next 3 seconds.
YES: 11 m, 13 m, 15 m.

CONCEPTUAL *Physics* PRACTICE PAGE

Chapter 4 Newton's Second Law of Motion
Mass and Weight

Learning physics is learning the connections among concepts in nature, and also learning to distinguish between closely-related concepts. Velocity and acceleration, previously treated, are often confused. Similarly in this chapter, we find that mass and weight are often confused. They aren't the same! Please review the distinction between mass and weight in your textbook. To reinforce your understanding of this distinction, circle the correct answers below.

Comparing the concepts of mass and weight, one is basic—fundamental—depending only on the internal makeup of an object and the number and kind of atoms that compose it. The concept that is fundamental is (mass) [weight].

The concept that additionally depends on location in a gravitational field is [mass] (weight).

(Mass) [Weight] is a measure of the amount of matter in an object and only depends on the number and kind of atoms that compose it.

It can correctly be said that (mass) [weight] is a measure of "laziness" of an object.

[Mass] (Weight) is related to the gravitational force acting on the object.

[Mass] (Weight) depends on an object's location, whereas (mass) [weight] does not.

In other words, a stone would have the same (mass) [weight] whether it is on the surface of Earth or on the surface of the Moon. However, its [mass] (weight) depends on its location.

On the Moon's surface, where gravity is only about 1/6th Earth gravity, (mass) [weight] [both the mass and the weight] of the stone would be the same as on Earth.

While mass and weight are not the same, they are (directly proportional) [inversely proportional] to each other. In the same location, twice the mass has (twice) [half] the weight.

The Standard International (SI) unit of mass is the (kilogram) [newton], and the SI unit of force is the [kilogram] (newton).

In the United States, it is common to measure the mass of something by measuring its gravitational pull to Earth, its weight. The common unit of weight in the U.S. is the (pound) [kilogram] [newton].

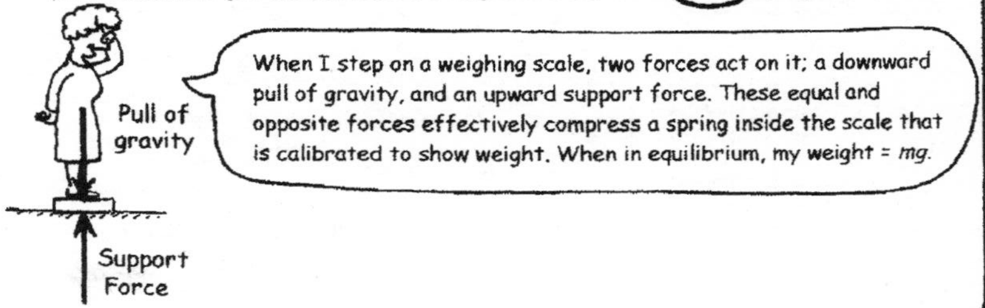

When I step on a weighing scale, two forces act on it: a downward pull of gravity, and an upward support force. These equal and opposite forces effectively compress a spring inside the scale that is calibrated to show weight. When in equilibrium, my weight = mg.

Pull of gravity

Support Force

thanx to Daniela Taylor

CONCEPTUAL *Physics* PRACTICE PAGE

Chapter 4 Newton's Second Law of Motion
Converting Mass to Weight

Objects with mass also have weight (although they can be weightless under special conditions). If you know the mass of something in **kilograms** and want its weight in **newtons**, at Earth's surface, you can take advantage of the formula that relates weight and mass.

Weight = mass × acceleration due to gravity

$W = mg$

This is in accord with Newton's 2nd law, written as $F = ma$. When the force of gravity is the only force, the acceleration of any object of mass m will be g, the acceleration of free fall. Importantly, g acts as a proportionality constant, 9.8 N/kg, which is equivalent to 9.8 m/s².

Sample Question:
How much does a 1-kg bag of nails weigh on Earth?

$W = mg = (1 \text{ kg})(9.8 \text{ m/s}^2) = 9.8 \text{ N}$,
or simply, $W = mg = (1 \text{ kg})(9.8 \text{ N/kg}) = 9.8 \text{ N}$.

From $F = ma$, we see that the unit of force equals the units [kg × m/s²]. Can you see the units [m/s²] = [N/kg]?

Answer the following questions:
Felicia the ballet dancer has a mass of 45.0 kg.

1. What is Felicia's weight in newtons at Earth's surface?   **441 N**

2. Given that 1 kilogram of mass corresponds to 2.2 pounds at Earth's surface, what is Felicia's weight in pounds on Earth?   **99 LB**

3. What would be Felicia's mass on the surface of Jupiter?   **45.0 kg**

4. What would be Felicia's weight on Jupiter's surface, where the acceleration due to gravity is 25.0 m/s²?   **1125 N**

Different masses are hung on a spring scale calibrated in newtons.
The force exerted by gravity on 1 kg = 9.8 N.

5. The force exerted by gravity on 5 kg = **49** N.

6. The force exerted by gravity on **10** kg = 98 N.

Make up your own mass and show the corresponding weight:
The force exerted by gravity on * _____ kg = * _____ N.
*ANY VALUE FOR kg AS LONG AS THE SAME VALUE IS MULTIPLIED BY 9.8 FOR N.

By whatever means (spring scales, measuring balances, etc.), find the mass of your physics book. Then complete the table.

OBJECT	MASS	WEIGHT
MELON	1 kg	9.8 N
APPLE	0.1 kg	1 N
BOOK		
A FRIEND	60 kg	588 N

CONCEPTUAL *Physics* PRACTICE PAGE

Chapter 4 Newton's Second Law of Motion
A Day at the Races with a = F/m

In each situation below, Cart A has a mass of **1 kg**. *Circle the correct answer* (A, B, or Same for both).

1. Cart A is pulled with a force of **1 N**.
Cart B also has a mass of **1 kg** and is pulled with a force of **2 N**.
Which undergoes the greater acceleration?

[A] **(B)** [Same for both]

2. Cart A is pulled with a force of **1 N**.
Cart B has a mass of **2 kg** and is also pulled with a force of **1 N**.
Which undergoes the greater acceleration?

(A) [B] [Same for both]

3. Cart A is pulled with a force of **1 N**.
Cart B has a mass of **2 kg** and is pulled with a force of **2 N**.
Which undergoes the greater acceleration?

[A] [B] **(Same for both)**

4. Cart A is pulled with a force of **1 N**.
Cart B has a mass of **3 kg** and is pulled with a force of **3 N**.
Which undergoes the greater acceleration?

[A] [B] **(Same for both)**

5. This time Cart A is pulled with a force of **4 N**.
Cart B has a mass of **4 kg** and is pulled with a force of **4 N**.
Which undergoes the greater acceleration?

(A) [B] [Same for both]

6. Cart A is pulled with a force of **2 N**.
Cart B has a mass of **4 kg** and is pulled with a force of **3 N**.
Which undergoes the greater acceleration?

(A) [B] [Same for both]

thanx to Dean Baird

Chapter 4 Newton's Second Law of Motion
Dropping Masses and Accelerating Cart

1. Consider a 1-kg cart being pulled by a 10-N applied force. According to Newton's 2nd law, acceleration of the cart is

$$a = \frac{F}{m} = \frac{10\ N}{1\ kg} = 10\ m/s^2.$$

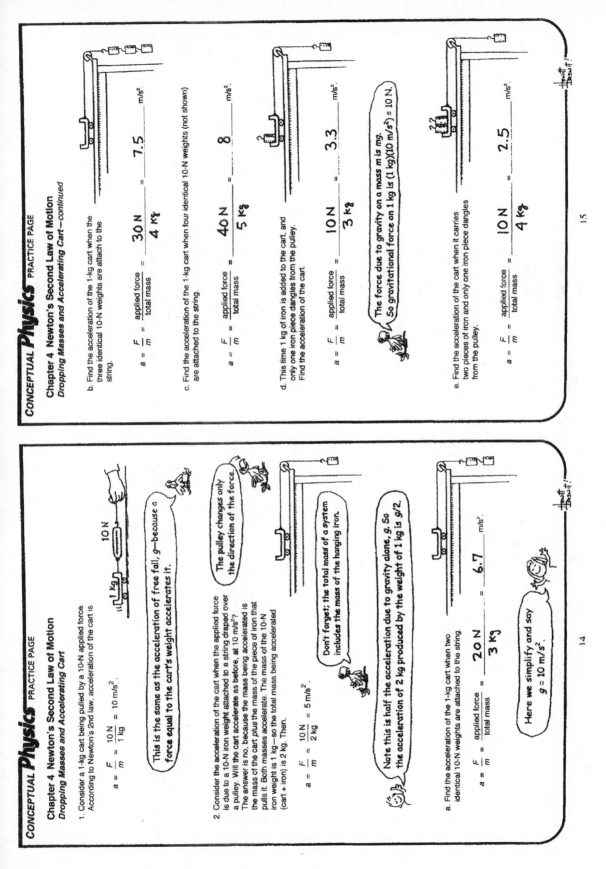

> This is the same as the acceleration of free fall, g—because a force equal to the cart's weight accelerates it.

2. Consider the acceleration of the cart when the applied force is due to a 10-N iron weight attached to a string draped over a pulley. Will the cart accelerate as before, at 10 m/s²? The answer is no, because the mass being accelerated is the mass of the cart *plus* the mass of the piece of iron that pulls it. Both masses accelerate. The mass of the 10-N iron weight is 1 kg—so the total mass being accelerated (cart + iron) is 2 kg. Then,

$$a = \frac{F}{m} = \frac{10\ N}{2\ kg} = 5\ m/s^2.$$

> The pulley changes only the direction of the force.

> Don't forget: the total mass of a system includes the mass of the hanging iron.

> Note this is half the acceleration due to gravity alone, g. So the acceleration of 2 kg produced by the weight of 1 kg is g/2.

a. Find the acceleration of the 1-kg cart when two identical 10-N weights are attached to the string.

$$a = \frac{F}{m} = \frac{applied\ force}{total\ mass} = \frac{20\ N}{3\ kg} = 6.7\ m/s^2.$$

> Here we simplify and say g = 10 m/s².

14

Chapter 4 Newton's Second Law of Motion
Dropping Masses and Accelerating Cart—continued

b. Find the acceleration of the 1-kg cart when the three identical 10-N weights are attach to the string.

$$a = \frac{F}{m} = \frac{applied\ force}{total\ mass} = \frac{30\ N}{4\ kg} = 7.5\ m/s^2.$$

c. Find the acceleration of the 1-kg cart when four identical 10-N weights (not shown) are attached to the string.

$$a = \frac{F}{m} = \frac{applied\ force}{total\ mass} = \frac{40\ N}{5\ kg} = 8\ m/s^2.$$

d. This time 1 kg of iron is added to the cart, and only one iron piece dangles from the pulley. Find the acceleration of the cart.

$$a = \frac{F}{m} = \frac{applied\ force}{total\ mass} = \frac{10\ N}{3\ kg} = 3.3\ m/s^2.$$

> The force due to gravity on a mass m is mg. So gravitational force on 1 kg is (1 kg)(10 m/s²) = 10 N.

e. Find the acceleration of the cart when it carries two pieces of iron and only one iron piece dangles from the pulley.

$$a = \frac{F}{m} = \frac{applied\ force}{total\ mass} = \frac{10\ N}{4\ kg} = 2.5\ m/s^2.$$

15

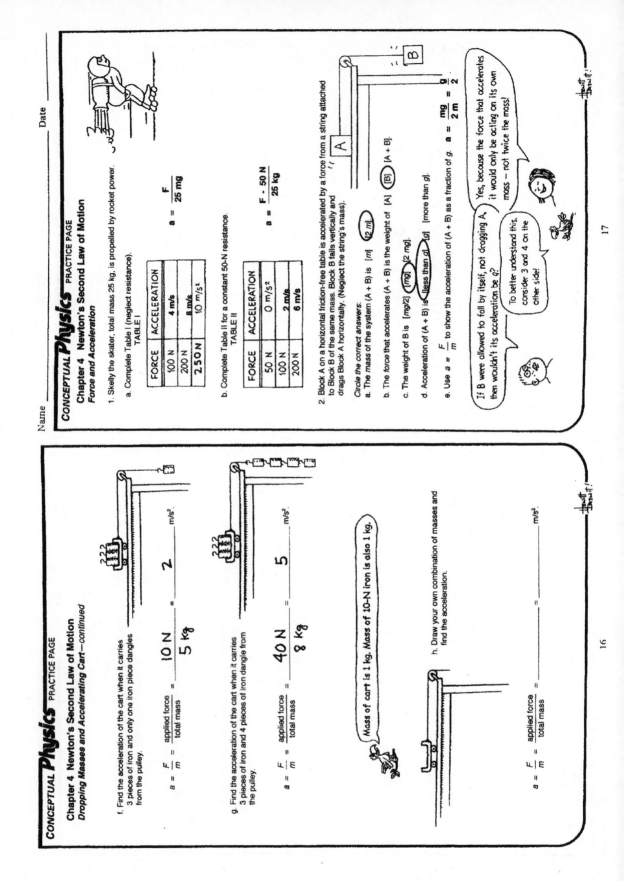

CONCEPTUAL Physics PRACTICE PAGE

Chapter 4 Newton's Second Law of Motion
Dropping Masses and Accelerating Cart—continued

f. Find the acceleration of the cart when it carries 3 pieces of iron and only one iron piece dangles from the pulley.

$$a = \frac{F}{m} = \frac{\text{applied force}}{\text{total mass}} = \frac{10\ N}{5\ kg} = 2 \ \_\_\_\_ \ m/s^2$$

g. Find the acceleration of the cart when it carries 3 pieces of iron and 4 pieces of iron dangle from the pulley.

$$a = \frac{F}{m} = \frac{\text{applied force}}{\text{total mass}} = \frac{40\ N}{8\ kg} = 5 \ \_\_\_\_ \ m/s^2$$

Mass of cart is 1 kg. Mass of 10-N iron is also 1 kg.

h. Draw your own combination of masses and find the acceleration.

$$a = \frac{F}{m} = \_\_\_\_ = \_\_\_\_ \ m/s^2$$

16

CONCEPTUAL Physics PRACTICE PAGE

Chapter 4 Newton's Second Law of Motion
Force and Acceleration

1. Skelly the skater, total mass 25 kg, is propelled by rocket power.

a. Complete Table I (neglect resistance).

TABLE I

FORCE	ACCELERATION
100 N	4 m/s
200 N	8 m/s
250 N	10 m/s²

$$a = \frac{F}{25\ mg}$$

b. Complete Table II for a constant 50-N resistance.

TABLE II

FORCE	ACCELERATION
50 N	0 m/s²
100 N	2 m/s
200 N	6 m/s

$$a = \frac{F - 50\ N}{25\ kg}$$

2. Block A on a horizontal friction-free table is accelerated by a force from a string attached to Block B of the same mass. Block B falls vertically and drags Block A horizontally. (Neglect the string's mass).

Circle the correct answers:

a. The *mass* of the system (A + B) is [*m*] (2 *m*).

b. The *force* that accelerates (A + B) is the weight of [A] (B) [A + B].

c. The *weight* of B is [*mg/2*] (*mg*) [2 *mg*].

d. *Acceleration* of (A + B) is [*g*] (less than *g*) [more than *g*].

e. Use $a = \dfrac{F}{m}$ to show the acceleration of (A + B) as a fraction of *g*. $a = \dfrac{mg}{2m} = \dfrac{g}{2}$

If B were allowed to fall by itself, not dragging A, then wouldn't its acceleration be *g*?

Yes, because the force that accelerates it would only be acting on its own mass — not twice the mass!

To better understand this, consider 3 and 4 on the other side!

17

138

Chapter 4 Newton's Second Law of Motion
Force and Acceleration—continued

3. Suppose Block A is still a 1-kg block, but B is a low-mass feather (or a coin).

a. Compared to the acceleration of the system of 2 equal-mass blocks

the acceleration of (A + B) is [(less)] [more]

and is [(close to zero)] [close to g].

b. In this case, the acceleration of B is [practically that of free fall] [(nearly zero)].

4. Suppose A is the feather or coin, and Block B has a mass of 1 kg.

a. The acceleration of (A + B) here is [close to zero] [(close to g)].

b. In this case, the acceleration of Block B is [practically that of free fall] [nearly zero].

5. Summarizing we see that when the weight of one object causes the acceleration of two objects, the range of possible accelerations is between [(zero and g)] [zero and infinity] [g and infinity].

6. For a change of pace, consider a ball that rolls down a uniform-slope ramp.

a. Speed of the ball is [decreasing] [constant] [(increasing)].

b. Acceleration is [decreasing] [(constant)] [increasing].

c. If the ramp were steeper, acceleration would be [(more)] [the same] [less].

d. When the ball reaches the bottom and rolls along the smooth level surface, it [continues to accelerate] [(does not accelerate)].

Chapter 4 Newton's Second Law of Motion
Friction

1. A crate filled with delicious junk food rests on a horizontal floor. Only gravity and the support force of the floor act on it, as shown by the vectors for weight **W** and normal force **N**.

a. The net force on the crate is [(zero)] [greater than zero].

b. Evidence for this is __NO ACCELERATION.__

2. A slight pull **P** is exerted on the crate, not enough to move it. A force of friction *f* now acts,

a. which is [less than] [(equal to)] [greater than] **P**.

b. Net force on the crate is [(zero)] [greater than zero].

3. Pull **P** is increased until the crate begins to move. It is pulled so that it moves with constant velocity across the floor.

a. Friction *f* is [less than] [(equal to)] [greater than] **P**.

b. Constant velocity means acceleration is [(zero)] [more than zero].

c. Net force on the crate is [less than] [(equal to)] [more than] zero.

4. Pull **P** is further increased and is now greater than friction *f*.

a. Net force on the crate is [less than] [equal to] [(greater than)] zero.

b. The net force acts toward the right, so acceleration acts toward the [left] [(right)].

5. If the pulling force **P** is 150 N and the crate doesn't move, what is the magnitude of *f*? __150 N__

6. If the pulling force **P** is 200 N and the crate doesn't move, what is the magnitude of *f*? __200 N__

7. If the force of sliding friction is 250 N, what force is necessary to keep the crate sliding at constant velocity? __250 N__

8. If the mass of the crate is 50 kg and sliding friction is 250 N, what is the acceleration of the crate

when the pulling force is 250 N? __0 m/s²__   300 N? __1 m/s²__   500 N? __5 m/s²__

CONCEPTUAL *Physics* PRACTICE PAGE

Chapter 4 Newton's Second Law of Motion
Falling and Air Resistance

Bronco skydives and parachutes from a stationary helicopter. Various stages of fall are shown in positions a through f. Using Newton's 2nd law,

$$a = \frac{F_{net}}{m} = \frac{W - R}{m}$$

find Bronco's acceleration at each position (answer in the blanks to the right). You need to know that Bronco's mass m is 100 kg so his weight is a constant 1000 N. Air resistance R varies with speed and cross-sectional area as shown.

a — W = 1000 N   R = 0 $a = $ __10 m/s²__

b — W = 1000 N   R = 400 N $a = $ __6 m/s²__

c — W = 1000 N   R = 1000 N $a = $ __0 m/s²__

d — W = 1000 N   R = 1200 N $a = $ __-2m/s²__

e — W = 1000 N   R = 2000 N $a = $ __-10 m/s²__

f — W = 1000 N   R = 1000 N $a = $ __0 m/s²__

Circle the correct answers:

1. When Bronco's speed is least, his acceleration is

[least] (most)

2. In which position(s) does Bronco experience a downward acceleration?

(a) (b) [c] [d] [e] [f]

3. In which position(s) does Bronco experience a upward acceleration?

[a] [b] [c] (d) (e) [f]

4. When Bronco experiences an upward acceleration, his velocity is (still downward) [upward also].

5. In which position(s) is Bronco's velocity constant?

[a] [b] (c) [d] [e] (f)

6. In which position(s) does Bronco experience terminal velocity?

[a] [b] (c) [d] [e] (f)

7. In which position(s) is terminal velocity greatest?

[a] [b] (c) [d] [e] (f)

8. If Bronco were heavier, his terminal velocity would be (greater) [less] [the same].

CONCEPTUAL *Physics* PRACTICE PAGE

Chapter 5 Newton's Third Law of Motion
Action and Reaction Pairs

1. In the example below, the action-reaction pair is shown by the arrows (vectors), and the action-reaction described in words. In *a* through *g*, draw the other arrow (vector) and state the reaction to the given action. Then make up your own example in *h*.

Example:

Fist hits wall.   *Wall hits fist.*

a. **BALL BUMPS HEAD.**   *Head bumps ball.*

b. **BUG HITS WINDSHIELD.**   *Windshield hits bug.*

c. **BALL HITS BAT.**   *Bat hits ball.*

d. **NOSE TOUCHES HAND.**   *Hand touches nose.*

e. **FLOWER PULLS ON HAND.**   *Hand pulls flower.*

f. **BAR PUSHES ATHLETE DOWNWARD.**   *Athlete pushes bar upward.*

g. **BALLOON SURFACE PUSHES COMPRESSED AIR UPWARD.**   *Compressed air pushes balloon surface outward.*

h. **THING A ACTS ON THING B.**   **THING B ACTS ON THING A.**

STUDENT DRAWING (OPEN)

2. Draw arrows to show the chain of at least six parts of action-reaction forces below.

YOU CAN'T TOUCH WITHOUT BEING TOUCHED— NEWTON'S THIRD LAW

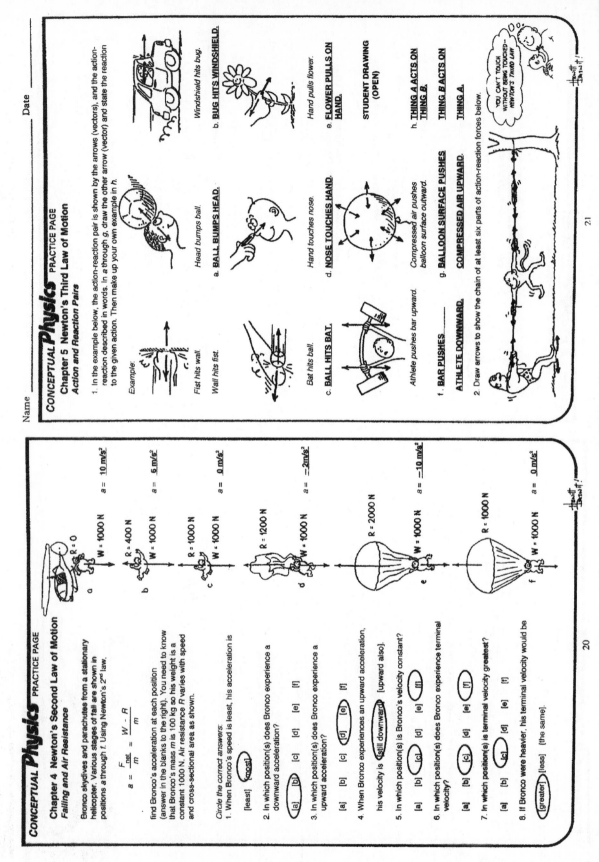

CONCEPTUAL *Physics* PRACTICE PAGE

Chapter 5 Newton's Third Law of Motion
Interactions

1. Nellie Newton holds an apple weighing 1 newton at rest on the palm of her hand. The force vectors shown are the forces that act on the apple.

a. To say the weight of the apple is 1 N is to say that a downward gravitational force of 1 N is exerted on the apple by [Earth] [her hand].

b. Nellie's hand supports the apple with normal force N, which acts in a direction opposite to W. We can say N [equals W] [has the same magnitude as W].

c. Since the apple is at rest, the net force on the apple is [zero] [nonzero].

d. Since N is equal and opposite to W, we [can] [cannot] say that N and W comprise an action-reaction pair. The reason is because action and reaction always [act on the same object] [act on different objects], and here we see N and W [both acting on the apple] [acting on different objects].

e. In accord with the rule, "If ACTION is A acting on B, then REACTION is B acting on A," if we say action is Earth pulling down on the apple, then reaction is [the apple pulling up on Earth] [N, Nellie's hand pushing up on the apple].

f. To repeat for emphasis, we see that N and W are equal and opposite to each other [and comprise an action-reaction pair] [but do not comprise an action-reaction pair].

To identify a pair of action-reaction forces in any situation, first identify the pair of interacting objects involved. Something is interacting with something else. In this case the whole Earth is interacting (gravitationally) with the apple. So Earth pulls downward on the apple (call it action), while the apple pulls upward on Earth (reaction).

[Simply put, Earth pulls on apple (action); apple pulls on Earth (reaction).]

[Better put, apple and Earth pull on each other with equal and opposite forces that comprise a single interaction.]

g. Another pair of forces is N as shown, and the downward force of the apple against Nellie's hand, not shown. This force pair [is] [isn't] an action-reaction pair.

h. Suppose Nellie now pushes upward on the apple with a force of 2 N. The apple [is still in equilibrium] [accelerates upward], and compared to W, the magnitude of N is [the same] [twice] [not the same, and not twice].

i. Once the apple leaves Nellie's hand, N is [zero] [only W] [still twice the magnitude of W], and the net force on the apple is [zero] [only W] [still W − N, a negative force].

141

CONCEPTUAL *Physics* PRACTICE PAGE

Chapter 5 Newton's Third Law of Motion
Vectors and the Parallelogram Rule

1. When two vectors **A** and **B** are at an angle to each other, they add to produce the resultant **C** by the *parallelogram rule*. Note that **C** is the diagonal of a parallelogram where **A** and **B** are adjacent sides. Resultant **C** is shown in the first two diagrams, *a* and *b*. Construct resultant **C** in diagrams *c* and *d*. Note that in diagram *d* you form a rectangle (a special case of a parallelogram).

2. Below we see a top view of an airplane being blown off course by wind in various directions. Use the parallelogram rule to show the resulting speed and direction of travel for each case. In which case does the airplane travel fastest across the ground? Slowest?

3. To the right we see the top views of 3 motorboats crossing a river. All have the same speed relative to the water, and all experience the same water flow.

Construct resultant vectors showing the speed and direction of the boats.

a. Which boat takes the shortest path to the opposite shore?
_____a_____

b. Which boat reaches the opposite shore first?
_____b_____

c. Which boat provides the fastest ride?
_____c_____

23

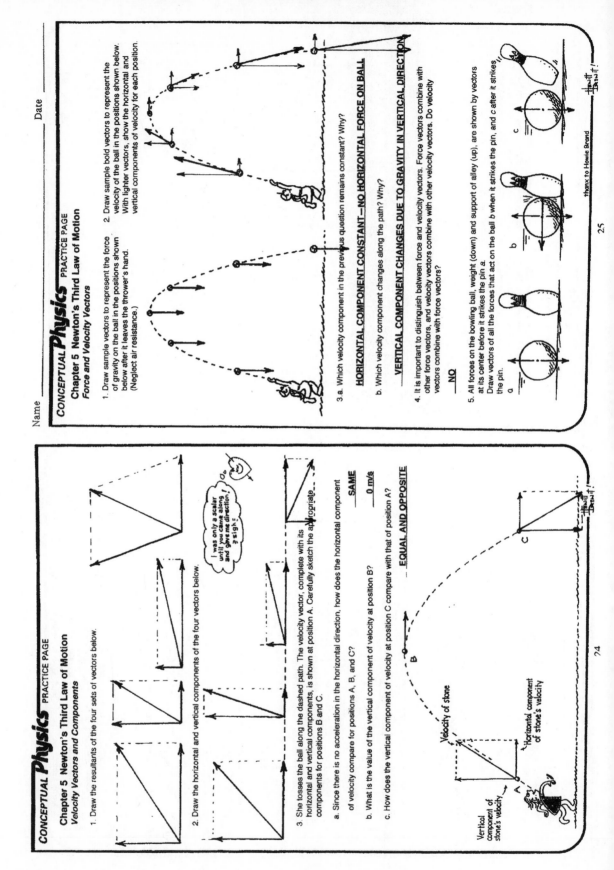

CONCEPTUAL *Physics* PRACTICE PAGE

Chapter 5 Newton's Third Law of Motion
Force and Velocity Vectors

1. Draw sample vectors to represent the force of gravity on the ball in the positions shown below after it leaves the thrower's hand. (Neglect air resistance.)

2. Draw sample bold vectors to represent the velocity of the ball in the positions shown below. With lighter vectors, show the horizontal and vertical components of velocity for each position.

3. a. Which velocity component in the previous question remains constant? Why?

HORIZONTAL COMPONENT CONSTANT—NO HORIZONTAL FORCE ON BALL

b. Which velocity component changes along the path? Why?

VERTICAL COMPONENT CHANGES DUE TO GRAVITY IN VERTICAL DIRECTION

4. It is important to distinguish between force and velocity vectors. Force vectors combine with other force vectors, and velocity vectors combine with other velocity vectors. Do velocity vectors combine with force vectors?

NO

5. All forces on the bowling ball, weight (down) and support of alley (up), are shown by vectors at its center before it strikes the pin *a*. Draw vectors of all the forces that act on the ball *b* when it strikes the pin, and *c* after it strikes the pin.

a   *b*   *c*

thanx to Howie Brand

25

CONCEPTUAL *Physics* PRACTICE PAGE

Chapter 5 Newton's Third Law of Motion
Velocity Vectors and Components

1. Draw the resultants of the four sets of vectors below.

I was only a scalar until you came along and gave me direction! ≥ sigh ≤

2. Draw the horizontal and vertical components of the four vectors below.

3. She tosses the ball along the dashed path. The velocity vector, complete with its horizontal and vertical components, is shown at position A. Carefully sketch the appropriate components for positions B and C.

a. Since there is no acceleration in the horizontal direction, how does the horizontal component of velocity compare for positions A, B, and C?

SAME

b. What is the value of the vertical component of velocity at position B?

0 m/s

c. How does the vertical component of velocity at position C compare with that of position A?

EQUAL AND OPPOSITE

Velocity of stone

Vertical component of stone's velocity

Horizontal component of stone's velocity

24

142

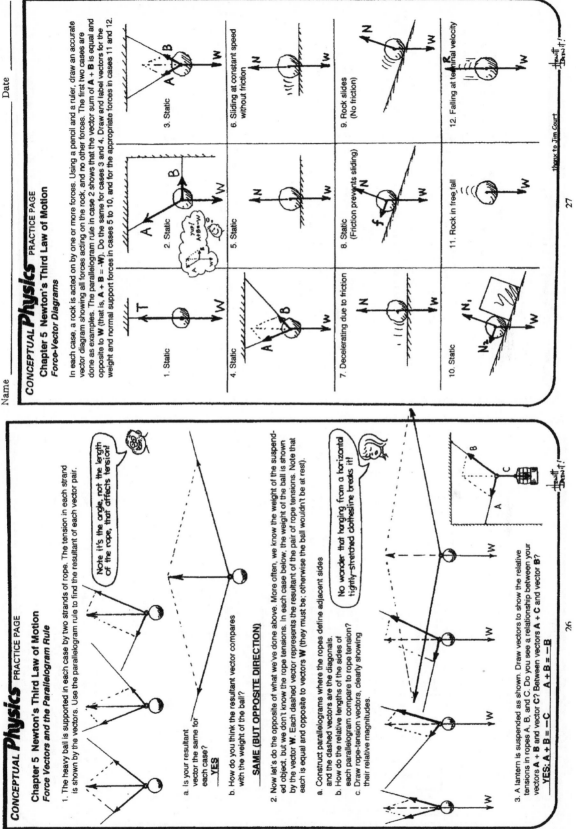

CONCEPTUAL *Physics* PRACTICE PAGE

Chapter 5 Newton's Third Law of Motion
Force Vectors and the Parallelogram Rule

1. The heavy ball is supported in each case by two strands of rope. The tension in each strand is shown by the vectors. Use the parallelogram rule to find the resultant of each vector pair.

> Note it's the angle, not the length of the rope, that affects tension!

a. Is your resultant vector the same for each case? **YES**

b. How do you think the resultant vector compares with the weight of the ball?

SAME (BUT OPPOSITE DIRECTION)

2. Now let's do the opposite of what we've done above. More often, we know the weight of the suspended object, but we don't know the rope tensions. In each case below, the weight of the ball is shown by the vector **W**. Each dashed vector represents the resultant of the pair of rope tensions. Note that each is equal and opposite to vectors **W** (they must be; otherwise the ball wouldn't be at rest).

a. Construct parallelograms where the ropes define adjacent sides and the dashed vectors are the diagonals.

b. How do the relative lengths of the sides of each parallelogram compare to rope tension?

c. Draw rope-tension vectors, clearly showing their relative magnitudes.

> No wonder that hanging from a horizontal tightly-stretched clothesline breaks it!

3. A lantern is suspended as shown. Draw vectors to show the relative tensions in ropes A, B, and C. Do you see a relationship between your vectors **A** + **C** and vector **C**? Between vectors **A** + **B** and vector **B**?

YES: A + B = –C   A + B = –B

26

CONCEPTUAL *Physics* PRACTICE PAGE

Chapter 5 Newton's Third Law of Motion
Force-Vector Diagrams

In each case, a rock is acted on by one or more forces. Using a pencil and a ruler, draw an accurate vector diagram showing all forces acting on the rock, and no other forces. The first two cases are done as examples. The parallelogram rule in case 2 shows that the vector sum of **A** + **B** is equal and opposite to **W** (that is, **A** + **B** = –**W**). Do the same for cases 3 and 4. Draw and label vectors for the weight and normal support forces in cases 5 to 10, and for the appropriate forces in cases 11 and 12.

1. Static

2. Static

> yur! A+B=–W

3. Static

4. Static

5. Static

6. Sliding at constant speed without friction

7. Decelerating due to friction

8. Static (Friction prevents sliding)

9. Rock slides (No friction)

10. Static

11. Rock in free fall

12. Falling at terminal velocity

thanx to Jim Court

27

143

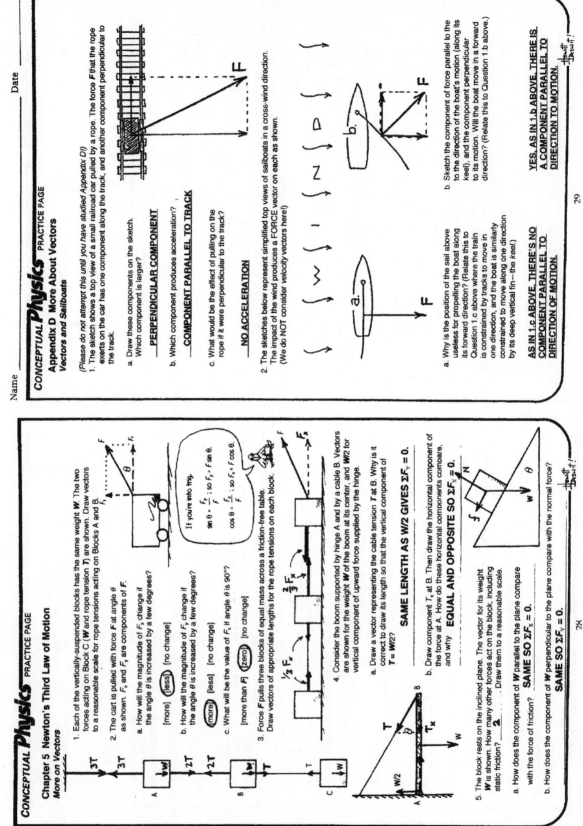

CONCEPTUAL Physics PRACTICE PAGE

Chapter 5 Newton's Third Law of Motion
More on Vectors

1. Each of the vertically-suspended blocks has the same weight W. The two forces acting on Block C (W and rope tension T) are shown. Draw vectors to a reasonable scale for rope tensions acting on Blocks A and B.

2. The cart is pulled with force F at angle θ as shown. F_x and F_y are components of F.
   a. How will the magnitude of F_x change if the angle θ is increased by a few degrees? [more] (less) [no change]
   b. How will the magnitude of F_y change if the angle θ is increased by a few degrees? (more) [less] [no change]
   c. What will be the value of F_x if angle θ is 90°? [more than F] (zero) [no change]

   If you're into trig.
   $$\sin\theta = \frac{F_y}{F} \text{ ; so } F_y = F\sin\theta.$$
   $$\cos\theta = \frac{F_x}{F} \text{ ; so } F_x = F\cos\theta.$$

3. Force F pulls three blocks of equal mass across a friction-free table. Draw vectors of appropriate lengths for the rope tensions on each block.

   $\frac{1}{3}F_x$ $\frac{2}{3}F_x$

4. Consider the boom supported by hinge A and by a cable B. Vectors are shown for the weight W of the boom at its center, and W/2 for vertical component of upward force supplied by the hinge.
   a. Draw a vector representing the cable tension T at B. Why is it correct to draw its length so that the vertical component of $T = W/2$? **SAME LENGTH AS W/2 GIVES $\Sigma F_y = 0$.**
   b. Draw component T_x at B. Then draw the horizontal component of the force at A. How do these horizontal components compare, and why **EQUAL AND OPPOSITE SO $\Sigma F_x = 0$.**

5. The block rests on the inclined plane. The vector for its weight W is shown. How many other forces act on the block, including static friction? __2__. Draw them to a reasonable scale.
   a. How does the component of W parallel to the plane compare with the force of friction? **SAME SO $\Sigma F_x = 0$.**
   b. How does the component of W perpendicular to the plane compare with the normal force? **SAME SO $\Sigma F_y = 0$.**

28

CONCEPTUAL Physics PRACTICE PAGE

Appendix D More About Vectors
Vectors and Sailboats

(Please do not attempt this until you have studied Appendix D!)

1. The sketch shows a top view of a small railroad car pulled by a rope. The force F that the rope exerts on the car has one component along the track, and another component perpendicular to the track.
   a. Draw these components on the sketch. Which component is larger? **PERPENDICULAR COMPONENT**
   b. Which component produces acceleration? **COMPONENT PARALLEL TO TRACK**
   c. What would be the effect of pulling on the rope if it were perpendicular to the track? **NO ACCELERATION**

2. The sketches below represent simplified top views of sailboats in a cross-wind direction. The impact of the wind produces a FORCE vector on each as shown. (We do NOT consider *velocity* vectors here!)

   WIND

   a. Why is the position of the sail above useless for propelling the boat along its forward direction? (Relate this to Question 1.c above where the train is constrained by tracks to move in one direction, and the boat is similarly constrained to move along one direction by its deep vertical fin—the *keel*.) **AS IN 1.c ABOVE, THERE'S NO COMPONENT PARALLEL TO DIRECTION OF MOTION.**

   b. Sketch the component of force parallel to the direction of the boat's motion (along its keel), and the component perpendicular to its motion. Will the boat move in a forward direction? (Relate this to Question 1.b above.) **YES, AS IN 1.b ABOVE, THERE IS A COMPONENT PARALLEL TO DIRECTION TO MOTION.**

29

CONCEPTUAL *Physics* PRACTICE PAGE

Appendix D More About Vectors
Vectors and Sailboats—continued

3. The boat to the right is oriented at an angle into the wind. Draw the force vector and its forward and perpendicular components.

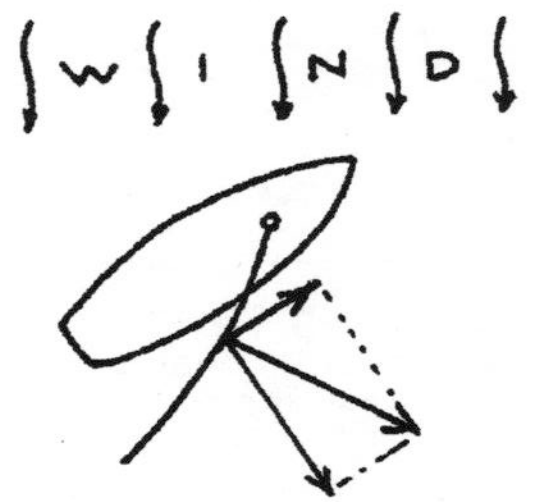

a. Will the boat move in a forward direction and tack into the wind? Why or why not?

YES, BECAUSE THERE IS A COMPONENT

OF FORCE PARALLEL TO THE DIRECTION

OF MOTION.

4. The sketch below is a top view of five identical sailboats. Where they exist, draw force vectors to represent wind impact on the sails. Then draw components parallel and perpendicular to the keels of each boat.

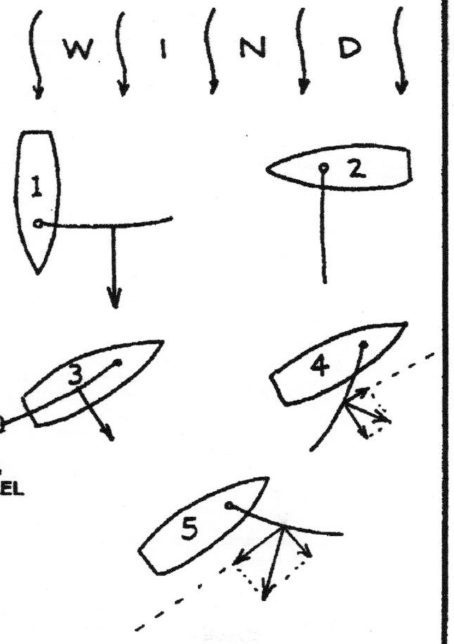

a. Which boat will sail the fastest in a forward direction?

**BOAT 4 (WILL USUALLY EXCEED
BOAT 1)**

b. Which will respond least to the wind?

BOAT 2 (OR BOAT 3)

c. Which will move in a backward direction?

BOAT 5

d. Which will experience decreasing wind impact with increasing speed?

BOAT 1 (NO IMPACT AT WIND SPEED)

**"THE WIND MISSES THE SAIL OF BOAT 2,
AND THERE'S NO COMPONENT PARALLEL
TO THE KEEL FOR BOAT 3.**

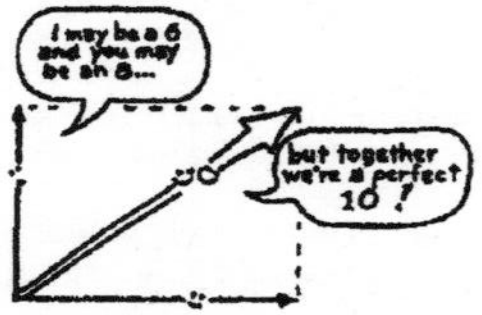

30

CONCEPTUAL *Physics* PRACTICE PAGE

Chapter 6 Momentum
Changing Momentum

1. A moving car has momentum. If it moves twice as fast, its momentum is ____TWICE____ as much.

2. Two cars, one twice as heavy as the other, move down a hill at the same speed. Compared with the lighter car, the momentum of the heavier car is ____TWICE____ as much.

3. The recoil momentum of a cannon that kicks is

[more than] [less than] (the same as)

the momentum of the cannonball it fires.
(Here we neglect friction and the momentum of the gases.)

ALTHOUGH SPEED AND ACCELERATION OF BULLET GREATER

4. Suppose you are traveling in a bus at highway speed on a nice summer day and the momentum of an unlucky bug is suddenly changed as it splatters onto the front window.

a. Compared to the force that acts on the bug, how much force acts on the bus?

[more] [less] (the same)

b. The time of impact is the same for both the bug and the bus. Compared to the impulse on the bug, this means the impulse on the bus is

[more] [less] (the same)

c. Although the momentum of the bus is very large compared to the momentum of the bug, the *change* in momentum of the bus, compared to the *change* of momentum of the bug is

[more] [less] (the same)

d. Which undergoes the greater acceleration?

[bus] [both the same] (bug)

e. Which therefore, suffers the greater damage?

[bus] [both the same] (bug of course!)

31

145

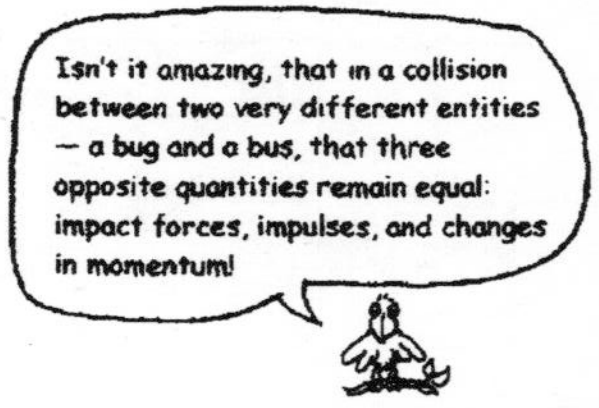

Chapter 6 Momentum
Changing Momentum—continued

5. Granny whizzes around the rink and is suddenly confronted with Ambrose at rest directly in her path. Rather than knock him over, she picks him up and continues in motion without "braking."

Consider both Granny and Ambrose as two parts of one system. Since no outside forces act on the system, the momentum of the system before collision equals the momentum of the system after collision.

a. Complete the before-collision data in the table below.

BEFORE COLLISION	
Granny's mass	80 kg
Granny's speed	3 m/s
Granny's momentum	__240 Kg·m/s__
Ambrose's mass	40 kg
Ambrose's speed	0 m/s
Ambrose's momentum	__0__
Total momentum	__240 Kg·m/s__

b. After collision, Granny's speed [increases] (decreases)

c. After collision, Ambrose's speed (increases) [decreases]

d. After collision, the total mass of Granny + Ambrose is __120 kg.__

e. After collision, the total momentum of Granny + Ambrose is
__240 kg·m/s__

f. Use the conservation of momentum law to find the speed of Granny and Ambrose together after collision. (Show your work in the space below.)

$$Mv + mv' = (M + m) V$$
$$(80 kg)(3 m/s) + 0 = (80 kg + 40 kg)V$$
$$240 kg·m/s = (120 kg)V$$
$$V = 2 m/s$$

New speed __2 m/s__

Chapter 6 Momentum
Systems

1. When the compressed spring is released, Blocks A and B will slide apart. There are 3 systems to consider, indicated by the closed dashed lines below—A, B, and A + B. Ignore the vertical forces of gravity and the support force of the table.

a. Does an external force act on System A? [Y] [N]

Will the momentum of System A change? [Y] [N]

b. Does an external force act on System B? [Y] [N]

Will the momentum of System B change? [Y] [N]

c. Does an external force act on System A + B? [Y] [N]

Will the momentum of System A + B change? [Y] [N]

Note that external forces on System A and System B are internal to System A+B, so they cancel

2. Billiard ball A collides with billiard ball B at rest. Isolate each system with a closed dashed line. Draw only the external force vectors that act on each system.

a. Upon collision, the momentum of System A [increases] [decreases] [remains unchanged].

b. Upon collision, the momentum of System B [increases] [decreases] [remains unchanged].

c. Upon collision, the momentum of System A + B [increases] [decreases] [remains unchanged].

3.a. A girl jumps upward. In the left sketch, draw a closed dashed line to indicate the system of the girl. Is there an external force acting on her?

Does her momentum change? [Y] [N]

Is the girl's momentum conserved? [Y] [N]

b. In the right sketch, draw a closed dashed line to indicate the system (girl + Earth). Is there an external force acting on the system due to the interaction between the girl and Earth? [Y] [N]

Does her momentum change? [Y] [N]

Is momentum conserved? [Y] [N]

4. A block strikes a blob of jelly. Isolate 3 systems with a closed dashed line and show the external force on each. In which system is momentum conserved?

5. A truck crashes into a wall. Isolate 3 systems with a closed dashed line and show the external force on each. In which system is momentum conserved?

ONE ON RIGHT

CONCEPTUAL Physics PRACTICE PAGE

Chapter 7 Energy
Work and Energy

1. How much work (energy) is needed to lift an object that weighs 200 N to a height of 4 meters?
   800 J

2. How much power is needed to lift the 200-N object to a height of 4 m in 4 seconds? **200 W**

3. What is the power output of an engine that does 60,000 J of work in 10 seconds? **6 kW**

4. The block of ice weighs 500 newtons. (Neglect friction.)

   a. How much force parallel to the incline is needed to push it to the top? **250 N**

   b. How much work is required to push it to the top of the incline? **1500 J**

   c. What is the potential energy of the block relative to ground level? **1500 J**

   d. What would be the potential energy if the block were simply lifted vertically 3 m? **1500 J**

5. All the ramps below are 5 meters high. We know that the KE of the block at the bottom of each ramp will be equal to the loss of PE (conservation of energy).
Find the speed of the block at ground level in each case. (Hint: Do you recall from earlier chapters how much time it takes something to fall a vertical distance of 5 m from a position of rest assuming $g = 10$ m/s² and how much speed a falling object acquires in this time?) This gives you the answer to Case 1.
Discuss with your classmates how energy conservation provides the answers to Cases 2 and 3.

Case 1 Speed __10__ m/s

Case 2 Speed __10__ m/s

Case 3 Speed __10__ m/s

SPEED SAME BECAUSE ΔKE SAME; BUT TIME IS DIFFERENT!

35

CONCEPTUAL Physics PRACTICE PAGE

Chapter 7 Energy
Work and Energy—continued

6. Which block reaches the bottom of the incline first? Assume no friction. (Be careful!) Explain your answer.
BLOCK A BECAUSE GREATER ACCELERATION AND LESS RAMP DISTANCE. SO A HAS SHORTER SLIDING TIME—BUT SAME SPEED

7. Both the KE and PE of a block freely sliding down a ramp are shown below only at the bottom position in the sketch. Fill in the missing values for the other positions.

   PE = 75 J, KE = 0

   PE = 50 J, KE = 25 J

   PE = 25 J, KE = 50 J

   PE = 0, KE = 75 J

8. A big metal bead slides due to gravity along an upright friction-free wire. It starts from rest at the top of the wire as shown in the sketch.

   How fast is it traveling as it passes

   Point B? __10 m/s__

   Point D? __10 m/s__

   Point E? __10 m/s__

   Maximum speed at Point __C__

9. Rows of wind-powered generators are used in various windy locations to generate electric power. Does the power generated affect the speed of the wind? Would locations behind the "windmills" be windier if they weren't there. Discuss this in terms of energy conservation with your classmates.
YES. BY CONSERVATION OF ENERGY, ENERGY GAINED BY WINDMILLS IS TAKEN FROM WIND KE, SO WIND MUST SLOW DOWN. LOCATIONS BEHIND WOULD BE WINDIER WITHOUT THE WINDMILLS!

THINK
ENERGY
CONSERVATION

36

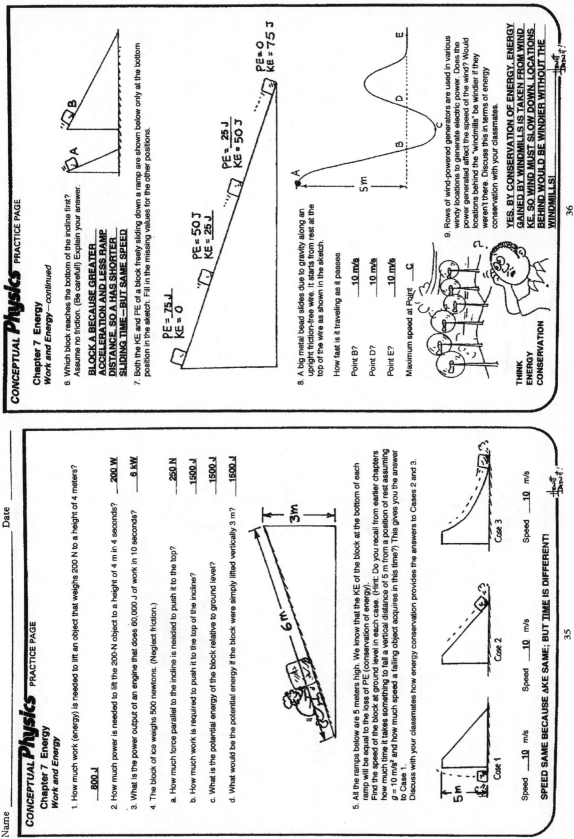

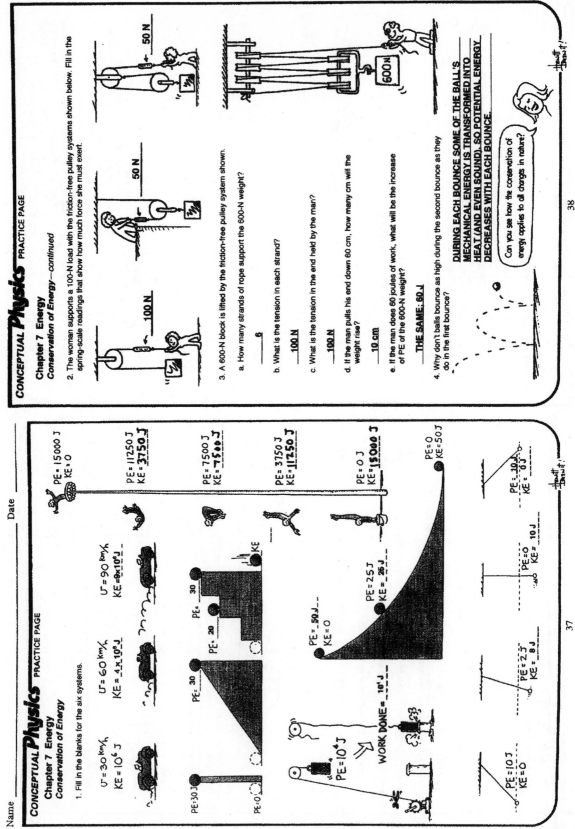

Page 37 (left)

Date _____

CONCEPTUAL Physics PRACTICE PAGE

Chapter 7 Energy
Conservation of Energy

1. Fill in the blanks for the six systems.

$v = 30$ km/h KE = 10^5 J
$v = 60$ km/h KE = 4×10^5 J
$v = 90$ km/h KE = 9×10^5 J

PE = 30 J   PE = 0

PE = 30   PE = 20   PE = 30   KE

PE = 10^4 J   PE = 10^4 J   WORK DONE = 10^4 J

PE = 50 J   KE = 0
PE = 25 J   KE = 25 J
PE = 0   KE = 50 J

PE = 10 J   KE = 0
PE = 2.5   KE = 8 J
PE = 0   KE = 10 J
PE = 10 J   KE = 0 J

Roller coaster:
PE = 15 000 J   KE = 0
PE = 11250 J   KE = 3750 J
PE = 7500 J   KE = 7500 J
PE = 3750 J   KE = 11250 J
PE = 0 J   KE = 15 000 J

37

Page 38 (right)

CONCEPTUAL Physics PRACTICE PAGE

Chapter 7 Energy
Conservation of Energy—continued

2. The woman supports a 100-N load with the friction-free pulley systems shown below. Fill in the spring-scale readings that show how much force she must exert.

100 N   50 N   50 N

3. A 600-N block is lifted by the friction-free pulley system shown.

a. How many strands of rope support the 600-N weight?

6

b. What is the tension in each strand?

100 N

c. What is the tension in the end held by the man?

100 N

d. If the man pulls his end down 60 cm, how many cm will the weight rise?

10 cm

e. If the man does 60 joules of work, what will be the increase of PE of the 600-N weight?

THE SAME: 60 J

4. Why don't balls bounce as high during the second bounce as they do in the first bounce?

DURING EACH BOUNCE SOME OF THE BALL'S MECHANICAL ENERGY IS TRANSFORMED INTO HEAT (AND EVEN SOUND), SO POTENTIAL ENERGY DECREASES WITH EACH BOUNCE.

Can you see how the conservation of energy applies to all changes in nature?

38

CONCEPTUAL Physics PRACTICE PAGE

Chapter 7 Energy
Momentum and Energy

Bronco Brown wants to put $Ft = \Delta mv$ to the test and try bungee jumping. Bronco leaps from a high cliff and experiences 3 s of free fall. Then the bungee cord begins to stretch, reducing his speed to zero in 2 s. Fortunately, the cord stretches to its maximum length just short of the ground below.

Bronco's mass is 100 kg.
Acceleration of free fall is 10 m/s².

Fill in the blanks:

Express values in SI units (*distance* in m, *velocity* in m/s, *momentum* in kg·m/s, *impulse* in N·s, and *deceleration* in m/s²).

t = 0 s   v = __0__
momentum = __0__

t = 1 s   v = __10 m/s__
momentum = __1000 kg·m/s__

t = 2 s   v = __20 m/s__
momentum = __2000 kg·m/s__

The 3-s free-fall distance of Bronco just before the bungee cord begins to stretch
= __45 m__

Δmv during the 3 to 5-s interval of free fall
= __3000 kg·m/s__

t = 3 s   v = __30 m/s__
momentum = __3000 kg·m/s__

Δmv during the 3 to 5-s of slowing down
= __3000 kg·m/s__

Impulse during the 3 to 5-s of slowing down
= __3000 N·s__

Average force exerted by the cord during the 3 to 5-s interval of slowing down
= __1500 N__

How about *work* and *energy*? How much KE does Bronco have 3 s after he first jumps?
__45,000 J__

t = 5 s   v = __0__
momentum = __0__

How much does gravitational PE decrease during this 3 s?
__45,000 J__

What two kinds of PE are changing during the 3 to 5-s slowing-down interval?

__GRAVITATIONAL AND ELASTIC__

CONCEPTUAL Physics PRACTICE PAGE

Chapter 7 Energy
Energy and Momentum

A Mini Cooper and a Lincoln Town Car are initially at rest on a horizontal parking lot at the edge of a steep cliff. For simplicity, we assume that the Town Car has twice as much mass as the Mini Cooper. Equal constant forces are applied to each car and they accelerate across equal distances (we ignore the effects of friction). When they reach the far end of the lot, the force is suddenly removed, whereupon they sail through the air and crash to the ground below. (The cars are wrecks to begin with, and this is a scientific experiment!)

Let equations guide your thinking!

1. Which vehicle has the greater acceleration? (Think $a = F/m$)

   __MINI COOPER (LESS MASS ACTED ON BY THE SAME FORCE)__

2. Which vehicle spends more time along the surface of the lot? (The faster or slower one?)

   __TOWN CAR (SLOWER DUE TO LESS ACCELERATION)__

3. Which vehicle has the larger impulse imparted to it by the applied force? (Think Impulse = Ft) Defend your answer.

   __TOWN CAR. SAME FORCE IS APPLIED OVER A LONGER TIME.__

4. Which vehicle has the greater momentum at the cliff's edge? (Think $Ft = \Delta mv$.) Defend your answer.

   __TOWN CAR. MORE IMPULSE PRODUCES MORE MOMENTUM CHANGE.__

5. Which vehicle has the greater work done on it by the applied force? (Think $W = Fd$.) Defend your answer in terms of the distance traveled.

   __SAME ON EACH. FORCE × DISTANCE IS SAME FOR EACH.__

6. Which vehicle has the greater kinetic energy at the edge of the cliff? (Think $W = \Delta KE$.) Does your answer follow from your explanation of Question 5? Does it contradict your answer to Question 3? Why or why not?

   __SAME, BECAUSE OF SAME WORK.__
   __YES.__
   __NO CONTRADICTION BECAUSE GREATER IMPULSE MEAN GREATER WORK.__

7. Which vehicle spends more time in the air, from the edge of the cliff to the ground below?

   __BOTH THE SAME!__

8. Which vehicle lands farther horizontally from the edge of the cliff onto the ground below?

   __THE MINI COOPER, WHICH IS MOVING FASTER.__

Challenge: Suppose the slower vehicle crashes a horizontal distance of 10 m from the ledge. Then at what horizontal distance does the faster car hit? __14 m (MINI COOPER MOVES √2 TIMES FASTER DUE TO EQUAL KE AT CLIFF EDGE. 1/2(2 m)v² = 1/2MV² WHERE V = √2v. SO √2 FASTER MEANS √2 FARTHER IN SAME TIME!)__

Impulse = Δmomentum
$Ft = \Delta mv$

Work = Fd $\Delta KE = \frac{1}{2}mv²$

Making this distinction between momentum and kinetic energy is high-level physics.

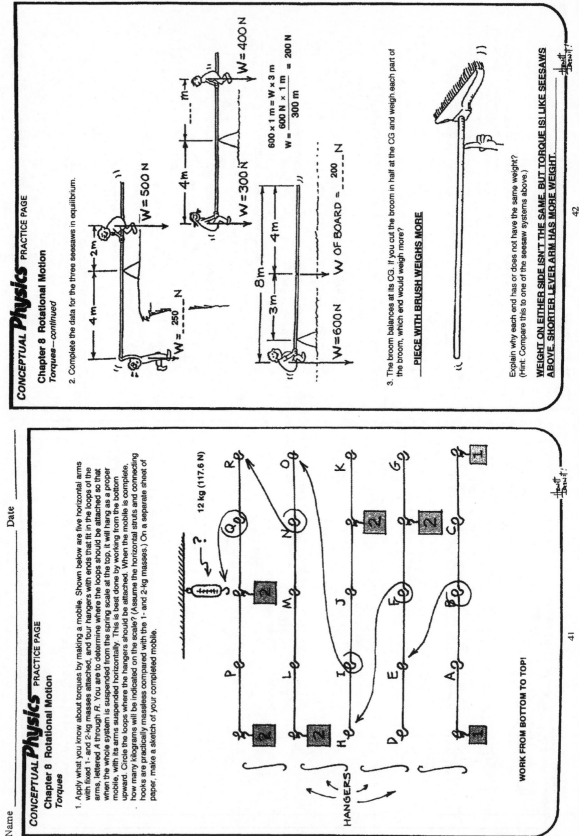

Name _____ Date _____

Chapter 8 Rotational Motion
Torques

1. Apply what you know about torques by making a mobile. Shown below are five horizontal arms with fixed 1- and 2-kg masses attached, and four hangers with ends that fit in the loops of the arms, lettered A through R. You are to determine where the loops should be attached so that when the whole system is suspended from the spring scale at the top, it will hang as a proper mobile, with its arms suspended horizontally. This is best done by working from the bottom upward. Circle the loops where the hangers should be attached. When the mobile is complete, how many kilograms will be indicated on the scale? (Assume the horizontal struts and connecting hooks are practically massless compared with the 1- and 2-kg masses.) On a separate sheet of paper, make a sketch of your completed mobile.

12 kg (117.6 N)

WORK FROM BOTTOM TO TOP!

HANGERS

41

Chapter 8 Rotational Motion
Torques—continued

2. Complete the data for the three seesaws in equilibrium.

W = 500 N   W = 400 N

2 m   4 m   m

W = ____ N   4 m
250   W = 300 N

$$600 \times 1\,m = W \times 3\,m$$
$$W = \frac{600\,N \times 1\,m}{300\,m} = 200\,N$$

8 m
3 m   4 m

W = 600 N   W OF BOARD = ____ N
200

3. The broom balances at its CG. If you cut the broom in half at the CG and weigh each part of the broom, which end would weigh more?

_____ PIECE WITH BRUSH WEIGHS MORE

Explain why each end has or does not have the same weight?
(Hint: Compare this to one of the seesaw systems above.)

WEIGHT ON EITHER SIDE ISN'T THE SAME, BUT TORQUE IS! LIKE SEESAWS ABOVE, SHORTER LEVER ARM HAS MORE WEIGHT.

42

CONCEPTUAL *Physics* PRACTICE PAGE

Chapter 8 Rotational Motion
Torques and Rotation

1. Pull the string gently and the spool rolls. The direction of roll depends on the way the torque is applied.

In (1) and (2) below, the force and lever arm are shown for the torque about the point where surface contact is made (shown by the triangular "fulcrum"). The lever arm is the heavy dashed line, which is different for each different pulling position.

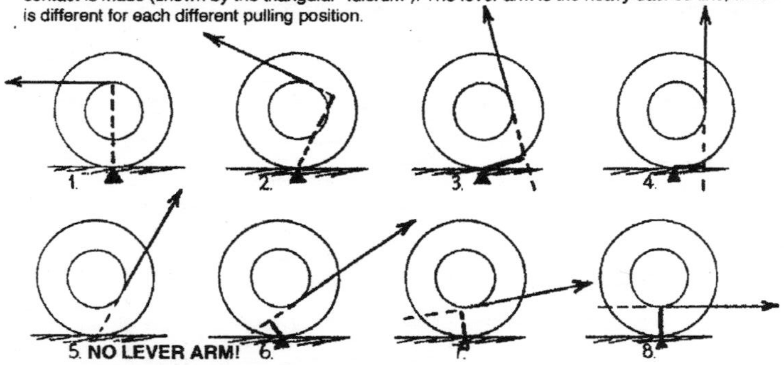

a. Construct the lever arm for the other positions.

b. Lever arm is longer when the string of the spool spindle is on the [top] [bottom].

c. For a given pull, the torque is greater when the string is on the [top] [bottom].

d. For the same pull, rotational acceleration is greater when the string is on the

[top] [bottom] [makes no difference].

e. At which position(s) does the spool roll to the left? __1,2,3,4__

f. At which position(s) does the spool roll to the right? __6,7,8__

g. At which position(s) does the spool not roll at all? __5__

h. Why does the spool slide rather than roll at this position?

5. NO LEVER ARM!

6.

LINE OF ACTION EXTENDS TO FULCRUM: NO LEVER ARM. NO TORQUE.

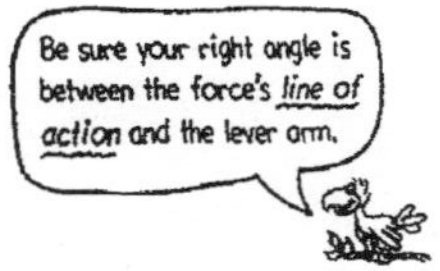

2. Relatively few people know that the reason a ball picks up rotational speed rolling down an incline is because of a torque. In sketch A, we see the ingredients of the torque acting on the ball—the force due to gravity and the lever arm to the point where surface contact is made.

a. Construct the lever arms for positions B and C.

b. As the incline becomes steeper, the torque [increases] [decreases].

Be sure your right angle is between the force's *line of action* and the lever arm.

43

CONCEPTUAL *Physics* PRACTICE PAGE

Chapter 8 Rotational Motion
Acceleration and Circular Motion

Newton's 2nd law, $a = F/m$, tells us that net force and its corresponding acceleration are always in the same direction. But force and acceleration vectors are not always in the direction of velocity (another vector).

1. You're in a car at a traffic light. The light turns green and the driver "steps on the gas." The sketch shows the top view of the car. Note the direction of the velocity and acceleration vectors.

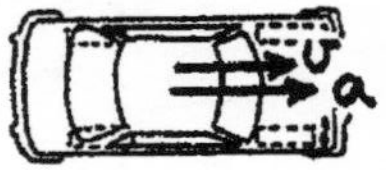

a. Your body tends to lurch [forward] [not at all] [backward]

b. The car accelerates [forward] [not at all] [backward].

c. The force on the car acts [forward] [not at all] [backward].

2. You're driving along and approach a stop sign. The driver steps on the brakes. The sketch shows the top view of the car. Draw vectors for velocity and acceleration.

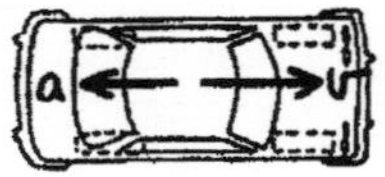

a. Your body tends to lurch [forward] [not at all] [backward].

b. The car accelerates [forward] [not at all] [backward].

c. The force on the car acts [forward] [not at all] [backward].

3. You continue driving, and round a sharp curve to the left at constant speed.

a. Your body tends to lean [inward] [not at all] [outward].

b. The direction of the car's acceleration is [inward] [not at all] [outward].

c. The force on the car acts [inward] [not at all] [outward].

Draw vectors for velocity and acceleration of the car.

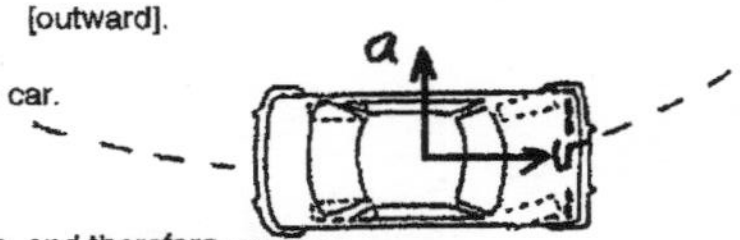

4. In general, the directions of lurch and acceleration, and therefore the directions of lurch and force are [the same] [not related] [opposite].

5. The whirling stone's direction of motion keeps changing.

a. If it moves faster, its direction changes [faster] [slower].

b. This indicates that as speed increases, acceleration [increases] [decreases] [stays the same].

6. Like Question 5, consider whirling the stone on a shorter string—that is, of smaller radius.

a. For a given speed, the rate that the stone changes direction is [less] [more] [the same].

b. This indicates that as the radius decreases, acceleration [increases] [decreases] [stays the same].

†thanx to Jim Harper

44

CONCEPTUAL *Physics* PRACTICE PAGE

Chapter 8 Rotational Motion
The Flying Pig

The toy pig flies in a circle at constant speed. This arrangement is called a conical pendulum because the supporting string sweeps out a cone. Neglecting the action of its flapping wings, only two forces act on the pig—gravitational mg, and string tension T.

Vector Component Analysis:
Note that vector T can be resolved into two components—horizontal T_x, and vertical T_y. These vector components are dashed to distinguish them from the tension vector T.

Circle the correct answers:

1. If T were somehow replaced with T_x and T_y, the pig **[would]** [would not] behave identically to being supported by T.

2. Since the pig doesn't accelerate vertically, compared with the magnitude of mg, component T_y must be [greater] [less] **[equal and opposite]**.

3. The velocity of the pig at any instant is [along the radius of] **[tangent to]** its circular path.

4. Since the pig continues in circular motion, component T_x must be a **[centripetal]** [centrifugal] [nonexistent] force, which equals [zero] **[mv^2/r]**. Furthermore, T_x is **[along the radius]** [tangent to] the circle swept out.

Vector Resultant Analysis:

5. Rather than resolving T into horizontal and vertical components, use your pencil to sketch the resultant of mg and T using the *parallelogram rule*.

6. The resultant lies in a **[horizontal]** [vertical] direction, and **[toward]** [away from] the center of the circular path. The resultant of mg and T is a **[centripetal]** [centrifugal] force.

For straight-line motion with no acceleration, $\Sigma F = 0$. But for uniform circular motion, $\Sigma F = mv^2/r$.

thanx to Pablo Robinson and Miss Piggy

CONCEPTUAL *Physics* PRACTICE PAGE

Chapter 8 Circular and Rotational Motion
Banked Airplanes

An airplane banks as it turns along a horizontal circular path in the air. Except for the thrust of its engines and air resistance, the two significant forces on the plane are gravitational mg (vertical), and lift L (perpendicular to the wings).

Vector Component Analysis:
With a ruler and a pencil, resolve vector L into two perpendicular components, horizontal L_x, and vertical L_y. Make these vectors dashed to distinguish them from L.

Circle the correct answers:

1. The velocity of the airplane at any instant is [along the radius of] **[tangent to]** its circular path.

2. If L were somehow replaced with L_x and L_y, the airplane **[would]** [would not] behave the same as being supported by L.

3. Since the airplane doesn't accelerate vertically, component L_y must be [greater than] [less than] **[equal and opposite to]** mg.

4. Since the plane continues in circular motion, component L_x, must equal [zero] **[mv^2/r]**, and be a **[centripetal]** [centrifugal] [nonexistent] force. Furthermore, L_x is **[along the radius of]** [tangent to] the circular path.

Vector Resultant Analysis:

5. Rather than resolving L into horizontal and vertical components, use your pencil to sketch the resultant of mg and L using the *parallelogram rule*.

6. The resultant lies in a **[horizontal]** [vertical] direction, and **[toward]** [away from] the center of the circular path. The resultant of mg and L is a **[centripetal]** [centrifugal] force.

7. The resultant of mg and L is the same as **[L_x]** [L_y].

Challenge: Explain in your own words why the resultant of two vectors can be the same as a single component of one of them. **For any pair of vectors to be added, if**

$$\Sigma v_y = 0, \text{ and } \Sigma v_x \neq 0, \text{ the resultant will be } \Sigma v_x.$$

Chapter 8 Rotational Motion
Banked Track

A car rounds a banked curve with just the right speed so that it has no tendency to slide down or up the banked road surface. Shown below are two main forces that act on the car perpendicular to its motion—gravitational *mg* and the normal force *N* (the support force of the surface).

Vector Component Analysis:

Note that vector *N* is resolved into two perpendicular components, horizontal N_x and vertical N_y. As usual, these vectors are dashed to distinguish them from *N*.

Circle the correct answers:

1. If *N* were somehow replaced with N_x and N_y, the car (would) [would not]

behave identically to being supported by *N*.

2. Since the car doesn't accelerate vertically, component N_y must be

[greater than] (equal and opposite to) [less than] *mg*.

3. The velocity of the car at any instant is [along the radius of] (tangent to) its circular path.

4. Since the car continues in uniform circular motion, component N_x must equal [zero] (mv^2/r)

and be a (centripetal) [centrifugal] [nonexistent] force. Furthermore, N_x

(lies along the radius of) [is tangent to] the circular path.

Vector Resultant Analysis:

5. Rather than resolving *N* into horizontal and vertical components, use your pencil to sketch the resultant of *mg* and *N* using the *parallelogram rule.*

6. The resultant lies in a (horizontal) [vertical]

direction, and (toward) [away from] the

center of the circular path. The resultant of

mg and *N* is a (centripetal) [centrifugal] force.

7. The resultant of *mg* and *N* is the same as

(N_x) [N_y], and provides the

(centripetal) [centrifugal] force.

Notice that when a component of *N* makes up a centripetal force, *N* > *mg*.

Chapter 8 Rotational Motion
Leaning On

When turning a corner on a bicycle, everyone knows that you've got to lean "into the curve." What is the physics of this leaning? It involves torque, friction, and centripetal force (mv^2/r).

First, consider the simple case of riding a bicycle along a straight-line path. Except for the force that propels the bike forward (friction of the road in the direction of motion) and air resistance (friction of air against the direction of motion), only two significant forces act: weight *mg* and the normal force *N*. (The vectors are drawn side-by-side, but actually lie along a single vertical line.)

Circle the correct answers:

1. Since there is no vertical acceleration, we can say that the magnitude of

[$N > mg$] [$N < mg$] ($N = mg$) which means that in the vertical direction,

[$\Sigma F_y > 0$] [$\Sigma F_y < 0$] ($\Sigma F_y = 0$)

2. Since the bike doesn't rotate or change in its rotational state, then the total

torque is (zero) [not zero].

Now consider the same bike rounding a corner. In order to safely make the turn, the bicyclist leans in the direction of the turn. A force of friction pushes sideways on the tire toward the center of the curve.

3. The friction force, *f*, provides the centripetal force that produces a

curved path. Then ($f = mv^2/r$) [$f = mv^2/r$]

4. Consider the net torque about the center of mass (*CM*) of the bike-rider system. Gravity produces no torque about this point, but *N* and *f* do. The torque involving *N* tends to produce

(clockwise) [counterclockwise] rotation, and the one involving *f*

[clockwise] (counterclockwise) rotation.

These torques cancel each other when the resultant of vectors *N* and *f* pass through the *CM*.

5. With your pencil, use the parallelogram rule and sketch in the resultant of vectors *N* and *f*. Label your resultant *R*. Note the *R* passes through the center of mass of the bike-rider system. That

means that *R* produces [a clockwise] [a counterclockwise] [no]

torque about the *CM*. Therefore the bike-rider system

[topples clockwise] [topples counterclockwise] (doesn't topple).

When learning how to turn on a bike, you lean so that the sum of the torques about your *CM* is zero. You may not be calculating torques, but your body learns to feel them.

thanx to Pablo Robinson

Name _____ Date _____

CONCEPTUAL *Physics* PRACTICE PAGE

Chapter 8 Rotational Motion
Simulated Gravity and Frames of Reference

Suzie Spacewalker and Bob Biker are in outer space. Bob experiences Earth–normal gravity in a rotating habitat, where centripetal force on his feet provides a normal support force that feels like weight. Suzie hovers outside in a weightless condition, motionless relative to the stars and the center of the habitat.

1. Suzie sees Bob rotating clockwise in a circular path at a linear speed of 30 km/h. Suzie and Bob are facing each other, and from Bob's point of view, he is at rest and he sees Suzie moving [clockwise] [counterclockwise].

Bob at rest on the floor
Suzie hovering in space

2. The rotating habitat seems like home to Bob—until he rides his bicycle. When he rides in the opposite direction as the habitat rotates, Suzie sees him moving [faster] [slower].

Bob rides counter-clockwise

3. As Bob's bicycle speedometer reading increases, his rotational speed [decreases] [remains unchanged] [increases] and the normal force that feels like weight [decreases] [remains unchanged] [increases]. So friction between the tires and the floor [decreases] [remains unchanged] [increases].

4. When Bob nevertheless gets his speed up to 30 km/h, Suzie sees him [motionless] [moving at 30 km/h] [moving at 60 km/h].

as indicated on his bicycle speedometer, Suzie sees him

thanx to Bob Becker

49

CONCEPTUAL *Physics* PRACTICE PAGE

Chapter 8 Rotational Motion
Simulated Gravity and Frames of Reference—continued

5. Bounding off the floor a bit while riding at 30 km/h, and neglecting wind effects, Bob [drifts toward the ceiling in midspace as the floor whizzes by him at 30 km/h] [falls as he would on Earth] [slams onto the floor with increased force]

and finds himself

[in the same frame of reference as Suzie]

[as if he rode at 30 km/h on Earth's surface]

[pressed harder against the bicyclist seat].

Bob rides at 30 km/h with respect to the floor

6. Bob maneuvers back to his initial condition, whirling at rest with the habitat, standing beside his bicycle. But not for long. Urged by Suzie, he rides in the opposite direction, clockwise with the rotation of the habitat. Now Suzie sees him moving [faster] [slower].

Bob rides clockwise

7. As Bob gains speed, the normal support force that feels like weight [decreases] [remains unchanged] [increases].

8. When Bob's speedometer reading gets up to 30 km/h, Suzie sees him moving [30 km/h] [not at all] [60 km/h] and Bob finds himself

[weightless like Suzie]

[just as if he rode at 30 km/h on Earth's surface]

[pressed harder against the bicyclist seat].

Next, Bob goes bowling. You decide whether the game depends on which direction the ball is rolled!

50

CONCEPTUAL Physics PRACTICE PAGE

Chapter 9 Gravity
Inverse-Square Law

1. Paint spray travels radially away from the nozzle of the can in straight lines. Like gravity, the strength (intensity) of the spray obeys an inverse-square law. Complete the diagram by filling in the blank spaces.

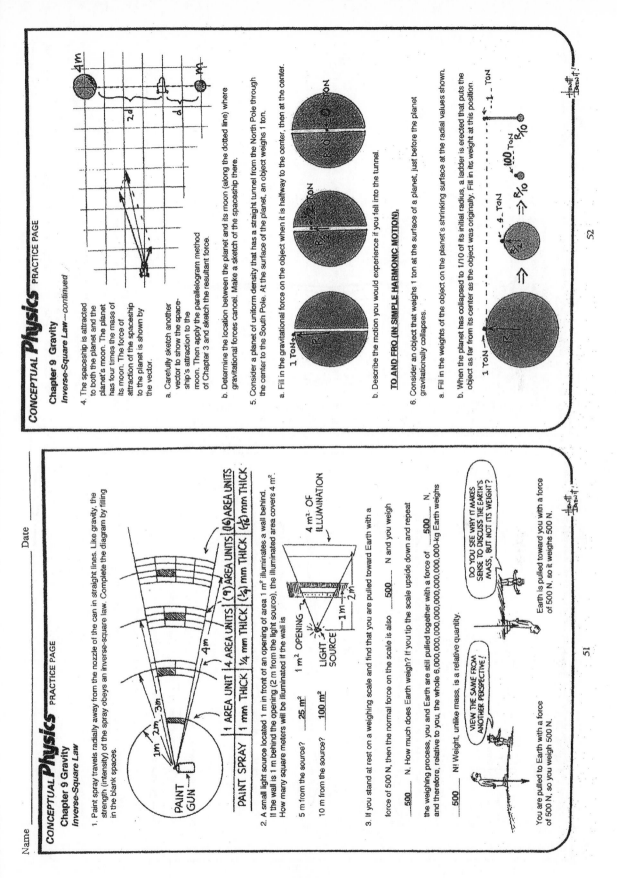

PAINT SPRAY	1 AREA UNIT	4 AREA UNITS	(**9**) AREA UNITS	(**16**) AREA UNITS
	1 mm THICK	¼ mm THICK	(**⅑**) mm THICK	(**1/16**) mm THICK

2. A small light source located 1 m in front of an opening of area 1 m² illuminates a wall behind. If the wall is 1 m behind the opening (2 m from the light source), the illuminated area covers 4 m². How many square meters will be illuminated if the wall is

5 m from the source? **25 m²**

10 m from the source? **100 m²**

3. If you stand at rest on a weighing scale and find that you are pulled toward Earth with a force of 500 N, then the normal force on the scale is also **500** N and you weigh **500** N. How much does Earth weigh? If you tip the scale upside down and repeat the weighing process, you and Earth are still pulled together with a force of **500** N, and therefore, relative to you, the whole 6,000,000,000,000,000,000,000,000-kg Earth weighs **500** N! Weight, unlike mass, is a relative quantity.

VIEW THE SAME FROM ANOTHER PERSPECTIVE!

DO YOU SEE WHY IT MAKES SENSE TO DISCUSS THE EARTH'S MASS, BUT NOT ITS WEIGHT?

You are pulled to Earth with a force of 500 N, so you weigh 500 N.

Earth is pulled toward you with a force of 500 N, so it weighs 500 N.

51

CONCEPTUAL Physics PRACTICE PAGE

Chapter 9 Gravity
Inverse-Square Law—continued

4. The spaceship is attracted to both the planet and the planet's moon. The planet has four times the mass of its moon. The force of attraction of the spaceship to the planet is shown by the vector.

a. Carefully sketch another vector to show the spaceship's attraction to the moon. Then apply the parallelogram method of Chapter 3 and sketch the resultant force.

b. Determine the location between the planet and its moon (along the dotted line) where gravitational forces cancel. Make a sketch of the spaceship there.

5. Consider a planet of uniform density that has a straight tunnel from the North Pole through the center to the South Pole. At the surface of the planet, an object weighs 1 ton.

a. Fill in the gravitational force on the object when it is halfway to the center, then at the center.

b. Describe the motion you would experience if you fell into the tunnel.

TO AND FRO (IN SIMPLE HARMONIC MOTION).

6. Consider an object that weighs 1 ton at the surface of a planet, just before the planet gravitationally collapses.

a. Fill in the weights of the object on the planet's shrinking surface at the radial values shown.

b. When the planet has collapsed to 1/10 of its initial radius, a ladder is erected that puts the object as far from its center as the object was originally. Fill in its weight at this position.

52

CONCEPTUAL *Physics* PRACTICE PAGE

Chapter 9 Gravity
Our Ocean Tides

1. Consider two equal-mass blobs of water, A and B, initially at rest in the Moon's gravitational field. The vector shows the gravitational force of the Moon on A.

   a. Draw a force vector on B due to the Moon's gravity.

   b. Is the force on B more or less than the force on A? __**LESS**__

   c. Why? __**FARTHER AWAY**__

   d. The blobs accelerate toward the Moon. Which has the greater acceleration? (A) [B]

   e. Because of the different accelerations, with time [A gets farther ahead of B] (A and B gain identical speeds) [decreases].
   (increases) [stays the same] and the distance between A and B

   f. If A and B were connected by a rubber band, with time the rubber band would [stretch] [not stretch].

   g. This (stretching) [nonstretching] is due to the ([difference]) [nondifference] in the Moon's gravitational pulls.

   h. The two blobs will eventually crash into the Moon. To orbit around the Moon instead of crashing into it, the blobs should move [away from the Moon] (tangentially). Then their accelerations will consist of changes in [speed] ([direction]).

2. Now consider the same two blobs located on opposite sides of Earth.

   a. Because of difference in the Moon's pull on the blobs, they tend to [spread away from each other] [approach each other].

   b. Does this spreading produce ocean tides? (Yes) [No]

   c. If Earth and Moon were closer, gravitational force between them would be (more) [the same] [less], and the difference in gravitational forces on the near and far parts of the ocean would be (more) [the same] [less].

   d. Because Earth's orbit about the Sun is slightly elliptical, Earth and Sun are closer in December than in June. Taking the Sun's tidal force into account, on a world average, ocean tides are greater in (December) [June] [no difference].

53

CONCEPTUAL *Physics* PRACTICE PAGE

Chapter 10 Projectile and Satellite Motion
Independence of Horizontal and Vertical Components of Motion

1. Above left: Use the scale 1 cm : 5 m and draw the positions of the dropped ball at 1-second intervals. Neglect air resistance and assume $g = 10 \text{ m/s}^2$. Estimate the number of seconds the ball is in the air. __4__ seconds

2. Above right: The four positions of the thrown ball with no gravity are at 1-second intervals. At 1 cm : 5 m, carefully draw the positions of the ball with gravity. Connect your positions with a smooth curve to show the path of the ball.
How is the motion in the vertical direction affected by motion in the horizontal direction? **ONLY VERTICAL MOTION AFFECTED BY GRAVITY: HORIZONTAL MOTION IS INDEPENDENT.**

55

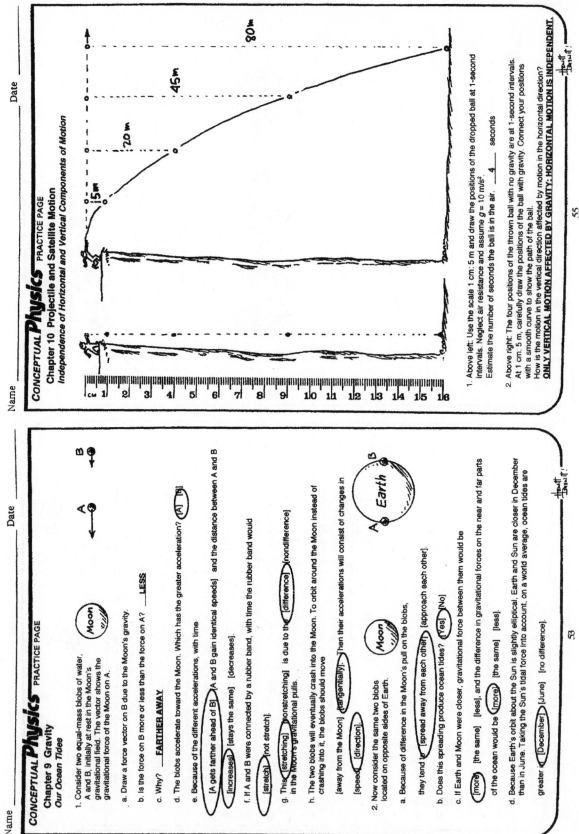

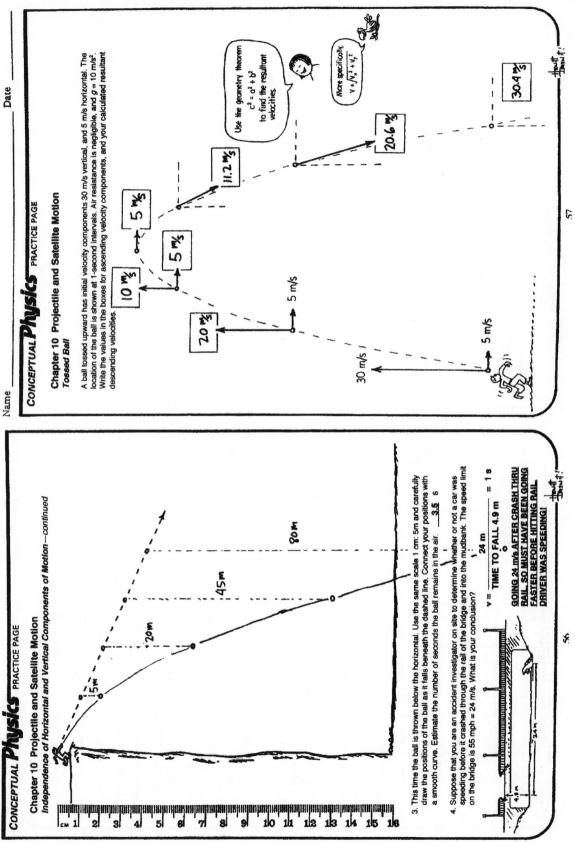

CONCEPTUAL Physics PRACTICE PAGE

Chapter 10 Projectile and Satellite Motion
Tossed Ball

A ball tossed upward has initial velocity components 30 m/s vertical, and 5 m/s horizontal. The location of the ball is shown at 1-second intervals. Air resistance is negligible, and $g = 10$ m/s². Write the values in the boxes for ascending velocity components, and your calculated resultant velocities.

Use the geometry theorem
$c^2 = a^2 + b^2$
to find the resultant velocities.

More specifically,
$v = \sqrt{v_x^2 + v_y^2}$

10 m/s	5 m/s
5 m/s	
20 m/s	5 m/s
11.2 m/s	20.6 m/s	30.4 m/s

30 m/s

5 m/s

57

CONCEPTUAL Physics PRACTICE PAGE

Chapter 10 Projectile and Satellite Motion
Independence of Horizontal and Vertical Components of Motion—continued

5m

20m

45m

80m

3. This time the ball is thrown below the horizontal. Use the same scale 1 cm: 5m and carefully draw the positions of the ball as it falls beneath the dashed line. Connect your positions with a smooth curve. Estimate the number of seconds the ball remains in the air. __3.5__ s

4. Suppose that you are an accident investigator on site to determine whether or not a car was speeding before it crashed through the rail of the bridge and into the mudbank. The speed limit on the bridge is 55 mph = 24 m/s. What is your conclusion?

$$v = \frac{24 \text{ m}}{\text{TIME TO FALL } 4.9 \text{ m} = 1 \text{ s}}$$

4.9m

24m

GOING 24 m/s AFTER CRASH THRU RAIL, SO MUST HAVE BEEN GOING FASTER BEFORE HITTING RAIL DRIVER WAS SPEEDING!

56

157

CONCEPTUAL *Physics* PRACTICE PAGE

Chapter 10 Projectile and Satellite Motion
Satellite in Circular Orbit

1. Figure A shows "Newton's Mountain," so high that its top is above the drag of the atmosphere. The cannonball is fired and hits the ground.

a. Draw a likely path that the cannonball might take if it were fired a little bit faster.

b. Repeat for a still greater speed, but less than 8 km/s.

c. Then draw its orbital path for a speed of 8 km/s.

d. What is the shape of the 8-km/s curve?

CIRCLE

e. What would be the shape of the orbital path if the cannonball were fired at a speed of 9 km/s?

ELLIPSE

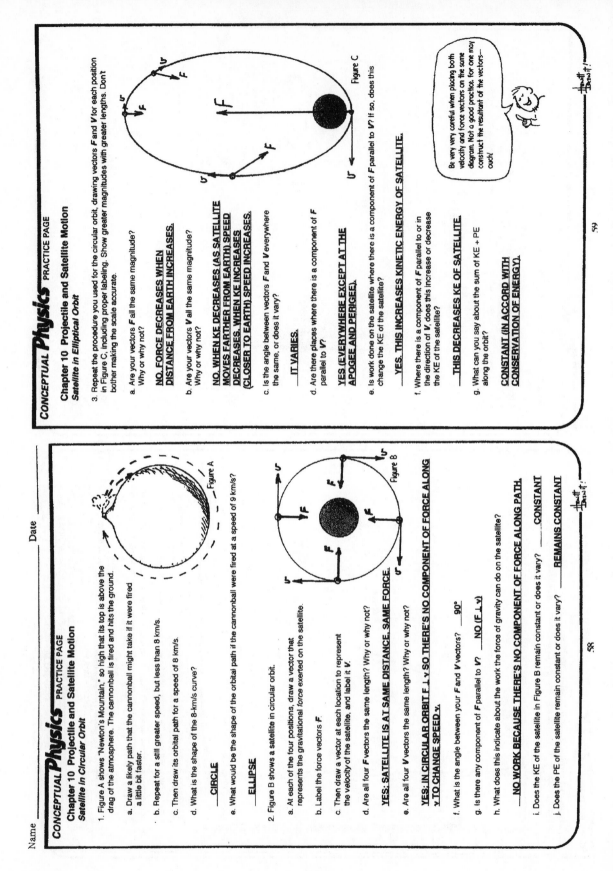

Figure A

Figure B

2. Figure B shows a satellite in circular orbit.

a. At each of the four positions, draw a vector that represents the gravitational *force* exerted on the satellite.

b. Label the force vectors **F**.

c. Then draw a vector at each location to represent the *velocity* of the satellite, and label it **v**.

d. Are all four **F** vectors the same length? Why or why not? **YES; SATELLITE IS AT SAME DISTANCE, SAME FORCE.**

e. Are all four **v** vectors the same length? Why or why not? **YES; IN CIRCULAR ORBIT F⊥v SO THERE'S NO COMPONENT OF FORCE ALONG v TO CHANGE SPEED v.**

f. What is the angle between your **F** and **v** vectors? **90°**

g. Is there any component of **F** parallel to **v**? **NO (F⊥v)**

h. What does this indicate about the work the force of gravity can do on the satellite? **NO WORK BECAUSE THERE'S NO COMPONENT OF FORCE ALONG PATH.**

i. Does the KE of the satellite in Figure B remain constant or does it vary? **CONSTANT**

j. Does the PE of the satellite remain constant or does it vary? **REMAINS CONSTANT**

CONCEPTUAL *Physics* PRACTICE PAGE

Chapter 10 Projectile and Satellite Motion
Satellite in Elliptical Orbit

3. Repeat the procedure you used for the circular orbit, drawing vectors *F* and *V* for each position in Figure C, including proper labeling. Show greater magnitudes with greater lengths. Don't bother making the scale accurate.

Figure C

a. Are your vectors *F* all the same magnitude? Why or why not? **NO. FORCE DECREASES WHEN DISTANCE FROM EARTH INCREASES.**

b. Are your vectors *V* all the same magnitude? Why or why not? **NO. WHEN KE DECREASES (AS SATELLITE MOVES FARTHER FROM EARTH) SPEED DECREASES. WHEN KE INCREASES (CLOSER TO EARTH) SPEED INCREASES.**

c. Is the angle between vectors *F* and *V* everywhere the same, or does it vary? **IT VARIES.**

d. Are there places where there is a component of *F* parallel to *V*? **YES (EVERYWHERE EXCEPT AT THE APOGEE AND PERIGEE).**

e. Is work done on the satellite where there is a component of *F* parallel to *V*? If so, does this change the KE of the satellite? **YES. THIS INCREASES KINETIC ENERGY OF SATELLITE.**

f. Where there is a component of *F* parallel to or in the direction of *V*, does this increase or decrease the KE of the satellite? **THIS DECREASES KE OF SATELLITE.**

g. What can you say about the sum of KE + PE along the orbit? **CONSTANT (IN ACCORD WITH CONSERVATION OF ENERGY).**

Be very careful when placing both velocity and force vectors on the same diagram. Not a good practice, for one may construct the resultant of the vectors—ouch!

CONCEPTUAL *Physics* PRACTICE PAGE
Mechanics Overview—Chapters 1 to 10

1. The sketch shows the elliptical path described by a satellite about Earth. In which of the labeled positions, A - D, (place an "S" for "same everywhere") does the satellite experience the maximum

a. gravitational force? __A__

b. speed? __A__

c. momentum? __A__

d. kinetic energy? __A__

e. gravitational potential energy? __C__

f. total energy (KE + PE)? __S__

g. acceleration? __A__

h. angular momentum? __S__

2. Answer the above questions for a satellite in circular orbit.

a. __S__   b. __S__   c. __S__   d. __S__

e. __S__   f. __S__   g. __S__   h. __S__

3. In which position(s) is there momentarily no work being done on the satellite by the force of gravity? Why?

__A AND C BECAUSE OF NO FORCE COMPONENTS IN DIRECTION OF MOTION.__

4. Work changes energy. Let the equation for work, $W = Fd$, guide your thinking on the following: Defend your answers in terms of $W = Fd$.

a. In which position will a several-minutes thrust of rocket engines pushing the satellite forward do the most work on the satellite and give it the greatest change in kinetic energy? (Hint: Think about where the most distance will be traveled during the application of a several-minutes thrust?)

__A. WHERE FORCE ACTS OVER LONGEST DISTANCE.__

b. In which position will a several-minutes thrust of rocket engines pushing the satellite forward do the least work on the satellite and give it the least boost in kinetic energy?

__C. WHERE FORCE ACTS OVER SHORTEST DISTANCE.__

c. In which position will a several-minutes thrust of a retro-rocket (pushing opposite to the satellite's direction of motion) do the most work on the satellite and change its kinetic energy the most?

__A. MOST "NEGATIVE WORK" DECREASES AND MOST AKE OCCURS WHERE FORCE ACTS OVER THE LONGEST DISTANCE.__

CONCEPTUAL *Physics* PRACTICE PAGE
Chapter 11 The Atomic Nature of Matter
Atoms and Atomic Nuclei

Use the periodic table in your text to help you answer the following questions.

1. When the atomic nuclei of hydrogen and lithium are squashed together (nuclear fusion) the element that is produced is

__BERYLLIUM__

2. When the atomic nuclei of a pair of lithium nuclei are fused, the element produced is

__CARBON__

3. When the atomic nuclei of a pair of aluminum nuclei are fused, the element produced is

__IRON__

4. When the nucleus of a nitrogen atom absorbs a proton, the resulting element is

__OXYGEN__

5. What element is produced when a gold nucleus gains a proton?   __MERCURY__

6. What element is produced when a gold nucleus loses a proton?   __PLATINUM__

7. What element is produced when a uranium nucleus ejects an elementary particle composed of two protons and two neutrons?

__THORIUM__

8. If a uranium nucleus breaks into two pieces (nuclear fission) and one of the pieces is zirconium (atomic number 40), the other piece is the element

__TELLURIUM (ATOMIC NUMBER 52)__

9. Which has more mass, a nitrogen molecule (N_2) or an oxygen molecule (O_2)?

__AN OXYGEN MOLECULE__

10. Which has the greater number of atoms, a gram of helium or a gram of neon?

__A GRAM OF HELIUM__

CONCEPTUAL *Physics* PRACTICE PAGE

Chapter 11 The Atomic Nature of Matter
Subatomic Particles

Three fundamental particles of the atom are the __PROTON__ , __NEUTRON__ , and
__ELECTRON__ . At the center of each atom lies the atomic __NUCLEUS__ which
consists of __PROTONS__ and __NEUTRONS__ . The atomic number refers to
the number of __PROTONS__ in the nucleus. All atoms of the same element have the same
number of __PROTONS__ hence, the same atomic number.

Isotopes are atoms that have the same number of __PROTONS__ but a different number of
__NEUTRONS__ . An isotope is identified by its atomic mass number, which is the total number
of __PROTONS__ and __NEUTRONS__ in the nucleus. A carbon isotope that has
6 __PROTONS__ and __NEUTRONS__ is identified as carbon-12, where 12 is the atomic
mass number. A carbon isotope having 6 __PROTONS__ and 8 __NEUTRONS__ on the
other hand is carbon-14.

1. *Complete the following table:*

ISOTOPE	ELECTRONS	NUMBER OF PROTONS	NEUTRONS
Hydrogen-1	1	1	0
Chlorine-36	17	17	19
Nitrogen-14	7	7	7
Potassium-40	19	19	21
Arsenic-75	33	33	42
Gold-197	79	79	118

2. Which results in a more valuable product—
adding or *subtracting* protons from gold nuclei?
__SUBTRACT FROM PLATINUM__
__(MORE VALUABLE)__

3. Which has more mass, a lead atom or
a uranium atom?
__NEON__

4. Which has a greater number of atoms,
a gram of lead or a gram of uranium?
__HELIUM!__

Of every 200 atoms in our bodies, 126 are hydrogen,
51 are oxygen, and just 19 are carbon. In addition to
carbon we need iron to manufacture hemoglobin,
cobalt for the creation of vitamin B-12, potassium
and a little sodium for our nerves, and molybdenum,
manganese, and vanadium to keep our enzymes
purring. Ah, we'd be nothing without atoms!

CONCEPTUAL *Physics* PRACTICE PAGE

Chapter 12 Solids
Scaling

1. Consider a cube 1 cm × 1 cm × 1 cm (a very small sugar cube). Its volume is 1 cm^3. The surface
area of one of its faces is 1 cm^2. The total surface area of the cube is 6 cm^2 because it has
6 sides. Now consider a second cube, scaled up by a factor of 2 so it is 2 cm × 2 cm × 2 cm.

a. What is the total surface area of each cube?

1st cube __6__ cm^2; 2nd cube __24__ cm^2

b. What is the volume of each cube?

1st cube __1__ cm^3; 2nd cube __8__ cm^3

c. Compare the ratio of surface area to volume for each cube.

1st cube of $\dfrac{\text{surface area}}{\text{volume}} = \dfrac{6}{1}$; 2nd cube of $\dfrac{\text{surface area}}{\text{volume}} = \dfrac{3}{1}$

2. Now consider a third cube, scaled up by a factor of 3 so it is 3 cm × 3 cm × 3 cm.

a. What is its total surface area? __54__ cm^2

b. What is its volume? __27__ cm^3

c. What is its ratio of surface area to volume?

$\dfrac{\text{surface area}}{\text{volume}} = \dfrac{2}{1}$

3. When the size of a cube is scaled up by a certain factor
(2 and then 3 for the above examples), the area increases as the __SQUARE__ of the factor,
and the volume increases as the __CUBE__ of the factor.

4. Does the ratio of surface area to volume increase or decrease as things are scaled up?
__RATIO DECREASES__

5. Does the rule for the scaling up of cubes also apply to other shapes? __YES__
Would your answers have been different if we started with a sphere of diameter 1 cm and
scaled it up to a sphere of diameter 2 cm, and then 3 cm? __NO; SAME RATIOS__

6. The effects of scaling are beneficial to some creatures and detrimental to others. Check either
(B) for beneficial or (D) for detrimental for each of the following:

a. an insect falling from a tree __B__ d. a big fish chasing a small fish __B__

b. an elephant falling from the same tree __D__ e. a hungry mouse __D__

c. a small fish trying to flee from a big fish __D__ f. an insect that falls in the water __D__

CONCEPTUAL *Physics* PRACTICE PAGE

Chapter 12 Solids
Scaling Circles

1. Complete the table below.

FOR THE CIRCUMFERENCE OF A CIRCLE, $C = 2\pi r$

AND FOR THE AREA OF A CIRCLE, $A = \pi r^2$

CIRCLES		
RADIUS	CIRCUMFERENCE	AREA
1 cm	$2\pi(1cm) = 2\pi$ cm	$\pi(1cm)^2 = \pi cm^2$
2 cm	$2\pi(2cm) = 4\pi cm$	$\pi(2cm)^2 = 4\pi cm^2$
3 cm	$2\pi(3cm) = 6\pi cm$	$\pi(3cm)^2 = 9\pi cm^2$
10 cm	$2\pi(10cm) = 20\pi cm$	$\pi(10cm)^2 = 100\pi cm^2$

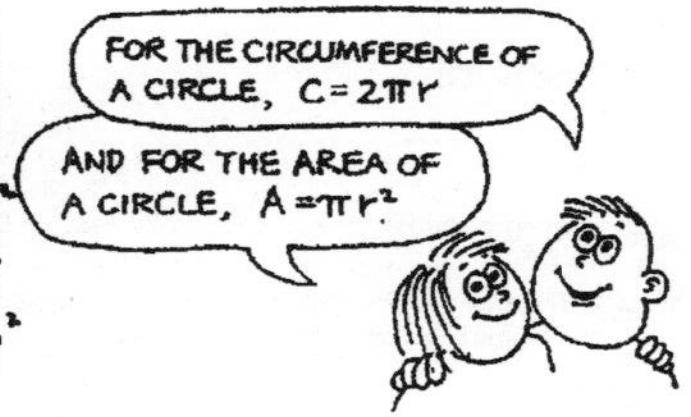

2. From your completed table, when the radius of a circle is doubled, its area increases by __4__.
When the radius is increased by a factor of 10, the area increases by __100__.

3. Consider a small pizza that costs $5.00. Another pizza of the same thickness has twice the diameter. How much should the larger pizza cost?

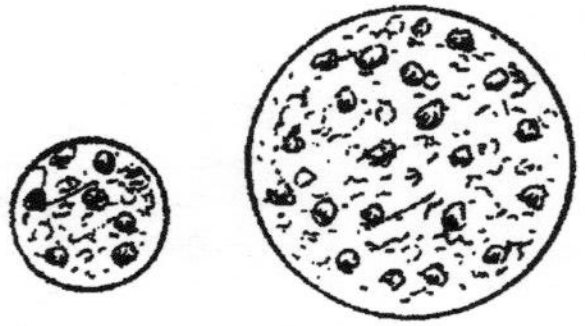

__$25.00__

Circle one:

4. [True] [False] If the radius of a circle is increased by a certain factor, say 5, then the area increases by the *square* of the factor, in this case 5^2 or 25.

Fill in the blank:
So if you scale up the radius of a circle by a factor of 10, its area will increase by

__100__

Application:

5. Suppose you raise chickens and purchase $50.00 worth of wire for a chicken pen. The shape of the pen that will accommodate the most number of chickens will be

[square] [circular] [either, for both provide the same area].

physics physics physics physics

64

CONCEPTUAL *Physics* PRACTICE PAGE

Chapter 13 Liquids
Archimedes' Principle I

1. Consider a balloon filled with 1 liter of water (1000 cm³) in equilibrium in a container of water, as shown in Figure 1.

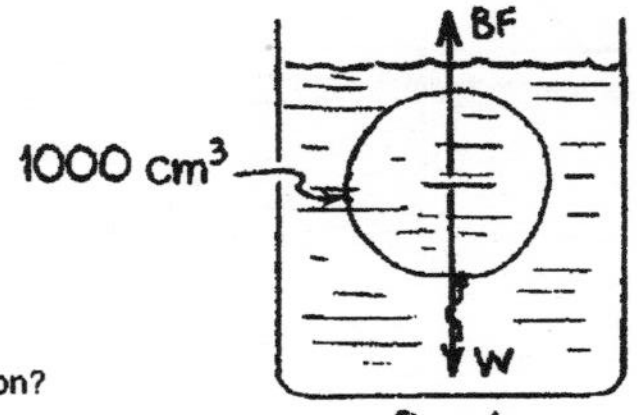

1000 cm³

Figure 1

a. What is the mass of the 1 liter of water?

__1 kg__

b. What is the weight of the 1 liter of water?

__9.8 N (OR 10 N)__

c. What is the weight of water displaced by the balloon?

__9.8 N__

d. What is the buoyant force on the balloon?

__9.8 N__

e. Sketch a pair of vectors in Figure 1: one for the weight of the balloon and the other for the buoyant force that acts on it. How do the size and directions of your vectors compare?

__VECTORS EQUAL IN MAGNITUDE, OPPOSITE IN DIRECTION__

WATER DOES NOT SINK IN WATER!

2. As a thought experiment, pretend we could remove the water from the balloon but still retain the same size of 1 liter. Then inside the balloon is a vacuum.

a. What is the mass of the liter of nothing?

__0 kg__

b. What is the weight of the liter of nothing?

__0 N__

c. What is the weight of water displaced by the nearly massless 1-liter balloon?

__9.8 N__

d. What is the buoyant force on the nearly massless balloon?

__9.8 N__

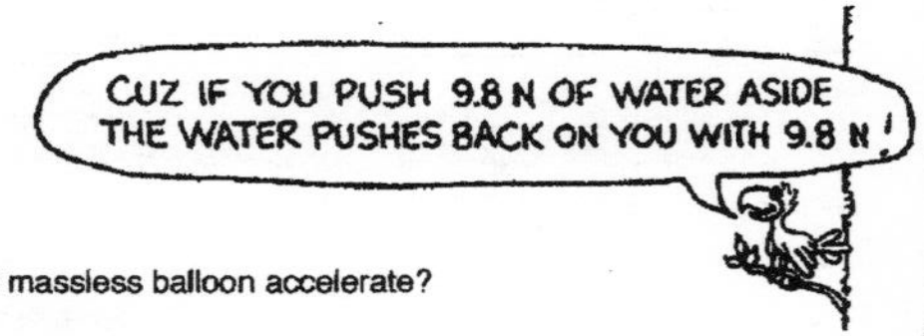

e. In which direction would the nearly massless balloon accelerate?

__UPWARD__

ANYTHING THAT DISPLACES 9.8 N OF WATER EXPERIENCES 9.8 N OF BUOYANT FORCE.

CUZ IF YOU PUSH 9.8 N OF WATER ASIDE THE WATER PUSHES BACK ON YOU WITH 9.8 N !

65

Left Page

CONCEPTUAL **Physics** PRACTICE PAGE

Chapter 13 Liquids
Archimedes' Principle I—continued

3. Assume the balloon is replaced by a 0.5-kilogram piece of wood that has exactly the same volume (1000 cm³), as shown in Figure 2. The wood is held in the same submerged position beneath the surface of the water.

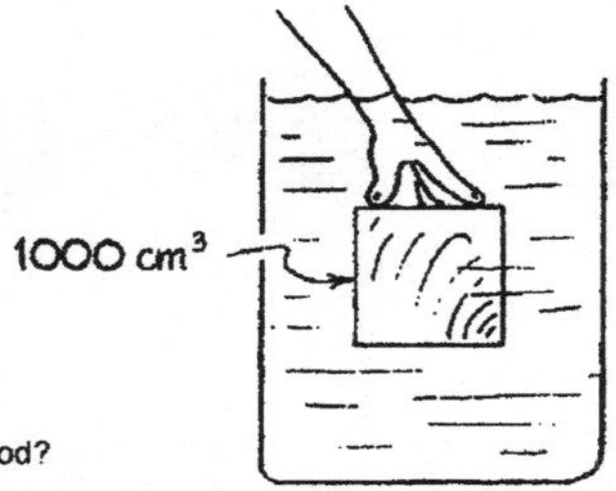

1000 cm³

Figure 2

a. What volume of water is displaced by the wood?

__1000 cm³ ≡ 1 L__

b. What is the mass of the water displaced by the wood?

__1 kg__

c. What is the weight of the water displaced by the wood?   __9.8 N__

d. How much buoyant force does the surrounding water exert on the wood?   __9.8 N__

e. When the hand is removed, what is the net force on the wood?
__NET FORCE = BUOYANT FORCE — WEIGHT OF WOOD = 9.8 N — 4.9 N = 4.9 N__
__(UPWARD)__

f. In which direction does the wood accelerate when released?   __UPWARD__

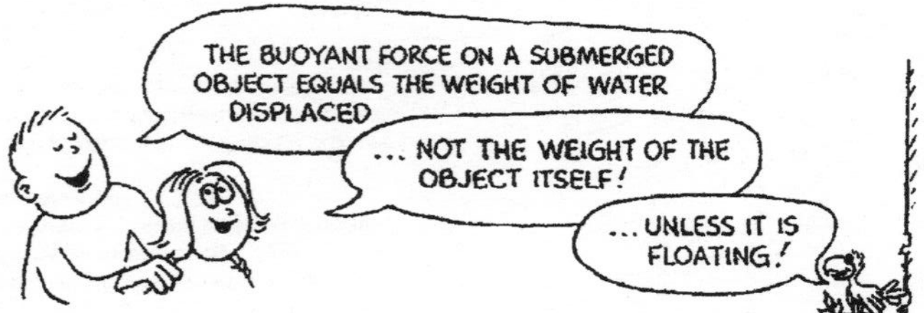

THE BUOYANT FORCE ON A SUBMERGED OBJECT EQUALS THE WEIGHT OF WATER DISPLACED

... NOT THE WEIGHT OF THE OBJECT ITSELF!

... UNLESS IT IS FLOATING!

4. Repeat parts a through f in the previous question for a 5-kg rock that has the same volume (1000 cm³), as shown in Figure 3. Assume the rock is suspended in the container of water by a string.

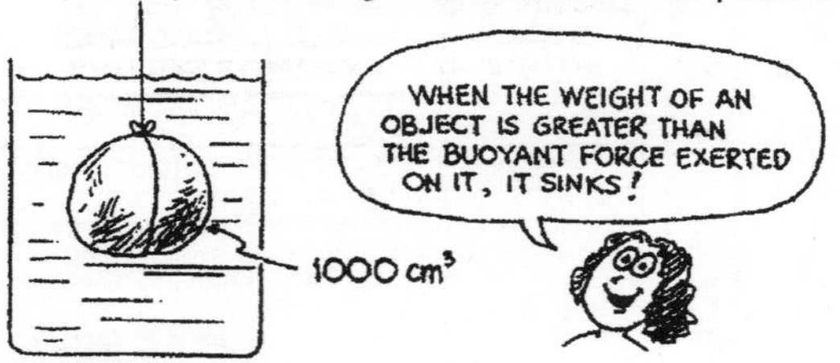

WHEN THE WEIGHT OF AN OBJECT IS GREATER THAN THE BUOYANT FORCE EXERTED ON IT, IT SINKS!

1000 cm³

Figure 3

a. __1000 cm³ (SAME)__

b. __1 kg (SAME)__

c. __9.8 N (SAME)__

d. __9.8 N (SAME)__

e. __39 N DOWNWARD*__

f. __DOWNWARD__

* NET FORCE = BUOYANT FORCE — WT ROCK = 9.8 N — 49 N = −39 N

Right Page

CONCEPTUAL **Physics** PRACTICE PAGE

Chapter 13 Liquids
Archimedes' Principle II

1. The water lines for the first three cases are shown. Sketch in the appropriate water lines for cases d and e, and make up your own for case f.

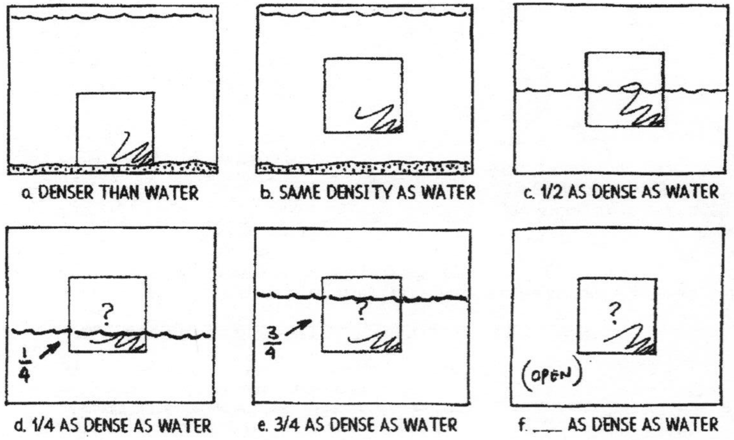

a. DENSER THAN WATER

b. SAME DENSITY AS WATER

c. 1/2 AS DENSE AS WATER

d. 1/4 AS DENSE AS WATER

e. 3/4 AS DENSE AS WATER

f. ____ AS DENSE AS WATER

2. If the weight of a ship is 100 million N, then the water it displaces weighs   __100 MILLION N__.

If a cargo weighing 1000 N is put on board, then the water it displaces weighs   __1000 N__   of water is displaced.

3. The first two sketches below show the water line for an empty and a loaded ship. Draw the appropriate water line for the third sketch.

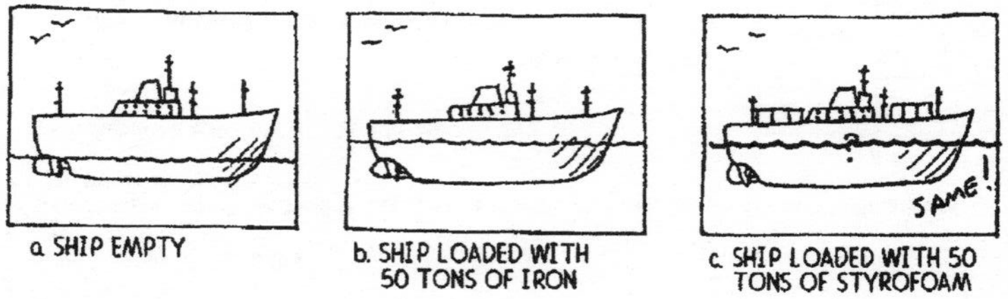

a. SHIP EMPTY

b. SHIP LOADED WITH 50 TONS OF IRON

c. SHIP LOADED WITH 50 TONS OF STYROFOAM

SAME!

CONCEPTUAL *Physics* PRACTICE PAGE

Chapter 13 Liquids
Archimedes' Principles II—continued

4. Here is an ice cube floating in a glass of ice water. Draw the water line after the ice cube melts. (Will the water line rise, fall, or remain the same?)

REMAINS THE SAME. VOLUME OF WATER WITH SAME WEIGHT OF ICE CUBE EQUALS VOLUME OF SUBMERGED PORTION OF ICE CUBE. THIS IS ALSO VOLUME OF WATER FROM MELTED ICE.

5. The air-filled balloon is weighted so it sinks in water. Near the surface, the balloon has a certain volume. Draw the balloon at the bottom (inside the dashed square) and show whether it is bigger, smaller, or the same size.

a. Since the weighted balloon sinks, how does its overall density compare to the density of water?

THE DENSITY OF BALLOON IS GREATER.

b. As the weighted balloon sinks, does its density increase, decrease, or remain the same?

DENSITY INCREASES (BECAUSE VOL DECREASES).

c. Since the weighted balloon sinks, how does the buoyant force on it compare to its weight?

BUOYANT FORCE IS LESS THAN ITS WEIGHT.

d. As the weighted balloon sinks deeper, does the buoyant force on it increase, decrease, or remain the same?

BUOYANT FORCE DECREASES (BECAUSE VOLUME DECREASES).

6. What would your answers be to the above questions (5.a to d) for a rock instead of an air-filled balloon?

a. **DENSITY OF ROCK IS GREATER.**

b. **DENSITY REMAINS THE SAME (SAME VOLUME).**

c. **BUOYANT FORCE IS LESS THAN ITS WEIGHT.**

d. **BUOYANT FORCE STAYS THE SAME (VOLUME STAYS THE SAME).**

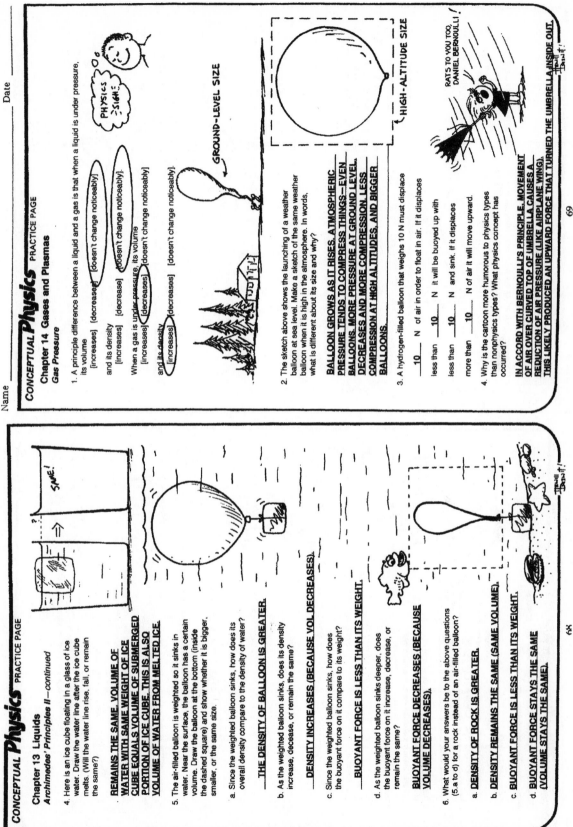

68

CONCEPTUAL *Physics* PRACTICE PAGE

Chapter 14 Gases and Plasmas
Gas Pressure

1. A principle difference between a liquid and a gas is that when a liquid is under pressure, its volume

[increases]   ([decreases])   [doesn't change noticeably]

and its density

([increases])   [decrease]   [doesn't change noticeably]

When a gas is under pressure, its volume

[increases]   ([decreases])   [doesn't change noticeably]

and its density

([increases])   [decreases]   [doesn't change noticeably].

2. The sketch above shows the launching of a weather balloon at sea level. Make a sketch of the same weather balloon when it is high in the atmosphere. In words, what is different about its size and why?

BALLOON GROWS AS IT RISES. ATMOSPHERIC PRESSURE TENDS TO COMPRESS THINGS—EVEN BALLOONS. MORE PRESSURE AT GROUND LEVEL DECREASES AND MORE COMPRESSION. LESS COMPRESSION AT HIGH ALTITUDES, AND BIGGER BALLOONS.

→ GROUND-LEVEL SIZE

→ HIGH-ALTITUDE SIZE

3. A hydrogen-filled balloon that weighs 10 N must displace

__10__ N of air in order to float in air. If it displaces

less than __10__ N it will be buoyed up with

less than __10__ N and sink. If it displaces

more than __10__ N of air it will move upward.

4. Why is the cartoon more humorous to physics types than nonphysics types? What physics concept has occurred?

IN ACCORD WITH BERNOULLI'S PRINCIPLE, MOVEMENT OF AIR OVER CURVED TOP OF UMBRELLA CAUSES A REDUCTION OF AIR PRESSURE (LIKE AIRPLANE WING). THIS LIKELY PRODUCED AN UPWARD FORCE THAT TURNED THE UMBRELLA INSIDE OUT.

RATS TO YOU TOO, DANIEL BERNOULLI!

69

CONCEPTUAL *Physics* PRACTICE PAGE

Chapter 15 Temperature, Heat, and Expansion
Measuring Temperatures

1. Complete the table:

TEMPERATURE OF MELTING ICE	0°C	32 °F	273K
TEMPERATURE OF BOILING WATER	100°C	212°F	373K

2. Suppose you apply a flame and warm one liter of water, raising its temperature 10°C. If you transfer the same heat energy to two liters, how much will the temperature rise? For three liters? Record your answers on the blanks in the drawing at the right.

$\Delta T = 10°C$ $\Delta T = \underline{5}°C$ $\Delta T = \underline{3.3}°C$

3. A thermometer is in a container half-filled with 20°C water.

a. When an equal volume of 20°C water is added, the temperature of the mixture will be
[10°C] (20°C) [40°C].

b. When instead an equal volume of 40°C water is added, the temperature of the mixture will be
[20°C] (30°C) [40°C].

c. When instead a small amount of 40°C water is added, the temperature of the mixture will be
[20°C] (between 20°C and 30°C) [30°C] [more than 30°C].

Circle one:
4. A small red-hot piece of iron is placed into a large bucket of cool water. (Ignore the heat transfer to the bucket.)

a. [True] (False) The decrease in iron temperature equals the increase in the water temperature.

b. (True) [False] The quantity of heat lost by the iron equals the quantity of heat gained by the water.

c. (True) [False] The iron and water both will eventually reach the same temperature.

d. [True] (False) The final temperature of the iron and water is halfway between the initial temperatures of each.

CAN COMMON ICE BE COLDER THAN 0°C? YES!

CONCEPTUAL *Physics* PRACTICE PAGE

Chapter 15 Temperature, Heat, and Expansion
Thermal Expansion

1. The weight hangs above the floor from the copper wire. When a candle is moved along the wire and warms it, what happens to the height of the weight above the floor? Why?

HEIGHT DECREASES AS WIRE LENGTHENS

2. The levels of water at 0°C and 1°C are shown below in the first two flasks. At these temperatures there is microscopic slush in the water. There is slightly more slush at 0°C than at 1°C. As the water is warmed, some of the slush collapses as it melts, and the level of the water falls in the tube. That's why the level of water is slightly lower in the 1°C-tube. Make rough estimates and sketch in the appropriate levels of water at the other temperatures shown. What is important about the level when the water reaches 4°C?

0°C   1°C   2°C   3°C   4°C   5°C   6°C
LOWEST

SINCE WATER IS MOST DENSE AT 4°C, WATER LEVEL IS LOWEST AT 4°C.

3. The diagram to the left shows an ice-covered pond. Fill in the blanks for likely temperatures of the water at the top and bottom of the pond.

ICE
0°C
4°C

WHICH WILL WEIGH MORE, 1 LITER OF ICE OR 1 LITER OF WATER? WATER (MORE DENSE)

I CAN'T GET THIS METAL LID OFF THE JAR... SHOULD I HEAT THE LID OR COOL IT? WHY? HEAT IT SO IT WILL EXPAND

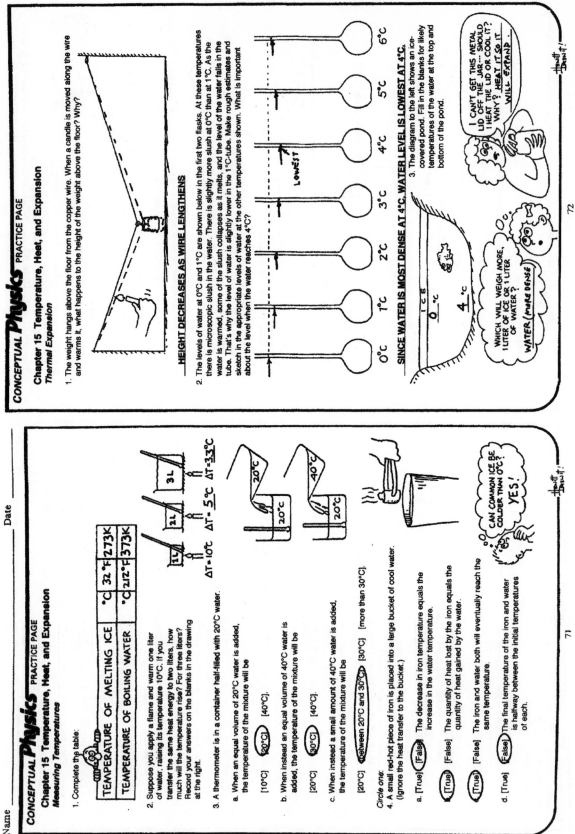

164

CONCEPTUAL *Physics* PRACTICE PAGE

Chapter 16 Heat Transfer
Transmission of Heat

Circle one:

1. The tips of both brass rods are held in the gas flame.

a. [True] [False] Heat is conducted only along Rod A.

b. [True] [False] Heat is conducted only along Rod B.

c. [True] [False] Heat is conducted equally along both Rod A and Rod B.

d. [True] [False] The idea that "heat rises" applies to heat transfer by *convection*, not by *conduction*.

WILL HEAT MOVE UPWARD?

WILL IT FLOW DOWNWARD?

2. Why does a bird fluff its feathers to keep warm on a cold day?

FLUFFED FEATHERS TRAP AIR THAT ACTS AS AN INSULATOR.

3. Why does a down-filled sleeping bag keep you warm on a cold night? Why is it useless if the down is wet?

AS IN #2, WHEN WATER TAKES PLACE OF TRAPPED AIR, INSULATION IS REDUCED.

4. What does *convection* have to do with the holes in the shade of the desk lamp?

WARMED AIR RISES THROUGH HOLES INSTEAD OF BEING TRAPPED.

5. The warmth of equatorial regions and coldness of polar regions on Earth can be understood by considering light from a flashlight striking a surface. If it strikes perpendicularly, light energy is more concentrated as it covers a smaller area; if it strikes at an angle, the energy spreads over a larger area. So the energy per unit area is less.

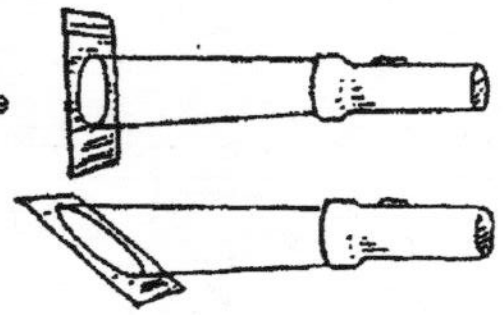

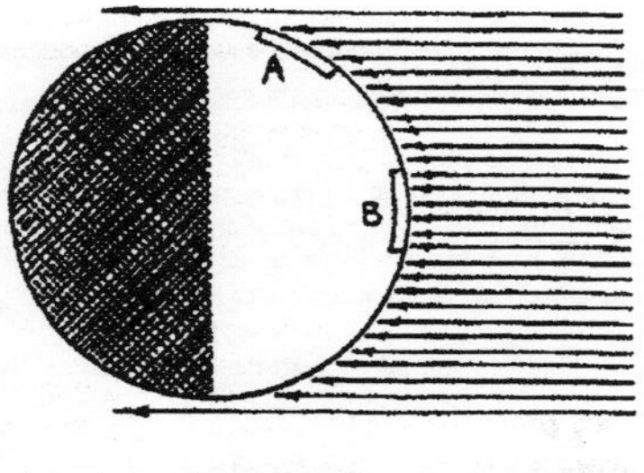

The arrows represent rays of light from the distant Sun incident upon Earth. Two areas of equal size are shown, Area A near the North Pole and Area B near the equator. Count the rays that reach each area, and explain why B is warmer than A.

3 ON A: 6 ON B.

AREA B GETS TWICE THE SOLAR ENERGY AS AREA A SO IT IS WARMER.

73

CONCEPTUAL *Physics* PRACTICE PAGE

Chapter 16 Heat Transfer
Transmission of Heat

6. The Earth's seasons arise from the 23.5-degree tilt of Earth's daily spin axis as it orbits the Sun. When Earth is at the position shown on the light in the sketch below (not to scale), the Northern Hemisphere tilts toward the Sun, and sunlight striking it is strong (more rays per area). Sunlight striking Southern Hemisphere is weak (fewer rays per area). Days in the north are warmer, and daylight is longer. You can see this by imagining Earth making its complete daily 24-hour spin.

Do two things on the sketch:
(i) Shade the part of Earth in nighttime darkness for all positions, as is already done in the left position.
(ii) Label each position with the proper month—March, June, September, or December.

(JUNE)

(SEPT.)

(MARCH)

(DEC.)

BE SURE TO DO THE SHADING BEFORE YOU ANSWER THE QUESTIONS BELOW!

a. When Earth is in any of the four positions shown, during one 24-hour spin, a location at the equator receives sunlight half the time and is in darkness the other half the time. This means that regions at the equator always receive about ___12___ hours of sunlight and ___12___ hours of darkness.

b. Can you see that in the June position regions farther north have longer daylight hours and shorter nights? Locations north of the Arctic Circle (dotted line in Northern Hemisphere) are continually in view of the Sun as Earth spins, so they get daylight ___24___ hours a day.

c. How many hours of light and darkness are there in June at regions south of the Antarctic Circle (dotted line in Southern Hemisphere)?

ZERO HOURS OF LIGHT, OR 24 HOURS OF DARKNESS PER DAY

d. Six months later, when Earth is at the December position, is the situation in the Antarctic Circle the same or is it the reverse? Count the rays that reach each area, and explain why B is warmer than A.

REVERSE: MORE SUNLIGHT PER AREA IN DECEMBER IN SOUTHERN HEMISPHERE

e. Why do South America and Australia enjoy warm weather in December instead of June?

IN DECEMBER THE SOUTHERN HEMISPHERE IS TILTED TOWARD THE SUN AND GETS MORE SUNLIGHT PER AREA THAN IN JUNE.

PHYSICS 2 YEA~

74

165

CONCEPTUAL *Physics* PRACTICE PAGE

Chapter 17 Change of Phase
Ice, Water, and Steam

All matter can exist in the solid, liquid, or gaseous phases. The solid phase normally exists at relatively low temperatures, the liquid phase at higher temperatures, and the gaseous phase at still higher temperatures. Water is the most common example, not only because of its abundance but also because the temperatures for all three phases are common. Study "Energy and Changes of Phase" in your textbook and then answer the following:

1. How many calories are needed to change 1 gram of 0°C ice to water?

    <u>80</u>

ICE 0°C ⟹ WATER 0°C

2. How many calories are needed to change the temperature of 1 gram of water by 1°C?

    <u>1</u>

T ⟹ T+1°C

3. How many calories are needed to melt 1 gram of 0°C ice and turn it to water at a room temperature of 23°C?

    <u>80 CAL + 23 CAL = 103 CALORIES</u>

0°C ⟹ 0°C ⟹ 23°C

4. A 50-gram sample of ice at 0°C is placed in a glass beaker that contains 200 g of water at 20°C.

a. How much heat is needed to melt the ice? <u>4000 CALORIES</u>
   SINCE THERE'S 50 g OF ICE, AND 80 CAL IS REQUIRED PER GRAM, HEAT REQUIRED IS 50 g × (80 CAL/g) = 4000 CAL

b. By how much would the temperature of the water change if it released this much heat to the ice? <u>BY 20°C</u>

c. What will be the final temperature of the mixture? (Disregard any heat absorbed by the glass or given off by the surrounding air.)

    <u>0°C</u>

5. How many calories are needed to change 1 gram of 100°C boiling water to 100°C steam?

    <u>540 CALORIES</u>

100°C

6. Fill in the number of calories at each step below for changing the phase of 1 gram of 0°C ice to 100°C steam.

CHANGE OF PHASE: 1 GRAM ICE 0°C ⟹ 1 GRAM WATER 0°C
TEMP. RISE: ⟹ 1 GRAM WATER 100°C
CHANGE OF PHASE: ⟹ 1 GRAM STEAM 100°C

HEAT NEEDED = <u>80</u> CAL + <u>100</u> CAL + <u>540</u> CAL = <u>720</u> CAL

CONCEPTUAL *Physics* PRACTICE PAGE

Chapter 17 Change of Phase
Ice, Water, and Steam—continued

7. One gram of steam at 100°C condenses, and the water cools to 22°C.

100°C ⟹ 100°C ⟹ 22°C

a. How much heat is released when the steam condenses? <u>540 CALORIES</u>

b. How much heat is released when the water cools from 100°C to 22°C? <u>78 CALORIES</u>
   (SINCE WATER COOLS BY 100°C — 22°C = 78°C)

c. How much heat is released altogether? <u>618 CALORIES</u>

8. In a household radiator 1000 g of steam at 100°C condenses, and the water cools to 90°C.

a. How much heat is released when the steam condenses? <u>540,000 CAL</u>

b. How much heat is released when the water cools from 100°C to 90°C?

    <u>10,000 CALORIES</u>

c. How much heat is released altogether? <u>550,000 CALORIES</u>

9. Why is it difficult to brew tea on the top of a high mountain?

    <u>WATER BOILS AT A LOWER TEMP, AND GETS NO HOTTER THAN THIS TEMP</u>

10. How many calories are given up by 1 gram of 100°C steam that condenses to 100°C water?

    <u>540 CALORIES</u>

11. How many calories are given up by 1 gram of 100°C steam that condenses and drops in temperature to 22°C water?

    <u>540 CALORIES + (100°C — 22°C) = 618 CALORIES</u>

12. How many calories are given to a household radiator when 1000 grams of 100°C steam condenses, and drops in temperature to 90°C water?

    <u>1000 CALORIES (540 CALORIES + [100°C — 90°C] = 550,000 CALORIES</u>

13. To get water from the ground, even in the hot desert, dig a hole about a half meter wide and a half meter deep. Place a cup at the bottom. Spread a sheet of plastic wrap over the hole and place stones along the edge to hold it secure. Weight the center of the plastic with a stone so it forms a cone shape. Why will water collect in the cup? (Physics can save your life if you're ever stranded in a desert!) <u>EVAPORATED WATER FROM GROUND IS TRAPPED, AND CONDENSES ON UNDERSIDE OF PLASTIC AND RUNS INTO THE CUP. (AT NIGHT, CONDENSATION FROM AIR COLLECTS ON *TOP* OF THE PLASTIC.)</u>

CONCEPTUAL *Physics* PRACTICE PAGE

Chapter 17 Change of Phase
Evaporation

1. Why do you feel colder when you swim in a pool on a windy day?

WATER EVAPORATES FROM YOUR BODY FASTER AND COOLS YOU.

2. Why does your skin feel cold when a little rubbing alcohol is applied to it?

ALCOHOL RAPIDLY EVAPORATES AND COOLS YOU IN PROCESS.

3. Briefly explain from a molecular point of view why evaporation is a cooling process.

THE MORE ENERGETIC AND FASTER MOLECULES ESCAPE INTO THE AIR.

ENERGY TAKEN WITH THEM REDUCES AVERAGE KE OF REMAINING MOLECULES.

4. When hot water rapidly evaporates, the result can be dramatic. Consider 4 g of boiling water spread over a large surface so that 1 g rapidly evaporates. Suppose further that the surface and surroundings are very very cold so that all 540 calories for evaporation come from the remaining 3 g of water.

a. How many calories are taken from each gram of water that remains?

$$\frac{540 \text{ CALORIES}}{3} = 180 \text{ CALORIES}$$

b. How many calories are released when 1 g of 100°C water cools to 0°C?

100 CALORIES

c. How many calories are released when 1 g of 0°C water changes to 0°C ice?

80 CALORIES

d. What happens in this case to the remaining 3 g of boiling water when 1 g rapidly evaporates?

THE REMAINING WATER FREEZES!

(EACH GRAM OF WATER RELEASES

180 CALORIES IN COOLING AND FREEZING.)

CONCEPTUAL *Physics* PRACTICE PAGE

Chapter 17 Change of Phase
Our Earth's Hot Interior

A major puzzle faced scientists in the 19th century. Volcanoes showed that Earth is molten beneath its crust. Penetration into the crust by bore holes and mines showed that Earth's temperature increases with depth. Scientists found that heat flows from the interior to the surface. They assumed that the source of Earth's internal heat was primordial, the afterglow of its fiery birth. Measurements of cooling rates indicated a relatively young Earth—some 25 to 30 millions years in age. But geological evidence indicated an older Earth. This puzzle wasn't solved until the discovery of radioactivity. Then it was learned that the interior is kept hot by the energy of radioactive decay. We now know the age of Earth is some 4.5 billions years—a much older Earth.

All rock contains trace amounts of radioactive minerals. Those in common granite release energy at the rate 0.03 Joule/kilogram•year. Granite at Earth's surface transfers this energy to the surroundings as fast as it is generated, so we don't find granite warm to the touch. But what if a sample of granite were thermally insulated? That is, suppose the increase of internal energy due to radioactivity were contained. Then it would get hotter. How much? Let's figure it out, using 790 joule/kilogram kelvin as the specific heat of granite.

Calculations to make:

1. How many joules are required to increase the temperature of 1 kg of granite by 1000 K?

$$Q = cm\Delta T = (790 \text{ J/kg•C°})(1 \text{ kg})(1000 \text{ C°}) = 790,000 \text{ J}$$

2. How many years would it take radioactive decay in a kilogram of granite to produce this many joules?

$$\underline{790,000 \text{ J/0.03 J/kg•yr} \times 1 \text{ kg} = 25.3 \text{ MILLION YEARS}}$$

Questions to answer:

1. How many years would it take a thermally insulated 1-kg chunk of granite to undergo a 1000 K increase in temperature?

SAME 26.3 MILLION YEARS

2. How many years would it take a thermally insulated one-million-kilogram chunk of granite to undergo a 1000 K increase in temperature?

SAME
(DUE TO CORRESPONDINGLY MORE RADIATION)

3. Why are your answers to the above the same (or different)?

THE ENERGY RELEASED PER KG IS THE SAME FOR BOTH. A BIGGER CHUNK GIVES MORE AND REQUIRES THE SAME AMOUNT MORE FOR A CHANGE IN TEMP.

Circle one:

4. [True] [False] The energy produced by Earth radioactivity ultimately becomes terrestrial radiation.

CONCEPTUAL *Physics* PRACTICE PAGE

Chapter 18 Thermodynamics
Absolute Zero

A mass of air is contained so that the volume can change but the pressure remains constant. Table I shows air volumes at various temperatures when the air is warmed slowly.

1. Plot the data in Table I on the graph and connect the points.

TABLE I

TEMP. (°C)	VOLUME (mL)
0	50
25	55
50	60
75	65
100	70

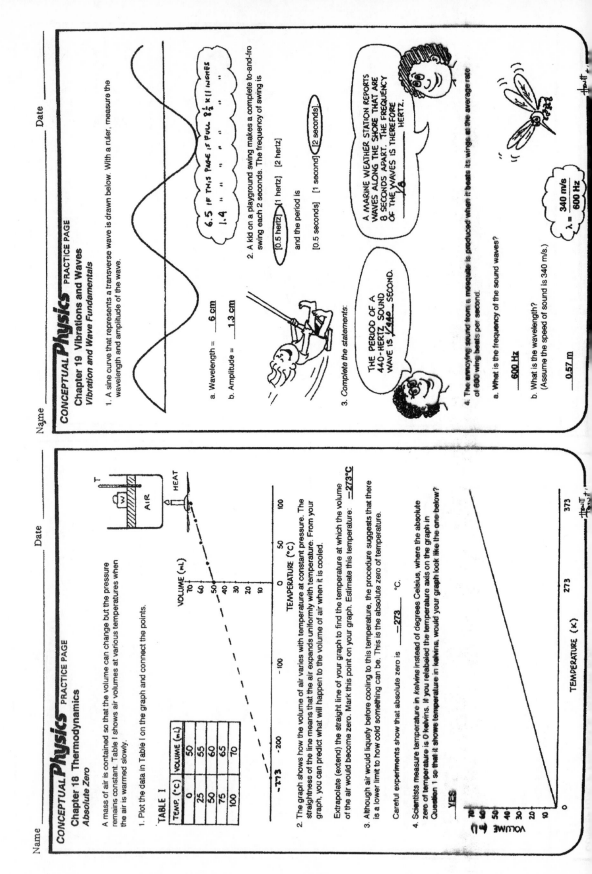

2. The graph shows how the volume of air varies with temperature at constant pressure. The straightness of the line means that the air expands uniformly with temperature. From your graph, you can predict what will happen to the volume of air when it is cooled.

Extrapolate (extend) the straight line of your graph to find the temperature at which the volume of the air would become zero. Mark this point on your graph. Estimate this temperature: **-273°C**

3. Although air would liquefy before cooling to this temperature, the procedure suggests that there is a lower limit to how cold something can be. This is the absolute zero of temperature.

Careful experiments show that absolute zero is **-273** °C.

4. Scientists measure temperature in *kelvins* instead of degrees Celsius, where the absolute zero of temperature is 0 kelvins. If you relabeled the temperature axis on the graph in Question 1 so that it shows temperature in *kelvins*, would your graph look like the one below?

YES

CONCEPTUAL *Physics* PRACTICE PAGE

Chapter 19 Vibrations and Waves
Vibration and Wave Fundamentals

1. A sine curve that represents a transverse wave is drawn below. With a ruler, measure the wavelength and amplitude of the wave.

6.5 IF THIS PAGE IS FULL 8½ x 11 INCHES
1.4 " " " " " "

a. Wavelength = **6 cm**

b. Amplitude = **1.3 cm**

2. A kid on a playground swing makes a complete to-and-fro swing each 2 seconds. The frequency of swing is

[0.5 hertz] [1 hertz] [2 hertz]

and the period is

[0.5 seconds] [1 second] [2 seconds].

3. *Complete the statements:*

THE PERIOD OF A 440-HERTZ SOUND WAVE IS **1/440** SECOND.

A MARINE WEATHER STATION REPORTS WAVES ALONG THE SHORE THAT ARE 8 SECONDS APART. THE FREQUENCY OF THE WAVES IS THEREFORE **1/8** HERTZ.

4. The annoying sound from a mosquito is produced when it beats its wings at the average rate of 600 wing beats per second.

a. What is the frequency of the sound waves?

600 Hz

b. What is the wavelength?
(Assume the speed of sound is 340 m/s.)

0.57 m

$\lambda = \dfrac{340 \text{ m/s}}{600 \text{ Hz}}$

Chapter 19 Vibrations and Waves
Vibration and Wave Fundamentals—continued

5. A machine gun fires 10 rounds per second. The speed of the bullets is 300 m/s.

a. What is the distance in the air between the flying bullets? ___30 m___

b. What happens to the distance between the bullets if the rate of fire is increased?

___DISTANCE BETWEEN BULLETS DECREASES___

6. Consider a wave generator that produces 10 pulses per second. The speed of the waves is 300 cm/s.

a. What is the wavelength of the waves? ___30 cm___

b. What happens to the wavelength if the frequency of pulses is increased?

___λ DECREASES, JUST AS DISTANCE BETWEEN BULLETS IN #5 DECREASES.___

7. The bird at the right watches the waves. If the portion of a wave between 2 crests passes the pole each second,

a. what is the speed of the waves? $v = f\lambda = 2 \times 1 \text{ m} = 2$ m/s

b. what is the period of wave motion? $T = \dfrac{1}{f} = \dfrac{1}{2} = 0.5$ s

c. If the distance between crests were 1.5 meters apart, and 2 crests pass the pole each second, what would be the speed of the wave?

___$v = f\lambda = 2 \times 1.5 = 3$ m/s___

d. What would the period of wave motion be for 7.c ?

___SAME (0.5 s)___

8. When an automobile moves toward a listener, the sound of its horn seems relatively

[low pitched] [high pitched] [normal]

and when moving away from the listener, its horn seems

[low pitched] [high pitched] [normal].

9. The changed pitch of the Doppler effect is due to changes in wave

[speed] [frequency] [both].

Chapter 19 Vibrations and Waves
Shock Waves

The cone-shaped shock wave produced by a supersonic aircraft is actually the result of overlapping spherical waves of sound, as indicated by the overlapping circles in Figure 19.19 in your textbook. Sketches a through e below show the "animated" growth of only one of the many spherical sound waves (shown as an expanding circle in the two-dimensional drawing).

The circle originates when the aircraft is in the position shown in a.

Sketch b shows both the growth of the circle and position of the aircraft at a later time.

Still later times are shown in c, d, and e. Note that the circle grows and the aircraft moves farther to the right. Note also that the aircraft is moving farther than the sound wave. This is because the aircraft is moving faster than sound.

Careful examination will reveal how fast the aircraft is moving compared to the speed of sound. Sketch e shows that in the same time the sound travels from O to A, the aircraft has traveled from O to B—twice as far. You can check with a ruler.

Circle the answer.

1. Inspect sketches b and d. Has the aircraft traveled twice as far as sound in the same time in these positions also?

(Yes) [No]

2. For greater speeds, the angle of the shock wave would be

[wider] [the same] [narrower].

DURING THE TIME THAT SOUND TRAVELS FROM O TO A, THE PLANE TRAVELS TWICE AS FAR —

SO IT'S FLYING AT TWICE THE SPEED OF SOUND !

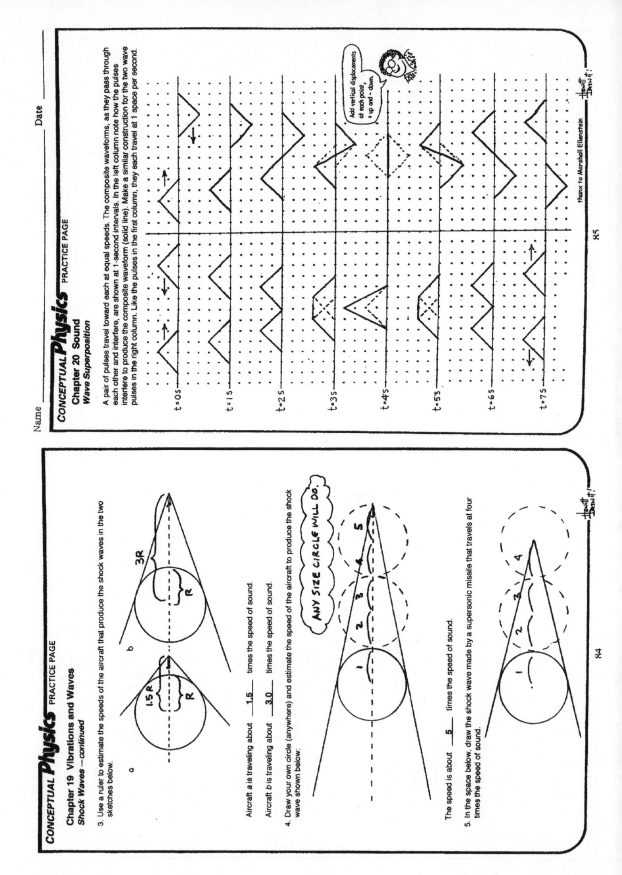

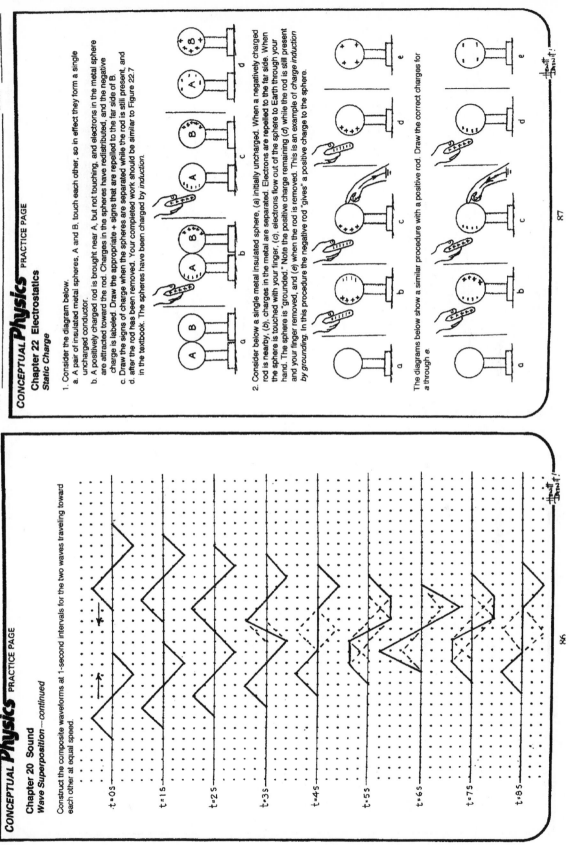

CONCEPTUAL **Physics** PRACTICE PAGE

Chapter 20 Sound
Wave Superposition—continued

Construct the composite waveforms at 1-second intervals for the two waves traveling toward each other at equal speed.

t = 0 s

t = 1 s

t = 2 s

t = 3 s

t = 4 s

t = 5 s

t = 6 s

t = 7 s

t = 8 s

86

CONCEPTUAL **Physics** PRACTICE PAGE

Chapter 22 Electrostatics
Static Charge

1. Consider the diagram below.

a. A pair of insulated metal spheres, A and B, touch each other, so in effect they form a single uncharged conductor.

b. A positively charged rod is brought near A, but not touching, and electrons in the metal sphere are attracted toward the rod. Charges in the spheres have redistributed, and the negative charge is labeled. Draw the appropriate + signs that are repelled to the far side of B.

c. Draw the signs of charge when the spheres are separated while the rod is still present, and

d. after the rod has been removed. Your completed work should be similar to Figure 22.7 in the textbook. The spheres have been charged by *induction*.

2. Consider below a single metal insulated sphere, (a) initially uncharged. When a negatively charged rod is nearby, (b), charges in the metal are separated. Electrons are repelled to the far side. When the sphere is touched with your finger, (c), electrons flow out of the sphere to Earth through your hand. The sphere is "grounded." Note the positive charge remaining (d) while the rod is still present and your finger removed, and (e) when the rod is removed. This is an example of *charge induction by grounding*. In this procedure the negative rod "gives" a positive charge to the sphere.

The diagrams below show a similar procedure with a positive rod. Draw the correct charges for a through e.

87

CONCEPTUAL *Physics* PRACTICE PAGE

Chapter 22 Electrostatics
Electric Potential

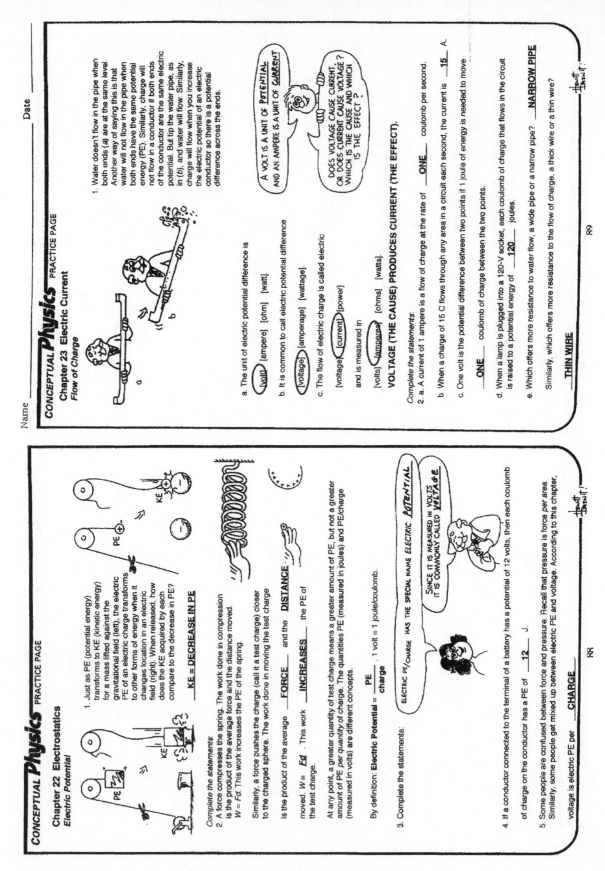

1. Just as PE (potential energy) transforms to KE (kinetic energy) for a mass lifted against the gravitational field (left), the electric PE of an electric charge transforms to other forms of energy when it changes location in an electric field (right). When released, how does the KE acquired by each compare to the decrease in PE?

KE = DECREASE IN PE

Complete the statements:

2. A force compresses the spring. The work done in compression is the product of the average force and the distance moved. $W = Fd$. This work increases the PE of the spring.

Similarly, a force pushes the charge (call it a test charge) closer to the charged sphere. The work done in moving the test charge

is the product of the average **FORCE** and the **DISTANCE**

moved. $W = $ **Fd** . This work **INCREASES** the PE of the test charge.

At any point, a greater quantity of test charge means a greater amount of PE, but not a greater amount of PE *per quantity of charge*. The quantities PE (measured in joules) and PE/charge (measured in volts) are different concepts.

By definition: **Electric Potential** = $\dfrac{\text{PE}}{\text{charge}}$. 1 volt = 1 joule/coulomb.

3. Complete the statements:

ELECTRIC PE/CHARGE HAS THE SPECIAL NAME ELECTRIC **POTENTIAL**

SINCE IT IS MEASURED IN VOLTS IT IS COMMONLY CALLED **VOLTAGE**

4. If a conductor connected to the terminal of a battery has a potential of 12 volts, then each coulomb of charge on the conductor has a PE of **12** J.

5. Some people are confused between force and pressure. Recall that pressure is force *per area*. Similarly, some people get mixed up between electric PE and voltage. According to this chapter,

voltage is electric PE per **CHARGE** .

CONCEPTUAL *Physics* PRACTICE PAGE

Chapter 23 Electric Current
Flow of Charge

1. Water doesn't flow in the pipe when both ends (a) are at the same level. Another way of saying this is that water will not flow in the pipe when both ends have the same potential energy (PE). Similarly, charge will not flow in a conductor if both ends of the conductor are the same electric potential. But tip the water pipe, as in (b), and water will flow. Similarly, charge will flow when you increase the electric potential of an electric conductor so there is a potential difference across the ends.

A VOLT IS A UNIT OF **POTENTIAL** AND AN AMPERE IS A UNIT OF **CURRENT**

DOES VOLTAGE CAUSE CURRENT, OR DOES CURRENT CAUSE VOLTAGE? WHICH IS THE CAUSE AND WHICH IS THE EFFECT?

a. The unit of electric potential difference is

(**volt**) [ampere] [ohm] [watt].

b. It is common to call electric potential difference

[voltage] [amperage] [wattage].

c. The flow of electric charge is called electric

[voltage] [**current**] [power]

and is measured in

[volts] [**amperes**] [ohms] [watts].

VOLTAGE (THE CAUSE) PRODUCES CURRENT (THE EFFECT).

Complete the statements:

2. a. A current of 1 ampere is a flow of charge at the rate of **ONE** coulomb per second.

b. When a charge of 15 C flows through any area in a circuit each second, the current is **15** A.

c. One volt is the potential difference between two points if 1 joule of energy is needed to move **ONE** coulomb of charge between the two points.

d. When a lamp is plugged into a 120-V socket, each coulomb of charge that flows in the circuit is raised to a potential energy of **120** joules.

e. Which offers more resistance to water flow, a wide pipe or a narrow pipe? **NARROW PIPE**

Similarly, which offers more resistance to the flow of charge, a thick wire or a thin wire?

THIN WIRE

CONCEPTUAL *Physics* PRACTICE PAGE

Chapter 23 Electric Current
Ohm's Law

MATH CRUTCH

CURRENT = VOLTAGE or $I = \frac{V}{R}$

USE OHM'S LAW IN THE TRIANGLE TO FIND THE QUANTITY YOU WANT. COVER THE LETTER WITH YOUR FINGER AND THE REMAINING TWO SHOW YOU THE FORMULA!

CONDUCTORS AND RESISTORS HAVE RESISTANCE TO THE CURRENT IN THEM.

1. How much current flows in a 1000-ohm resistor when 1.5 volts are impressed across it?

   0.0015 A

2. If the filament resistance in an automobile headlamp is 3 ohms, how many amps does it draw when connected to a 12-volt battery?

   4 A

3. The resistance of the side lights on an automobile are 10 ohms. How much current flows in them when connected to 12 volts?

   1.2 A

4. What is the current in the 30-ohm heating coil of a coffee maker that operates on a 120-volt circuit?

   4 A

5. During a lie detector test, a voltage of 6 V is impressed across two fingers. When a certain question is asked, the resistance between the fingers drops from 400,000 ohms to 200,000 ohms.

   a. What is the current initially through the fingers?   0.000015 A (15 μA)

   b. What is the current through the fingers when the resistance between them drops?
   0.000030 A (30 μA)

6. How much resistance allows an impressed voltage of 6 V to produce a current of 0.006 A?

   1000 Ω

7. What is the resistance of a clothes iron that draws a current of 12 A at 120 V?

   10 Ω

OHM MY GOODNESS !

8. What is the voltage across a 100-ohm circuit element that draws a current of 1 A?

   100 V

9. What voltage will produce 3 A through a 15-ohm resistor?

   45 V

10. The current in an incandescent lamp is 0.5 A when connected to a 120-V circuit, and 0.2 A when connected to a 10-V source. Does the resistance of the lamp change in these cases? Explain your answer and defend it with numerical values.
    YES. RESISTANCE INCREASES WITH HIGHER TEMP OR GREATER CURRENT.
    AT 0.2 A, R = 10 V/0.2 A = 50 Ω; AT 0.5 A, R = 120 V/0.5 A = 240 Ω
    (APPRECIABLY GREATER).

CONCEPTUAL *Physics* PRACTICE PAGE

Chapter 23 Electric Current
Electric Power

Recall that the rate at which energy is converted from one form to another is *power*.

$$\text{Power} = \frac{\text{energy converted}}{\text{time}} = \frac{\text{voltage} \times \text{charge}}{\text{time}} = \text{voltage} \times \frac{\text{charge}}{\text{time}} = \text{voltage} \times \text{current}$$

The unit of power is the *watt* (or *kilowatt*), so in units form,

Electric power (*watts*) = current (*amperes*) × voltage (*volts*), where 1 *watt* = 1 *ampere* × 1 *volt*.

THAT'S RIGHT... VOLTAGE = $\frac{\text{ENERGY}}{\text{CHARGE}}$, SO ENERGY = VOLTAGE × CHARGE ... AND $\frac{\text{CHARGE}}{\text{TIME}}$ = CURRENT ≥ HEAT

A 100-WATT BULB CONVERTS ELECTRIC ENERGY INTO HEAT AND LIGHT MORE QUICKLY THAN A 25-WATT BULB. THAT'S WHY FOR THE SAME VOLTAGE A 100-WATT BULB GLOWS BRIGHTER THAN A 25-WATT BULB!

WHICH DRAWS MORE CURRENT... THE 100-WATT OR THE 25-WATT BULB?

WATT'S HAPPENING ?

1. What is the power when a voltage of 120 V drives a 2-A current through a device?

   240 W

2. What is the current when a 60-W lamp is connected to 120 V?

   0.5 A

3. How much current does a 100-W lamp draw when connected to 120 V?

   0.83 A

4. If part of an electric circuit dissipates energy at 6 W when it draws a current of 3 A, what voltage is impressed across it?

   2 V

5. The equation

   $$\text{power} = \frac{\text{energy converted}}{\text{time}}$$

   rearranged gives energy converted =   POWER × TIME

6. Explain the difference between a kilowatt and a kilowatt-hour.

A KILOWATT IS A UNIT OF POWER: KW-HOUR IS UNIT OF ENERGY (POWER × TIME)

7. One deterrent to burglary is to leave your front porch light constantly on. If your fixture contains a 60-W bulb at 120 V, and your local power utility sells energy at 10 cents per kilowatt-hour, how much will it cost to leave the light on for the entire month? Show your work on the other side of this page.

   E = P × t = 60 W × 1 mo × 30 day/1 mo × 24 h/1 day × 1 kW/1000 W = 43.2 kWh
   MULTIPLY BY $0.10/kWh = $4.32

Name _____ Date _____

Chapter 23 Electric Current
Series Circuits

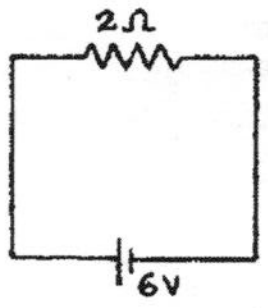

1. In the circuit shown at the right, a voltage of 6 V pushes charge through a single resistor of 2 Ω. According to Ohm's law, the current in the resistor (and therefore in the whole circuit) is

3 A.

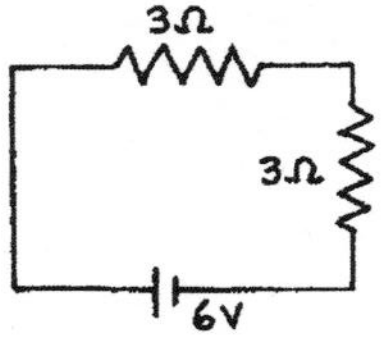

2. Two 3-Ω resistors and a 6-V battery comprise the circuit on the right. The total resistance of the circuit is **6** Ω.

The current in the circuit is then **1** A.

3. The equivalent resistance of three 4-Ω resistors in series would be **12** Ω.

THE EQUIVALENT RESISTANCE OF RESISTORS IN SERIES IS SIMPLY THEIR SUM!

4. Does current flow *through* a resistor, or *across* a resistor? **THROUGH**

Is voltage established *through* a resistor, or *across* a resistor? **ACROSS**

5. Does current in the lamps of a circuit occur simultaneously, or does charge flow first through one lamp, then the other, and finally the last in turn? **SIMULTANEOUSLY (SPEED OF LIGHT)**

6. Circuits *a* and *b* below are identical with all bulbs rated at equal wattage (therefore equal resistance). The only difference between the circuits is that Bulb 5 has a short circuit, as shown.

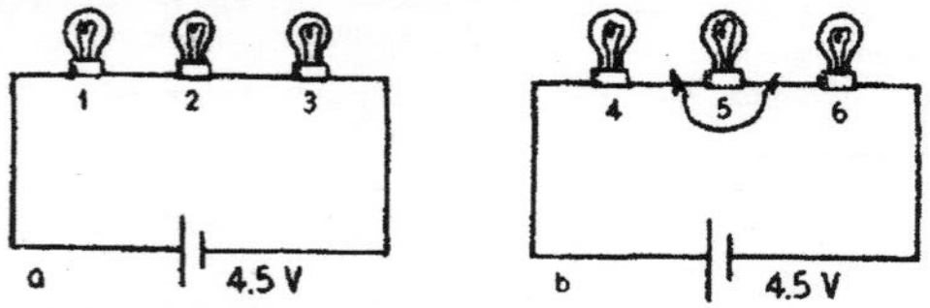

a. In which circuit is the current greater? **b**

b. In which circuit are all three bulbs equally bright? **a**

c. Which bulbs are the brightest? **4 AND 6**

d. Which bulb is the dimmest? **5 (NOT LIT)**

e. Which bulbs have the largest voltage drops across them? **4 AND 6 (2.25 V EACH)**

f. Which circuit dissipates more power? **b (GREATER CURRENT, SAME VOLTAGE)**

g. Which circuit produces more light? **b (MORE POWER)**

93

Chapter 23 Electric Current
Parallel Circuits

1. In the circuit shown below, there is a voltage drop of 6 V across each 2 Ω resistors.

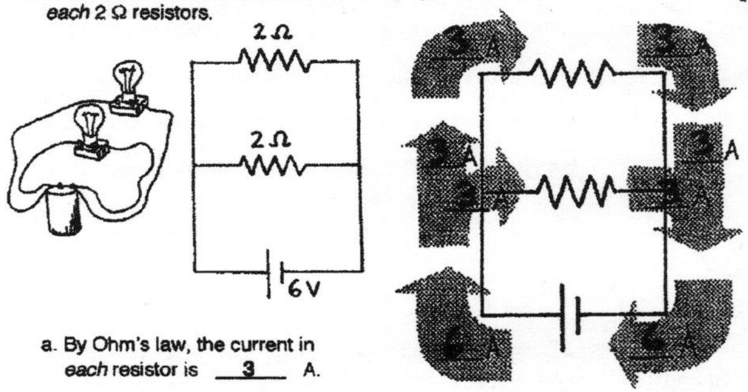

a. By Ohm's law, the current in *each* resistor is **3** A.

b. The current through the battery is the sum of the currents in the resistors, **6** A.

c. Fill in the current in the eight blank spaces in the diagram above of the same circuit.

THE SUM OF THE CURRENTS IN THE TWO BRANCH VEINS EQUALS THE CURRENT BEFORE IT DIVIDES.

2. Cross out the circuit below that is *not* equivalent to the circuit above.

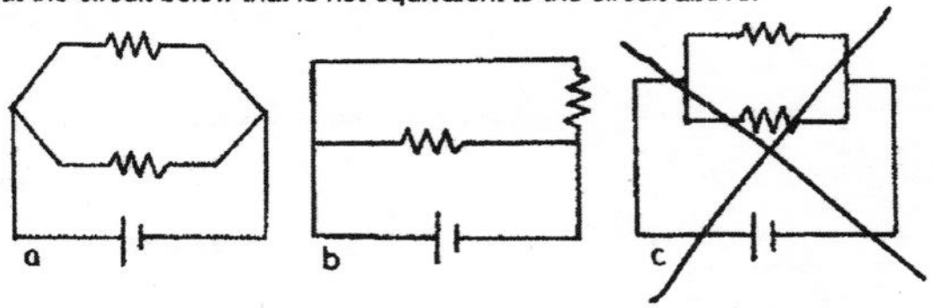

a   b   c

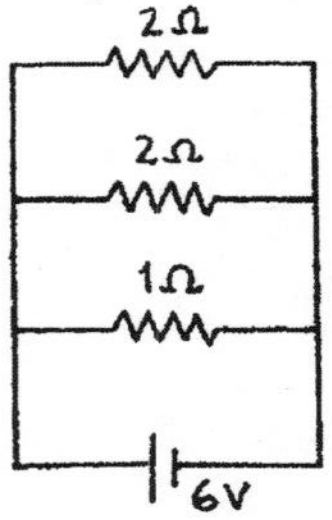

3. Consider the parallel circuit at the right.

a. The voltage drop across each resistor is **6** V.

b. The current in each branch is:

2-Ω resistor **3** A.

2-Ω resistor **3** A.

1-Ω resistor **6** A.

c. The current through the battery equals the sum of the currents which equals **12** A.

d. The equivalent resistance of the circuit equals **0.5** Ω.

THE EQUIVALENT RESISTANCE OF A PAIR OF RESISTORS IN PARALLEL IS THEIR PRODUCT DIVIDED BY THEIR SUM!

94

CONCEPTUAL *Physics* PRACTICE PAGE

Chapter 23 Electric Current
Circuit Resistance

> Figure what the resistances are, then show their values in the blanks to the left of each lamp.

All circuits below have the same lamp A with resistance of 6 Ω, and the same 12-volt battery with negligible resistance. The unknown resistances of lamps B through L are such that the current in lamp A remains 1 ampere. *Fill in the blanks:*

Circuit a: How much current flows through the battery? ___1___ A.

Circuit b: Assume lamps C and D are identical. Current through lamp D is ___½___ A.

Circuit c: Identical lamps E and F replace lamp D. Current through lamp C is ___½___ A.

Circuit d: Lamps G and H replace lamps E and F, and the resistance of lamp G is twice that of lamp H. Current through lamp H is ___½___ A.

> Handy rule: For a pair of resistors in parallel:
>
> Equivalent resistance = product of resistances / sum of resistances

Circuit e: Identical lamps K and L replace lamp H. Current through lamp L is ___¼___ A.

The equivalent resistance of a circuit is the value of a single resistor that will replace all the resistors of the circuit to produce the same load on the battery. How do the equivalent resistances of the circuits a through e compare?

ALL SAME, 12 Ω (THEY MUST BE FOR SAME 1-A CURRENT IN BATTERY)

CONCEPTUAL *Physics* PRACTICE PAGE

Chapter 23 Electric Current
Electric Power in Circuits

The table beside circuit a below shows the current through each resistor, the voltage across each resistor, and the power dissipated as heat in each resistor. Find the similar correct values for circuits b through d, and write your answers in the tables shown.

CURRENT IN EACH BRANCH = **VOLTAGE DROP ACROSS BRANCH / EQUIVALENT RESISTANCE OF BRANCH**

a.

RESISTANCE	CURRENT	× VOLTAGE	= POWER
2Ω	2A	4V	8W
4Ω	2A	8V	16W
6Ω	2A	12V	24W

b.

RESISTANCE	CURRENT	× VOLTAGE	= POWER
1Ω	2A	2V	4W
2Ω	2A	4V	8W

c.

RESISTANCE	CURRENT	× VOLTAGE	= POWER
6Ω	1A	6V	6W
3Ω	2A	6V	12W

d.

RESISTANCE	CURRENT	× VOLTAGE	= POWER
2Ω	1.5A	3V	4.5W
2Ω	1.5A	3V	4.5W
1Ω	3A	3V	9W

NOTE THAT TOTAL POWER DISSIPATED BY ALL RESISTORS IN A CIRCUIT EQUALS THE POWER SUPPLIED BY THE BATTERY (VOLTAGE × CURRENT THRU BATTERY)

175

CONCEPTUAL *Physics* PRACTICE PAGE

Chapter 24 Magnetism
Magnetic Fundamentals

Fill in the blanks:

1. Attraction or repulsion of charges depends on their *signs*, positives or negatives. Attraction or repulsion of magnets depends on their magnetic __POLES__ :

__NORTH__ or __SOUTH__.

2. Opposite poles attract; like poles __REPEL__.

3. A magnetic field is produced by the __MOTION__ of electric charge.

4. Clusters of magnetically aligned atoms are magnetic __DOMAINS__.

5. A magnetic __FIELD__ surrounds a current-carrying wire.

6. When a current-carrying wire is made to form a coil around a piece of iron, the result is an __ELECTROMAGNET__.

7. A charged particle moving in a magnetic field experiences a deflecting __FORCE__ that is maximum when the charge moves __PERPENDICULAR__ to the field.

8. A current-carrying wire experiences a deflecting __FORCE__ that is maximum when the wire and magnetic field are __PERPENDICULAR__ to one another.

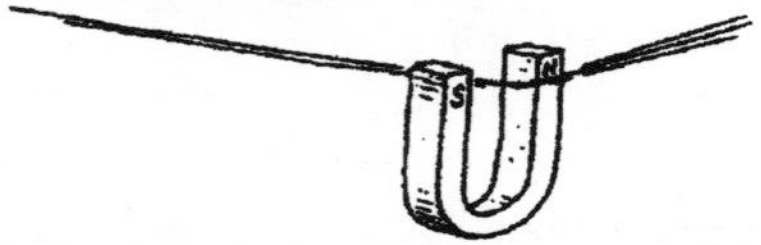

9. A simple instrument designed to detect electric current is the __GALVANOMETER__ ; when calibrated to measure current, it is an __AMMETER__ ; when calibrated to measure voltage, it is a __VOLTMETER__.

10. The largest size magnet in the world is the __WORLD (OR EARTH)__ itself.

YOU HAVE A MAGNETIC PERSONALITY!

THEN TO REALLY MAKE THINGS "SIMPLE", THERE'S THE RIGHT-HAND RULE!

CONCEPTUAL *Physics* PRACTICE PAGE

Chapter 24 Magnetism
Magnetic Fundamentals—continued

11. The illustration below is similar to Figure 24.2 in your textbook. Iron filings trace out patterns of magnetic field lines about a bar magnet. In the field are some magnetic compasses. The compass needle in only one compass is shown. Draw in the needles with proper orientation in the other compasses.

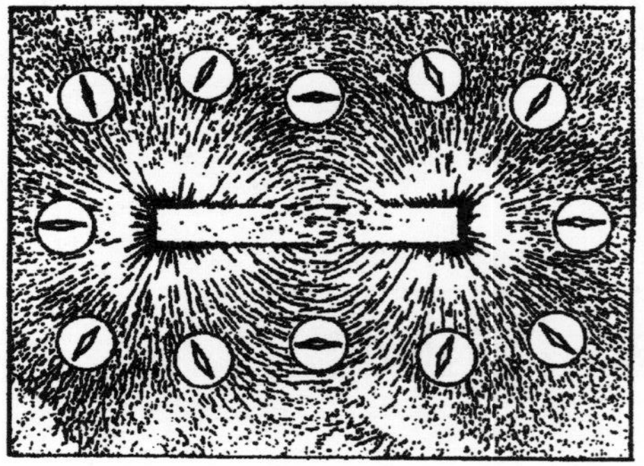

12. The illustration below is similar to Figure 24.10b in your textbook. Iron filings trace out magnetic field pattern about the loop of current-carrying wire. Draw in the compass needle orientations for all the compasses.

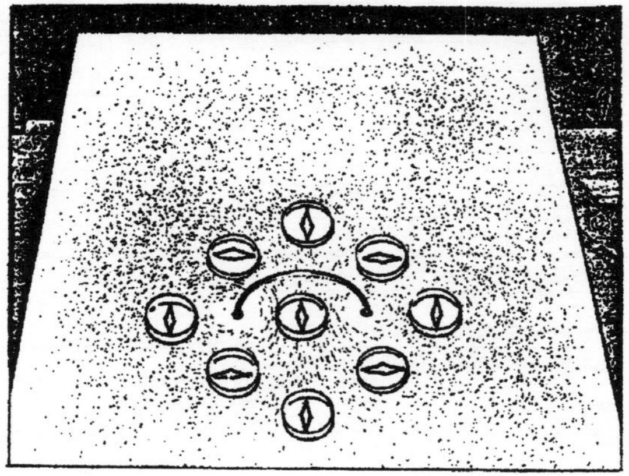

176

CONCEPTUAL *Physics* PRACTICE PAGE

Chapter 25 Electromagnetic Induction
Faraday's Law

Circle the correct answers:

1. Hans Christian Oersted discovered that magnetism and electricity are [**related**] [independent of each other].

   Magnetism is produced by [batteries] [**motion of electric charges**].

   Faraday and Henry discovered that electric current can be produced by [batteries] [**motion of a magnet**].

   More specifically, voltage is induced in a loop of wire if there is a change in [batteries] [**magnetic field in the loop**].

   This phenomenon is called [electromagnetism] [**electromagnetic induction**].

2. When a magnet is plunged in and out of a coil of wire, voltage is induced in the coil. If the rate of the in-and-out motion of the magnet is doubled, the induced voltage [**doubles**] [halves] [remains the same].

   If instead the number of loops in the coil is doubled, the induced voltage [**doubles**] [halves] [remains the same].

3. A rapidly changing magnetic field in any region of space induces a rapidly changing [**electric field**] [magnetic field] [gravitational field]

   which in turn induces a rapidly changing [**magnetic field**] [electric field] [baseball field].

   This generation and regeneration of electric and magnetic fields make up [**electromagnetic waves**] [sound waves] [both of these].

CONCEPTUAL *Physics* PRACTICE PAGE

Chapter 25 Electromagnetic Induction
Transformers

Consider a simple transformer that has a 100-turn primary coil and a 1000-turn secondary coil. The primary is connected to a 120-V AC source and the secondary is connected to an electrical device with a resistance of 1000 ohms.

1. What will be the voltage output of the secondary?

   __1200__ V.

2. What current flows in the secondary circuit?

   __1.2__ A.

3. Now that you know the voltage and the current, what is the power in the secondary coil?

   __1440__ W.

4. Neglecting small heating losses, and knowing that energy is conserved, what is the power in the primary coil?

   __1440__ W.

5. Now that you know the power and the voltage across the primary coil, what is the current drawn by the primary coil?

   __12__ A.

Circle the answers:

6. The results show voltage is stepped [**up**] [down] from primary to secondary, and that current is correspondingly stepped [up] [**down**].

7. For a step-up transformer, there are [**more**] [fewer] turns in the secondary coil than in the primary.

   For such a transformer, there is [more] [**less**] current in the secondary than in the primary.

8. A transformer can step up [**voltage**] [energy and power], but in no way can it step up [voltage] [**energy and power**].

9. If 120 V is used to power a toy electric train that operates on 6 V, then a [step up] [**step down**] transformer should be used that has a primary to secondary turns ratio of [1/20] [**20/1**].

10. A transformer operates on [dc] [**ac**] because the magnetic field within the iron core must [**continually change**] [remain steady].

CONCEPTUAL *Physics* PRACTICE PAGE

Chapter 26 Properties of Light
Speed, Wavelength, and Frequency

1. The first investigation that led to a determination of the speed of light was performed in about 1675 by the Danish astronomer Olaus Roemer. He made careful measurements of the period of Io, a moon about the planet Jupiter, and was surprised to find an irregularity in Io's observed period. While Earth was moving away from Jupiter, the measured periods were slightly longer than average. While Earth approached Jupiter, they were shorter than average. Roemer estimated that the cumulative discrepancy amounted to about 16.5 minutes. Later interpretations showed that what occurs is that light takes about 16.5 minutes to travel the extra 300,000,000-km distance across Earth's orbit. Aha! We have enough information to calculate the speed of light!

a. Write a formula for speed in terms of the distance traveled and the time spent traveling that distance.

$$v = \frac{d}{t} = \frac{300,000,000 \text{ km}}{16.5 \text{ min}}$$

b. Using Roemer's data, and changing 16.5 minutes to seconds, calculate the speed of light.

$$16.5 \text{ min} \times \frac{60 \text{ s}}{1 \text{ min}} = 990 \text{ s}$$

$$\frac{300,000,000 \text{ km}}{990 \text{ s}} = 3 \times 10^5 \frac{\text{km}}{\text{s}} = 3 \times 10^8 \frac{\text{m}}{\text{s}}$$

Study Figure 26.3 in your textbook and answer the following:
2. a. Which has the longer *wavelengths*? (radio waves) [light waves].

b. Which has the longer *wavelengths*? (light waves) [gamma waves].

c. Which has the higher *frequencies*? [ultraviolet waves] (infrared waves).

d. Which has the higher *frequencies*? [ultraviolet waves] (gamma rays).

LIGHT IS THE ONLY THING WE SEE!

Carefully study the section "Transparent Materials" in your textbook and answer the following:
3. a. Exactly what do vibrating electrons emit?

<u>ELECTROMAGNETIC WAVES</u>

b. When ultraviolet light shines on glass, what does it do to electrons in the glass structure?

<u>UV CAUSES ELECTRONS TO VIBRATE IN RESONANCE WITH THE INCIDENT UV</u>

c. When energetic electrons in the glass structure vibrate against neighboring atoms, what happens to the energy of vibration?

<u>BECOMES THERMAL ENERGY (HEAT)</u>

d. What happens to the energy of a vibrating electron that does not collide with neighboring atoms?

<u>EMITTED AS LIGHT</u>

PHYSICS — YEA!

CONCEPTUAL *Physics* PRACTICE PAGE

Chapter 26 Properties of Light
Speed, Wavelength, and Frequency—continued

e. Light in which range of frequencies is absorbed in glass? [visible] (ultraviolet).

f. Light in which range of frequencies is transmitted through glass? (visible) [ultraviolet].

g. How is the speed of light in glass affected by the succession of time delays that accompany the absorption and re-emission of light from atom to atom in the glass?

<u>THE AVERAGE SPEED OF LIGHT IS LESS IN GLASS THAN IN AIR</u>

h. How does the speed of light compare in water, glass, and diamond?

<u>SPEED OF LIGHT IS 0.75c IN WATER; 0.41c IN A DIAMOND</u>

4. The Sun normally shines on both Earth and Moon. Both cast shadows. Sometimes the Moon's shadow falls on Earth, and at other times Earth's shadow falls on the Moon.

a. The sketch shows the Sun and Earth. Draw the Moon at a position for a solar eclipse.

MOON'S SHADOW FALLS ON EARTH
SUN — EARTH

b. This sketch also shows the Sun and Earth. Draw the Moon at a position for a lunar eclipse.

EARTH'S SHADOW FALLS ON MOON
SUN — EARTH

5. The diagram shows the limits of light rays when a large lamp makes a shadow of a small object on a screen. Make a sketch of the shadow on the screen, shading the umbra darker than the penumbra. In what part of the shadow could an ant on the screen see part of the lamp?

<u>PENUMBRA</u>

LAMP — APPLE — DRAW COMPLETE SHADOW OF APPLE ON SCREEN

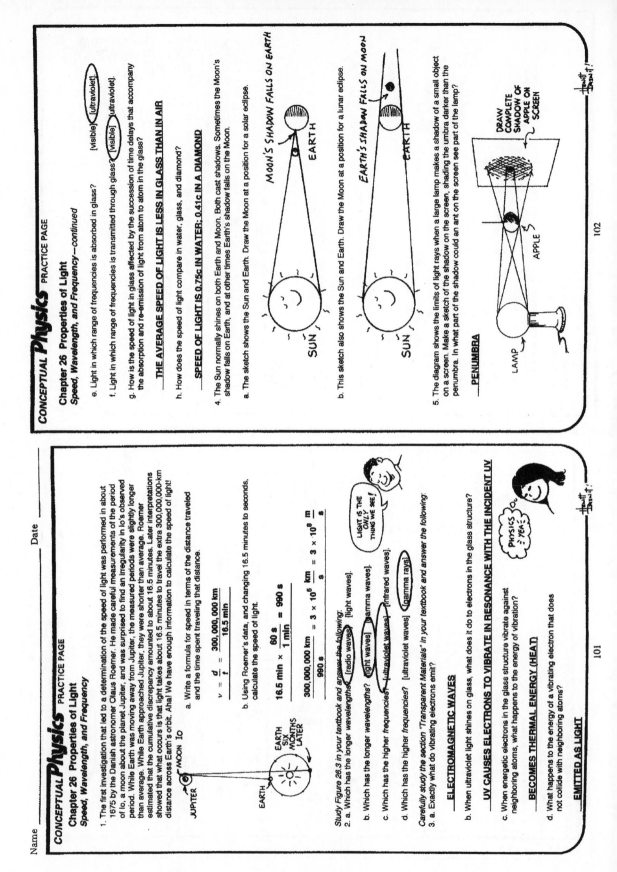

Name _____   Date _____

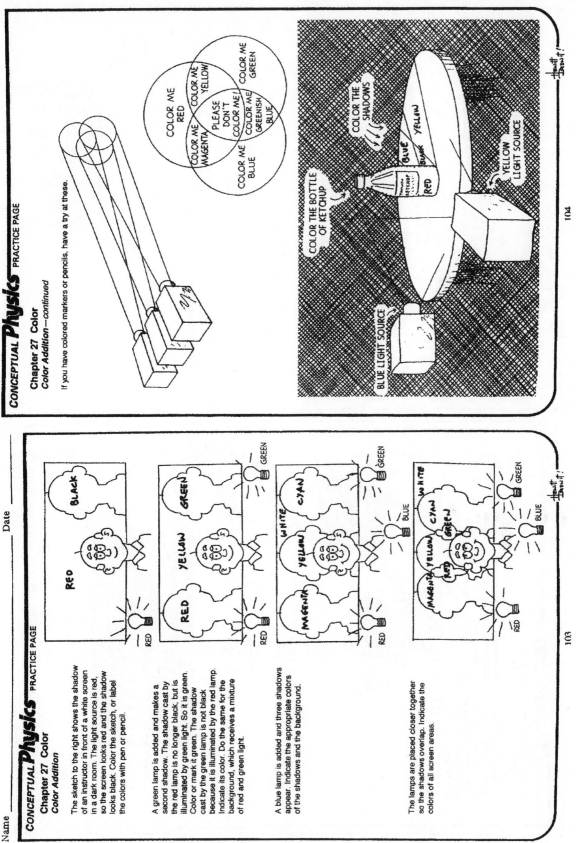

Left panel (page 103)

Chapter 27 Color
Color Addition

The sketch to the right shows the shadow of an instructor in front of a white screen in a dark room. The light source is red, so the screen looks red and the shadow looks black. Color the sketch, or label the colors with pen or pencil.

RED — BLACK

A green lamp is added and makes a second shadow. The shadow cast by the red lamp is no longer black, but is illuminated by green light. So it is green. Color or mark it green. The shadow cast by the green lamp is not black because it is illuminated by the red lamp. Indicate its color. Do the same for the background, which receives a mixture of red and green light.

RED — YELLOW — GREEN

A blue lamp is added and three shadows appear. Indicate the appropriate colors of the shadows and the background.

MAGENTA — WHITE — YELLOW — CYAN

The lamps are placed closer together so the shadows overlap. Indicate the colors of all screen areas.

MAGENTA — YELLOW — RED — GREEN — CYAN — WHITE

103

Right panel (page 104)

Chapter 27 Color
Color Addition—continued

If you have colored markers or pencils, have a try at these.

COLOR ME RED
COLOR ME MAGENTA
COLOR ME YELLOW
PLEASE DON'T COLOR ME!
COLOR ME GREENISH BLUE
COLOR ME GREEN
COLOR ME BLUE

COLOR THE BOTTLE OF KETCHUP
COLOR THE SHADOWS
BLUE — BLACK — YELLOW — RED

BLUE LIGHT SOURCE
YELLOW LIGHT SOURCE

104

CONCEPTUAL *Physics* PRACTICE PAGE

Chapter 28 Reflection and Refraction
Pool Room Optics

The law of reflection for optics is useful in playing pool. A ball bouncing off the bank of a pool table behaves like a photon reflecting off a mirror. As the sketch shows, angles become straight lines with the help of mirrors. The diagram shows a top view of this, with a flattened "mirrored" region. Note that the angled path on the table appears as a straight line (dashed) in the mirrored region.

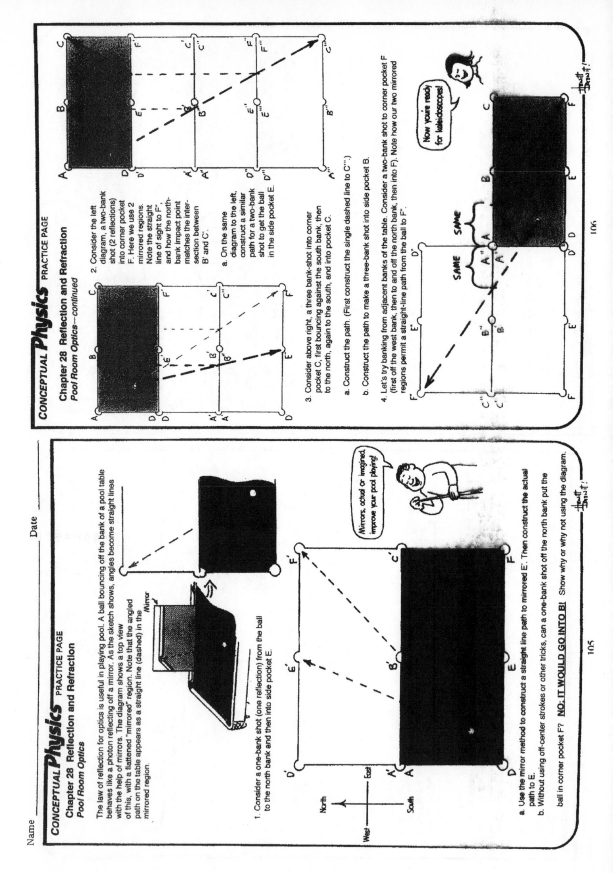

1. Consider a one-bank shot (one reflection) from the ball to the north bank and then into side pocket E.

North
West — East
South

Mirrors, actual or imagined, improve your pool playing!

a. Use the mirror method to construct a straight line path to mirrored E'. Then construct the actual path to E.

b. Without using off-center strokes or other tricks, can a one-bank shot off the north bank put the ball in corner pocket F? __NO: IT WOULD GO INTO B!__ Show why or why not using the diagram.

CONCEPTUAL *Physics* PRACTICE PAGE

Chapter 28 Reflection and Refraction
Pool Room Optics—continued

2. Consider the left diagram, a two-bank shot (2 reflections) into corner pocket F. Here we use 2 mirrored regions. Note the straight line of sight to F", and how the north-bank impact point matches the intersection between B' and C'.

a. On the same diagram to the left, construct a similar path for a two-bank shot to get the ball in the side pocket E.

3. Consider above right, a three bank-shot into corner pocket C, first bouncing against the south bank, then to the north, again to the south, and into pocket C.

a. Construct the path. (First construct the single dashed line to C''' .)

b. Construct the path to make a three-bank shot into side pocket B.

4. Let's try banking from adjacent banks of the table. Consider a two-bank shot to corner pocket F (first off the west bank, then to and off the north bank, then into F). Note how our two mirrored regions permit a straight-line path from the ball to F'.

SAME   SAME   SAME

Now you're ready for kaleidoscopes!

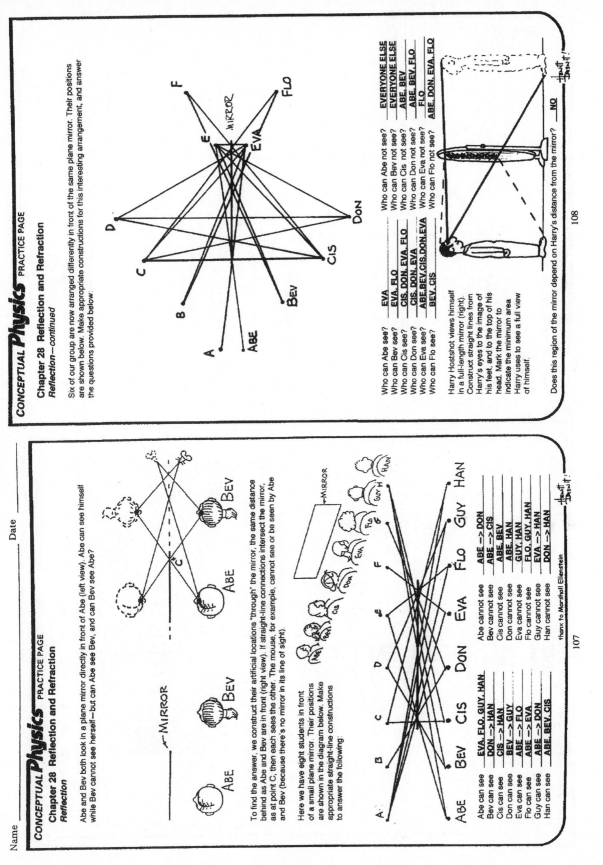

CONCEPTUAL *Physics* PRACTICE PAGE

Chapter 28 Reflection and Refraction

Reflection

Abe and Bev both look in a plane mirror directly in front of Abe (left view). Abe can see himself while Bev cannot see herself—but can Abe see Bev, and can Bev see Abe?

◄— MIRROR

ABE   BEV

To find the answer, we construct their artificial locations "through" the mirror, the same distance behind as Abe and Bev are in front (right view). If straight-line connections intersect the mirror, as at point C, then each sees the other. The mouse, for example, cannot see or be seen by Abe and Bev (because there's no mirror in its line of sight).

◄—MIRROR

Here we have eight students in front of a small plane mirror. Their positions are shown in the diagram below. Make appropriate straight-line constructions to answer the following:

Abe can see	EVA, FLO, GUY, HAN	Abe cannot see	ABE —> DON
Bev can see	DON —> HAN	Bev cannot see	ABE —> CIS
Cis can see	CIS —> HAN	Cis cannot see	ABE, BEV
Don can see	BEV —> GUY	Don cannot see	ABE, HAN
Eva can see	ABE —> FLO	Eva cannot see	GUY, HAN
Flo can see	ABE —> EVA	Flo cannot see	FLO, GUY, HAN
Guy can see	ABE —> DON	Guy cannot see	EVA —> HAN
Han can see	ABE, BEV, CIS	Han cannot see	DON —> HAN

thanx to Marshall Ellenstein

107

CONCEPTUAL *Physics* PRACTICE PAGE

Chapter 28 Reflection and Refraction

Reflection—continued

Six of our group are now arranged differently in front of the same plane mirror. Their positions are shown below. Make appropriate constructions for this interesting arrangement, and answer the questions provided below:

MIRROR

Who can Abe see?	EVA	Who can Abe not see?	EVERYONE ELSE
Who can Bev see?	EVA, FLO	Who can Bev not see?	EVERYONE ELSE
Who can Cis see?	CIS, DON, EVA, FLO	Who can Cis not see?	ABE, BEV
Who can Don see?	CIS, DON, EVA	Who can Don not see?	ABE, BEV, FLO
Who can Eva see?	ABE,BEV,CIS,DON,EVA	Who can Eva not see?	FLO
Who can Flo see?	BEV, CIS	Who can Flo not see?	ABE, DON, EVA, FLO

Harry Hotshot views himself in a full-length mirror (right). Construct straight lines from Harry's eyes to the image of his feet, and to the top of his head. Mark the mirror to indicate the minimum area Harry uses to see a full view of himself.

Does this region of the mirror depend on Harry's distance from the mirror? **NO**

108

Chapter 28 Reflection and Refraction
Reflected Views

1. The ray diagram below shows the extension of one of the reflected rays from the plane mirror.

Complete the above diagram:
a. Carefully draw the three other reflected rays.
b. Extend your drawn rays behind the mirror to locate the image of the flame. (Assume the candle and image are viewed by an observer on the left.)

2. A girl takes a photograph of the bridge as shown. Which of the two sketches below correctly shows the reflected view of the bridge? Defend your answer.

NOTE THAT RELECTED VIEW IS AS IF SEEN FROM HERE!

THE RIGHT-SIDE VIEW IS CORRECT. SHOWING THE UNDERSIDE OF BRIDGE. OR WHAT YOUR EYE WOULD SEE IF AS FAR BELOW THE REFLECTING SURFACE AS IT IS ABOVE. (PLACE A MIRROR ON THE FLOOR IN FRONT OF A TABLE. STUDENTS WILL SEE THAT THE REFLECTED VIEW OF THE TABLE SHOWS ITS BOTTOM!

Chapter 28 Reflection and Refraction
More Reflection

1. Light from a flashlight shines on a mirror and illuminates one of the cards. Draw the reflected beam to indicate the illuminated card.

2. A periscope has a pair of mirrors in it. Draw the light path from the object "O" to the eye of the observer.

3. The ray diagram below shows the reflection of one of the rays that strikes the parabolic mirror. Notice that the law of reflection is obeyed, and the angle of incidence (from the normal, the dashed line) equals the angle of reflection (from the normal). Complete the diagram by drawing the reflected rays of the other three rays that are shown. (Do you see why parabolic mirrors are used in automobile headlights?)

Be the first to invent a surface that is 100% reflecting!

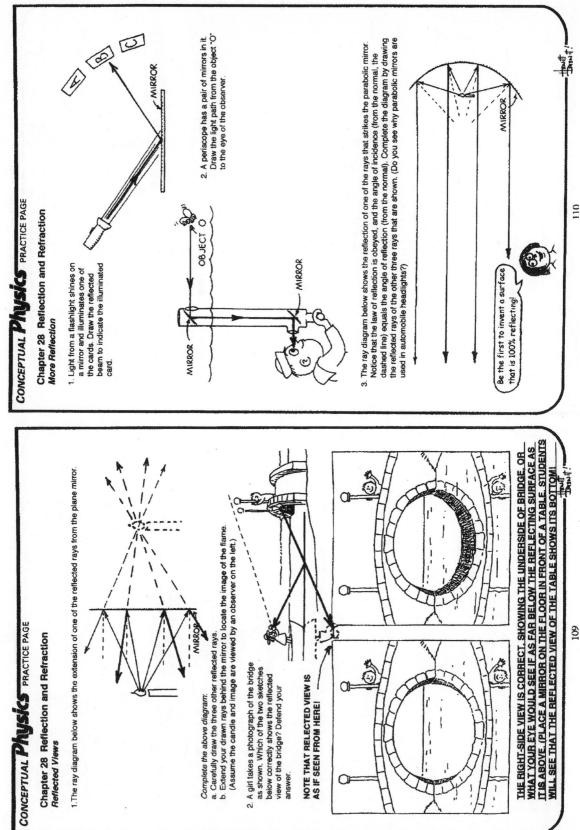

CONCEPTUAL *Physics* PRACTICE PAGE

Chapter 28 Reflection and Refraction
Refraction

1. A pair of toy cart wheels are rolled obliquely from a smooth surface onto two plots of grass—a rectangular plot on the left, and a triangular plot on the right. The ground is on a slight incline so that after slowing down in the grass, the wheels speed up again when emerging on the smooth surface. Finish each sketch and show some positions of the wheels inside the plots and on the other side. Clearly indicate their paths and directions of travel.

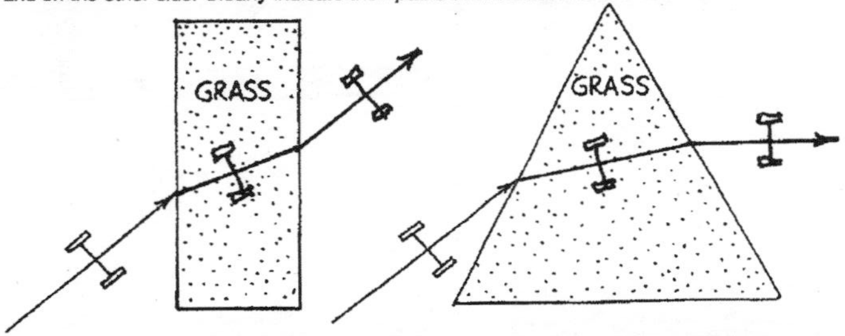

2. Red, green, and blue rays of light are incident upon a glass prism as shown below. The average speed of red light in the glass is less than in air, so the red ray is refracted. When it emerges into the air it regains its original speed and travels in the direction shown. Green light takes longer to get through the glass. Because of its slower speed it is refracted as shown. Blue light travels even slower in glass. Complete the diagram by estimating the path of the blue ray.

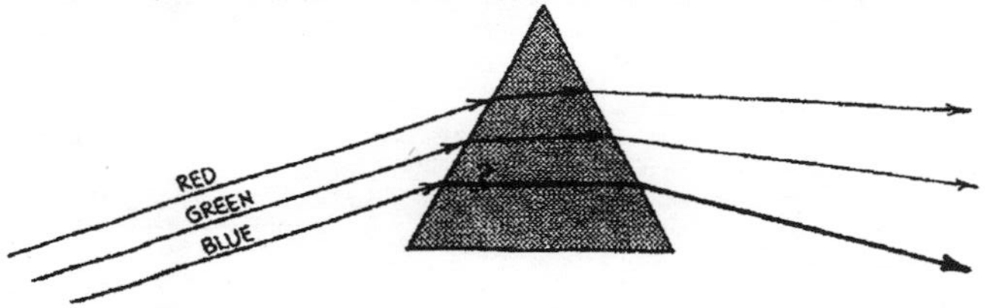

3. Below we consider a prism-shaped hole in a piece of glass—that is, an "air prism." Complete the diagram, showing likely paths of the beams of red, green, and blue light as they pass through this "prism" and then into glass.

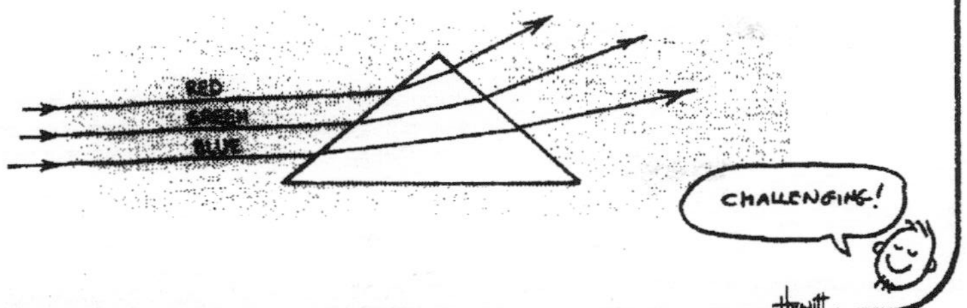

CHALLENGE!

CONCEPTUAL *Physics* PRACTICE PAGE

Chapter 28 Reflection and Refraction
Refraction—continued

4. Light of different colors diverges when emerging from a prism. Newton showed that with a second prism he could make the diverging beams become parallel again. Which placement of the second prism will do this?

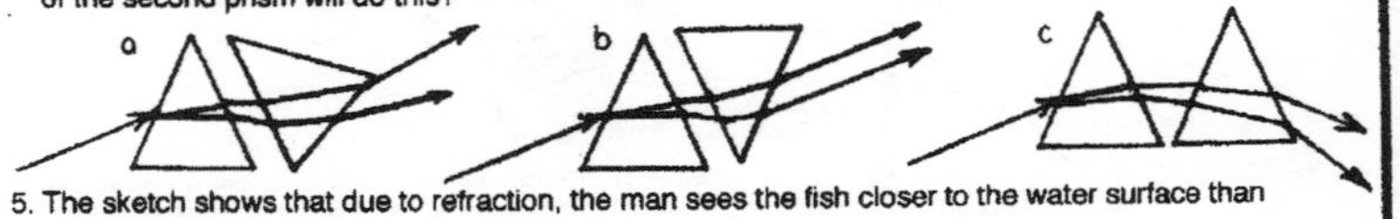

5. The sketch shows that due to refraction, the man sees the fish closer to the water surface than it actually is.

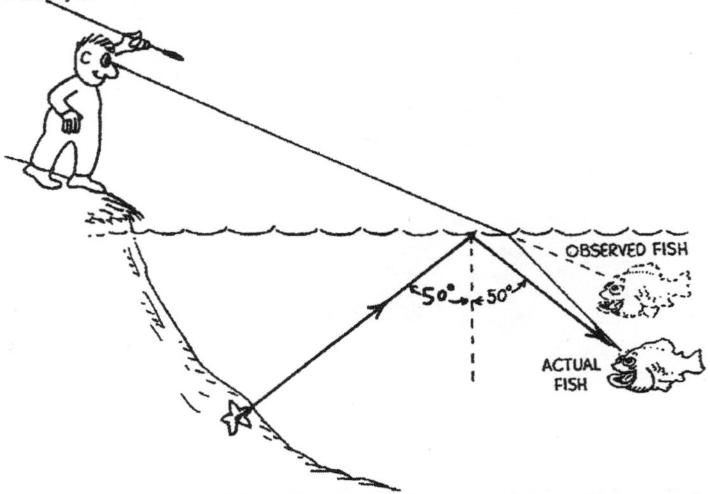

a. Draw a ray beginning at the fish's eye to show the line of sight of the fish when it looks upward at 50° to the normal at the water surface. Draw the direction of the ray after it meets the surface of water.

b. At the 50° angle, does the fish see the man, or does it see the reflected view of the starfish at the bottom of the pond? Explain. **FISH SEES REFLECTED VIEW OF STARFISH (50° ≥ 48° CRITICAL ANGLE, SO THERE IS TOTAL INTERNAL REFLECTION).**

c. To see the man, should the fish look higher or lower than the 50° path? **HIGHER, SO LINE OF SIGHT TO THE WATER IS LESS THAN 48° WITH NORMAL**

d. If the fish's eye were barely above the water surface, it would see the world above in a 180° view, horizon to horizon. The fisheye view of the world above as seen beneath the water, however, is very different. Due to the 48° critical angle of water, the fish sees a normally 180° horizon-to-horizon view compressed within an angle of _____96°_____.

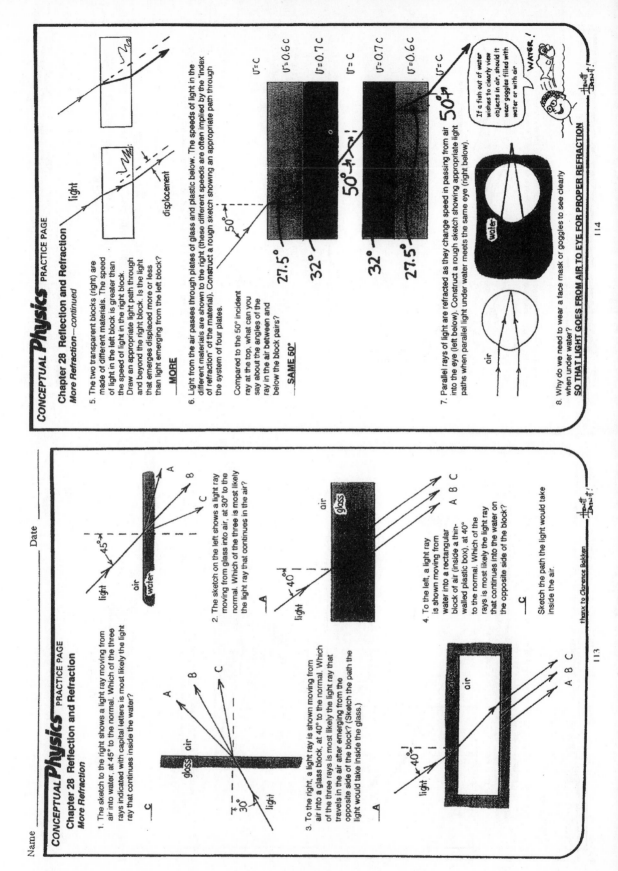

CONCEPTUAL Physics PRACTICE PAGE

Chapter 28 Reflection and Refraction
More Refraction

1. The sketch to the right shows a light ray moving from air into water, at 45° to the normal. Which of the three rays indicated with capital letters is most likely the light ray that continues inside the water?

C

2. The sketch on the left shows a light ray moving from glass into air, at 30° to the normal. Which of the three is most likely the light ray that continues in the air?

A

3. To the right, a light ray is shown moving from air into a glass block, at 40° to the normal. Which of the three rays is most likely the light ray that travels in the air after emerging from the opposite side of the block? (Sketch the path the light would take inside the glass.)

A

4. To the left, a light ray is shown moving from water into a rectangular block of air (inside a thin-walled plastic box), at 40° to the normal. Which of the rays is most likely the light ray that continues into the water on the opposite side of the block?

C

Sketch the path the light would take inside the air.

thanx to Clarence Bakken

113

CONCEPTUAL Physics PRACTICE PAGE

Chapter 28 Reflection and Refraction
More Refraction—continued

5. The two transparent blocks (right) are made of different materials. The speed of light in the left block is greater than the speed of light in the right block. Draw an appropriate light path through and beyond the right block. Is the light that emerges displaced more or less than light emerging from the left block?

MORE

6. Light from the air passes through plates of glass and plastic below. The speeds of light in the different materials are shown to the right (these different speeds are often implied by the "index of refraction" of the material). Construct a rough sketch showing an appropriate path through the system of four plates.

Compared to the 50° incident ray at the top, what can you say about the angles of the ray in the air between and below the block pairs?

SAME 50°

$v = c$
$v = 0.6c$
$v = 0.7c$
$v = c$
$v = 0.7c$
$v = 0.6c$
$v = c$

50°
27.5°
32°
50°
32°
27.5°
50°

7. Parallel rays of light are refracted as they change speed in passing from air into the eye (left above). Construct a rough sketch showing appropriate light paths when parallel light under water meets the same eye (right below).

air

water

If a fish out of water wishes to clearly view objects in air, should it wear goggles filled with water or with air? WATER!

8. Why do we need to wear a face mask or goggles to see clearly when under water?
SO THAT LIGHT GOES FROM AIR TO EYE FOR PROPER REFRACTION

114

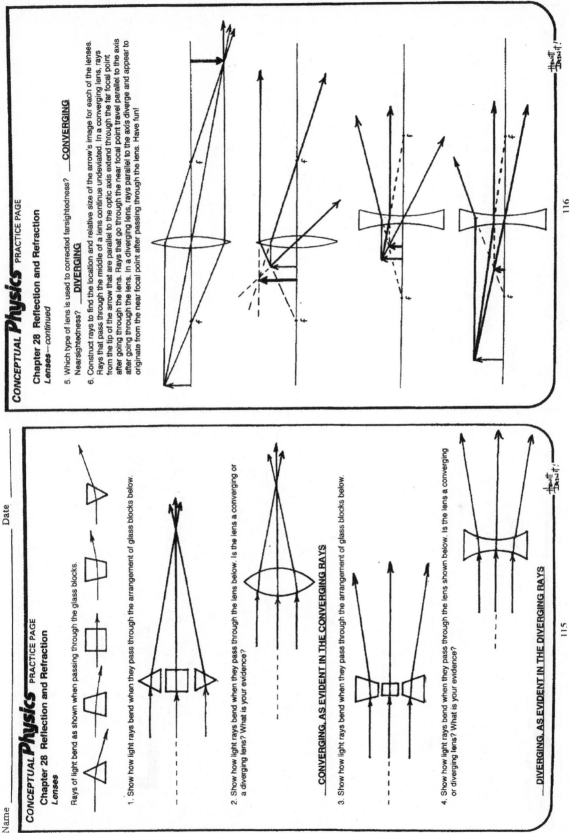

CONCEPTUAL **Physics** PRACTICE PAGE

Chapter 28 Reflection and Refraction
Lenses

Rays of light bend as shown when passing through the glass blocks.

1. Show how light rays bend when they pass through the arrangement of glass blocks below.

2. Show how light rays bend when they pass through the lens below. Is the lens a converging or a diverging lens? What is your evidence?

CONVERGING, AS EVIDENT IN THE CONVERGING RAYS

3. Show how light rays bend when they pass through the arrangement of glass blocks below.

4. Show how light rays bend when they pass through the lens shown below. Is the lens a converging or diverging lens? What is your evidence?

DIVERGING, AS EVIDENT IN THE DIVERGING RAYS

CONCEPTUAL **Physics** PRACTICE PAGE

Chapter 28 Reflection and Refraction
Lenses—continued

5. Which type of lens is used to corrected farsightedness? **CONVERGING**
Nearsightedness? **DIVERGING**

6. Construct rays to find the location and relative size of the arrow's image for each of the lenses. Rays that pass through the middle of a lens continue undeviated. In a converging lens, rays from the tip of the arrow that are parallel to the optic axis extend through the far focal point after going through the lens. Rays that go through the near focal point travel parallel to the axis after going through the lens. In a diverging lens, rays parallel to the axis diverge and appear to originate from the near focal point after passing through the lens. Have fun!

Name _____ Date _____

Chapter 29 Light Waves
Diffraction and Interference

1. Shown are concentric solid and dashed circles, each different in radius by 1 cm. Consider the circular pattern a top view of water waves, where the solid circles are crests and the dashed circles are troughs.

   a. Draw another set of the same concentric circles with a compass. Choose any part of the paper for your center (except the present central point). Let the circles run off the edge of the paper.

   b. Find where a dashed line crosses a solid line and draw a large dot at the intersection. Do this for ALL places where a solid and dashed line intersect.

   c. With a wide felt marker, connect the dots with the solid lines. These *nodal lines* lie in regions where the waves have cancelled — where the crest of one wave overlaps the trough of another (see Figures 29.15 and 29.16 in your textbook).

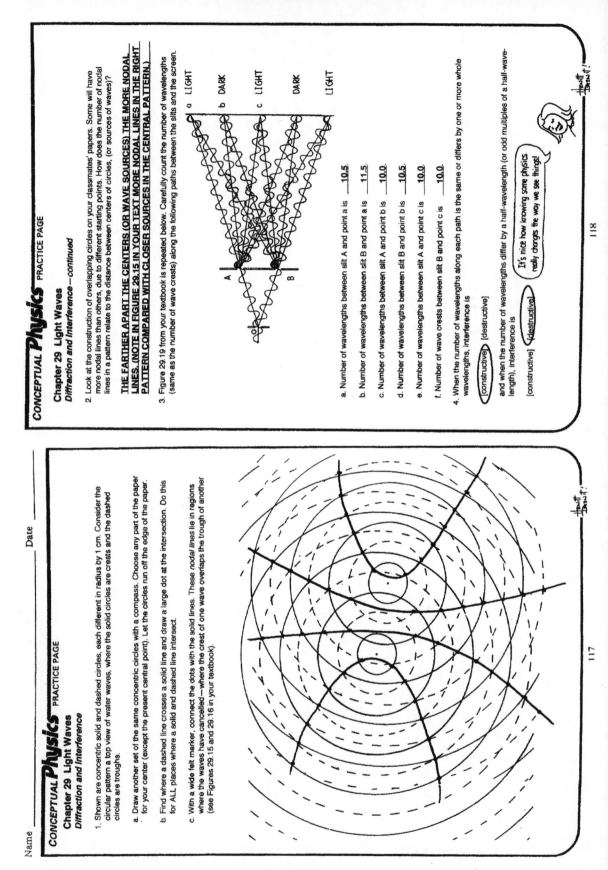

117

Chapter 29 Light Waves
Diffraction and Interference—continued

2. Look at the construction of overlapping circles on your classmates' papers. Some will have more nodal lines than others, due to different starting points. How does the number of nodal lines in a pattern relate to the distance between centers of circles, (or sources of waves)?

   THE FARTHER APART THE CENTERS (OR WAVE SOURCES) THE MORE NODAL LINES. (NOTE IN FIGURE 29.15 IN YOUR TEXT MORE NODAL LINES IN THE RIGHT PATTERN COMPARED WITH CLOSER SOURCES IN THE CENTRAL PATTERN.)

3. Figure 29.19 from your textbook is repeated below. Carefully count the number of wavelengths (same as the number of wave crests) along the following paths between the slits and the screen.

   a. Number of wavelengths between slit A and point a is _**10.5**_

   b. Number of wavelengths between slit B and point a is _**11.5**_

   c. Number of wavelengths between slit A and point b is _**10.0**_

   d. Number of wavelengths between slit B and point b is _**10.5**_

   e. Number of wavelengths between slit A and point c is _**10.0**_

   f. Number of wave crests between slit B and point c is _**10.0**_

4. When the number of wavelengths along each path is the same or differs by one or more whole wavelengths, interference is

   [constructive] [destructive]

   and when the number of wavelengths differ by a half-wavelength (or odd multiples of a half-wavelength), interference is

   [constructive] [destructive]

   It's nice how knowing some physics really changes the way we see things!

118

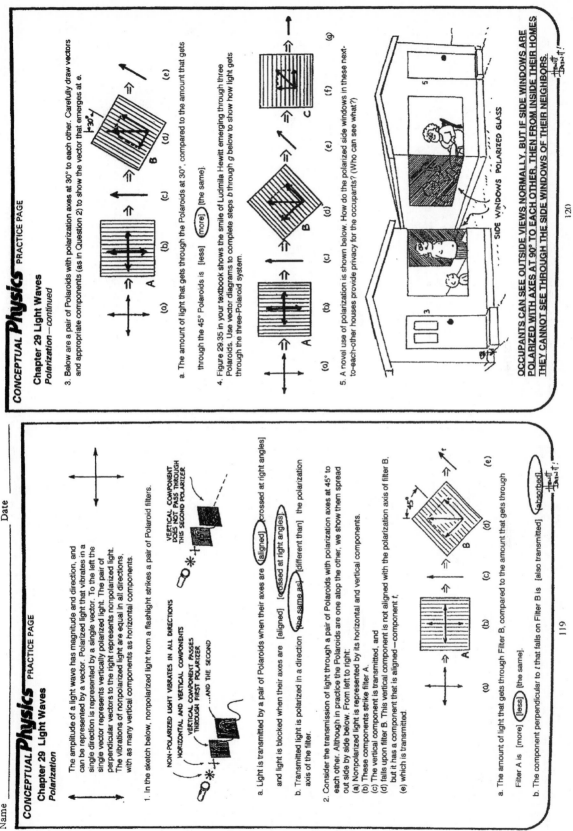

CONCEPTUAL *Physics* PRACTICE PAGE

Chapter 29 Light Waves
Polarization

The amplitude of a light wave has magnitude and direction, and can be represented by a vector. Polarized light that vibrates in a single direction is represented by a single vector. To the left the single vector represents vertically polarized light. The pair of perpendicular vectors to the right represents nonpolarized light. The vibrations of nonpolarized light are equal in all directions, with as many vertical components as horizontal components.

1. In the sketch below, nonpolarized light from a flashlight strikes a pair of Polaroid filters.

NON-POLARIZED LIGHT VIBRATES IN ALL DIRECTIONS

HORIZONTAL AND VERTICAL COMPONENTS

VERTICAL COMPONENT PASSES THROUGH FIRST POLARIZER

...AND THE SECOND

VERTICAL COMPONENT DOES NOT PASS THROUGH THIS SECOND POLARIZER

a. Light is transmitted by a pair of Polaroids when their axes are [aligned] [crossed at right angles] and light is blocked when their axes are [aligned] [crossed at right angles].

b. Transmitted light is polarized in a direction [the same as] [different than] the polarization axis of the filter.

2. Consider the transmission of light through a pair of Polaroids with polarization axes at 45° to each other. Although in practice the Polaroids are one atop the other, we show them spread out side by side below. From left to right:
(a) Nonpolarized light is represented by its horizontal and vertical components.
(b) These components strike filter A.
(c) The vertical component is transmitted, and
(d) falls upon filter B. This vertical component is not aligned with the polarization axis of filter B, but it has a component that is aligned—component t,
(e) which is transmitted.

a. The amount of light that gets through Filter B, compared to the amount that gets through Filter A is [more] [less] [the same].

b. The component perpendicular to t that falls on Filter B is [also transmitted] [absorbed].

119

CONCEPTUAL *Physics* PRACTICE PAGE

Chapter 29 Light Waves
Polarization—continued

3. Below are a pair of Polaroids with polarization axes at 30° to each other. Carefully draw vectors and appropriate components (as in Question 2) to show the vector that emerges at e.

a. The amount of light that gets through the Polaroids at 30°, compared to the amount that gets through the 45° Polaroids is [less] [more] [the same].

4. Figure 29.35 in your textbook shows the smile of Ludmila Hewitt emerging through three Polaroids. Use vector diagrams to complete steps b through g below to show how light gets through the three-Polaroid system.

5. A novel use of polarization is shown below. How do the polarized side windows in these next-to-each-other houses provide privacy for the occupants? (Who can see what?)

OCCUPANTS CAN SEE OUTSIDE VIEWS NORMALLY, BUT IF SIDE WINDOWS ARE POLARIZED WITH AXES AT 90° TO EACH OTHER, THEN FROM INSIDE THEIR HOMES THEY CANNOT SEE THROUGH THE SIDE WINDOWS OF THEIR NEIGHBORS.

SIDE WINDOWS POLARIZED GLASS

120

CONCEPTUAL *Physics* PRACTICE PAGE

Chapters 31 and 32 Light Quanta and The Atom and the Quantum
Light Quanta

1. To say that light is quantized means that light is made up of

   (elemental units)   [waves].

2. Compared to photons of low-frequency light, photons of higher-frequency light have more

   [energy]   [speed]   [quanta].

   E=hf

3. The photoelectric effect supports the

   [wave model of light]   (particle model of light).

4. The photoelectric effect is evident when light shone on certain

   photosensitive materials ejects   [photon]   (electrons).

5. The photoelectric effect is more effective with violet light than with red light because the photons

   [resonate with the atoms in the material]

   (deliver more energy to the material)

   [are more numerous].

6. According to De Broglie's wave model of matter, a beam of light

   and a beam of electrons   [are fundamentally different]   (are similar).

7. According to De Broglie, the greater the speed of an electron beam, the

   [longer is its wavelength]   (shorter is its wavelength).

8. The discreteness of the energy levels of electrons about the atomic nucleus is best understood

   by considering the electron to be a (wave)   [particle].

9. Heavier atoms are not appreciably larger in size than lighter atoms. The main reason for this is that the greater nuclear charge

   (pulls surrounding electrons into tighter orbits)

   [holds more electrons about the atomic nucleus]

   [produces a denser atomic structure].

10. Whereas in the everyday macroworld the study of motion is called *mechanics*, in the microworld the study of quanta is called

    [Newtonian mechanics]   (quantum mechanics).

    A QUANTUM MECHANIC!

CONCEPTUAL *Physics* PRACTICE PAGE

Chapter 33 Atomic Nucleus and Radioactivity
Radioactivity

Complete the following statements:

1. a. A lone neutron spontaneously decays into a proton plus an ___ELECTRON___ .

   PHYSICS = SIGH!

   b. Alpha and beta rays are made of streams of particles, whereas gamma rays are streams of

   ___PHOTONS___ .

   c. An electrically charged atom is called an ___ION___ .

   d. Different ___ISOTOPES___ of an element are chemically identical but differ in the number of neutrons in the nucleus.

   e. Transuranic elements are those beyond atomic number ___92___ .

   f. If the amount of a certain radioactive sample decreases by half in four weeks, in four more weeks the amount remaining should be ___ONE-FOURTH___ the original amount.

   g. Water from a natural hot spring is warmed by ___RADIOACTIVITY___ inside Earth.

2. The gas in the little girl's balloon is made up of former alpha and beta particles produced by radioactive decay.

   a. If the mixture is electrically neutral, how many more beta particles than alpha particles are in the balloon?

   ___THERE ARE TWICE AS MANY BETA___
   ___PARTICLES AS ALPHA PARTICLES.___

   b. Why is your answer to the above not the "same"?

   ___AN ALPHA HAS DOUBLE CHARGE: THE___
   ___CHARGE OF 2 BETAS = MAGNITUDE OF___
   ___CHARGE OF 1 ALPHA PARTICLE.___

   c. Why are the alpha and beta particles no longer harmful to the child?

   ___THEY HAVE LONG LOST THEIR HIGH KE,___

   ___WHICH BECOMES THE THERMAL ENERGY___

   ___ENERGY OF RANDOM MOLECULAR MOTION.___

   d. What element does this mixture make?

   ___HELIUM___

CONCEPTUAL *Physics* PRACTICE PAGE

Chapter 33 Atomic Nucleus and Radioactivity
Nuclear Reactions

Complete these nuclear reactions:

1. $^{238}_{92}U \rightarrow {}^{234}_{90}Th + {}^{4}_{2}\underline{He}$

2. $^{234}_{90}Th \rightarrow {}^{234}_{91}Pa + {}^{0}_{-1}\underline{e}$

3. $^{234}_{91}Pa \rightarrow {}^{230}_{89}\underline{Ac} + {}^{4}_{2}He$

4. $^{220}_{86}Rn \rightarrow {}^{216}_{84}\underline{Po} + {}^{4}_{2}He$

5. $^{216}_{84}Po \rightarrow {}^{216}_{85}\underline{At} + {}^{0}_{-1}e$

6. $^{216}_{84}Po \rightarrow {}^{212}_{82}\underline{Pb} + {}^{4}_{2}He$

7. $^{210}_{83}Bi \rightarrow {}^{210}_{84}\underline{Po} + {}^{0}_{-1}e$

8. $^{1}_{0}n + {}^{10}_{5}B \rightarrow {}^{7}_{3}\underline{Li} + {}^{4}_{2}He$

THORIUM LATE, I OVERTHLEPT?

NUCLEAR PHYSICS... IT'S THE SAME TO ME WITH THE FIRST TWO LETTERS INTERCHANGED?

CONCEPTUAL *Physics* PRACTICE PAGE

Chapter 33 Atomic Nucleus and Radioactivity
Natural Transmutation

Fill in the decay-scheme diagram below, similar to that shown in Figure 33.14 in your textbook, but beginning with U-235 and ending with an isotope of lead. Use the table at the left, and identify each element in the series with its chemical symbol.

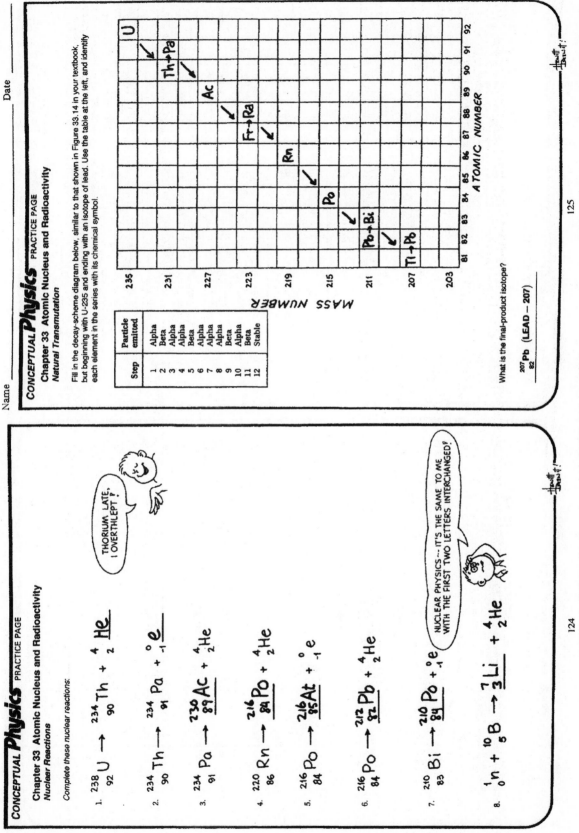

Step	Particle emitted
1	Alpha
2	Beta
3	Alpha
4	Alpha
5	Beta
6	Alpha
7	Alpha
8	Alpha
9	Beta
10	Alpha
11	Beta
12	Stable

What is the final-product isotope?

$^{207}_{82}Pb$ **(LEAD – 207)**

189

CONCEPTUAL *Physics* PRACTICE PAGE

Chapter 34 Nuclear Fission and Fusion
Nuclear Reactions

1. Complete the table for a chain reaction in which two neutrons from each step individually cause a new reaction.

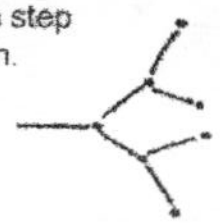

EVENT	1	2	3	4	5	6	7
NO. OF REACTIONS	1	2	4	8	16	32	64

2. Complete the table for a chain reaction where three neutrons from each reaction cause a new reaction.

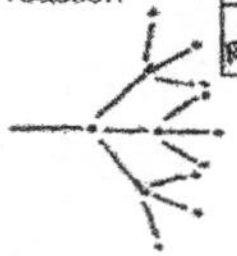

EVENT	1	2	3	4	5	6	7
NO. OF REACTIONS	1	3	9	27	81	243	729

3. Complete these beta reactions, which occur in a breeder reactor.

$$^{239}_{92}U \rightarrow\ ^{239}_{93}Np + ^{0}_{-1}e$$

$$^{239}_{93}Np \rightarrow\ ^{239}_{94}Pu + ^{0}_{-1}e$$

4. Complete the following fission reactions.

$$^{1}_{0}n + ^{235}_{92}U \rightarrow\ ^{143}_{54}Xe + ^{90}_{38}Sr + 3(^{1}_{0}n)$$

$$^{1}_{0}n + ^{235}_{92}U \rightarrow\ ^{152}_{60}Nd + ^{80}_{32}Ge + 4(^{1}_{0}n)$$

$$^{1}_{0}n + ^{239}_{94}Pu \rightarrow\ ^{141}_{54}Xe + ^{97}_{40}Zr + 2(^{1}_{0}n)$$

5. Complete the following fusion reactions.

$$^{2}_{1}H + ^{2}_{1}H \rightarrow\ ^{3}_{2}He + ^{1}_{0}n$$

$$^{2}_{1}H + ^{3}_{1}H \rightarrow\ ^{4}_{2}He + ^{1}_{0}n$$

KNOW NUKES!

CONCEPTUAL *Physics* PRACTICE PAGE

Chapter 35 Special Theory of Relativity
Time Dilation

Chapter 35 in your textbook discusses *The Twin Trip*, in which a traveling twin takes a 2-hour journey while a stay-at-home brother records the passage of 2 ½ hours. Quite remarkable! Times in both frames of reference are indicated by flashes of light, sent each 6 minutes from the spaceship, and received on Earth at 12-minute intervals for the spaceship leaving, and 3-minute intervals for the spaceship returning. Read this section in the book carefully, and fill in the clock readings aboard the spaceship when each flash is emitted, and on Earth when each flash is received.

SHIP LEAVING EARTH

FLASH	TIME ON SHIP WHEN FLASH SENT	TIME ON EARTH WHEN FLASH SEEN
0	12:00	12:00
1	12:06	12:12
2	12:12	12:24
3	12:18	12:36
4	12:24	12:48
5	12:30	1:00
6	12:36	1:12
7	12:42	1:24
8	12:48	1:36
9	12:54	1:48
10	1:00	2:00

SHIP APPROACHING EARTH

FLASH	TIME ON SHIP WHEN FLASH SENT	TIME ON EARTH WHEN FLASH SEEN
11	1:06	2:03
12	1:12	2:06
13	1:18	2:09
14	1:24	2:12
15	1:30	2:15
16	1:36	2:18
17	1:42	2:21
18	1:48	2:24
19	1:54	2:27
20	2:00	2:30

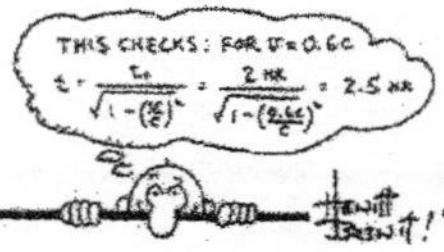

THIS CHECKS! FOR $v = 0.6c$ $t = \dfrac{t_o}{\sqrt{1-(v/c)^2}} = \dfrac{2\,hr.}{\sqrt{1-(0.6)^2}} = 2.5\,hr.$

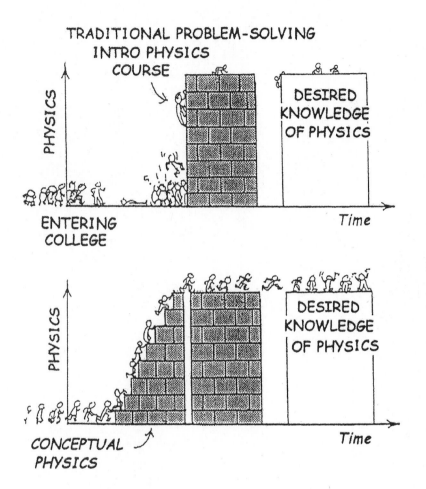

ANSWERS TO THE ODD-NUMBERED EXERCISES AND PROBLEMS
TO CONCEPTUAL PHYSICS—TENTH EDITION

ANSWERS TO CHAPTER 1 EXERCISES (About Science)

1. The penalty for fraud is professional excommunication.

3. Aristotle's hypotheses was partially correct, for material that makes up the plant comes partly from the soil, but mainly from the air and water. An experiment would be to weigh a pot of soil with a small seedling, then weigh the potted plant later after it has grown. The fact that the grown plant will weigh more is evidence that the plant is composed of more material than the soil offers. By keeping a record of the weight of water used to water the plant, and covering the soil with plastic wrap to minimize evaporation losses, the weight of the grown plant can be compared with the weight of water it absorbs. How can the weight of air taken in by the plant be estimated?

5. The examples are endless. Knowledge of electricity, for example, has proven to be extremely useful. The number of people who have been harmed by electricity who understood it is far fewer than the number of people who are harmed by it who don't understand it. A fear of electricity is much more harmful than useful to one's general health and attitude.

7. Yes, there is a geometric connection between the two ratios. As the sketch shows, they are approximately equal.

$$\frac{\text{Pole shadow}}{\text{Pole height}} = \frac{\text{Alexandria - Syene distance}}{\text{Earth radius}}$$

From this pair of ratios, given the distance between Alexandria and Syene, the radius of the Earth can be calculated!

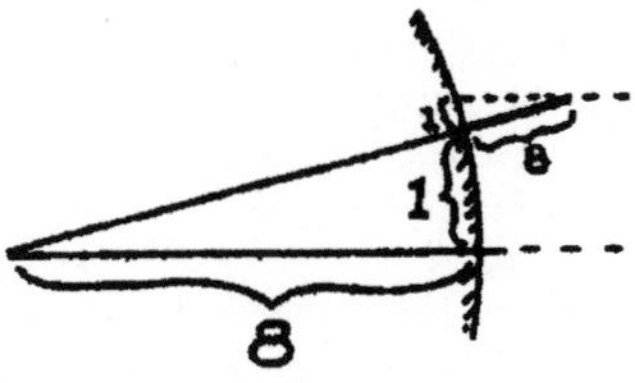

9. What is likely being misunderstood is the distinction between theory and hypothesis. In common usage, "theory" may mean a guess or hypothesis, something that is tentative or speculative. But in science a theory is a synthesis of a large body of validated information (e.g., cell theory or quantum theory). The value of a theory is its usefulness (not its "truth").

ANSWERS TO CHAPTER 2 EXERCISES (Newton's First Law of Motion—Inertia)

1. The tendency of a rolling ball is to continue rolling—in the absence of a force. The fact that it slows down is due to the force of friction.

3. He discredited Aristotle's idea that the rate at which bodies fall is proportional to their weight.

5. Galileo came up with the concept of inertia before Newton was born.

7. Nothing keeps the probe moving. In the absence of a propelling force it would continue moving in a straight line.

9. You should disagree with your friend. In the absence of external forces, a body at rest tends to remain at rest; if moving, it tends to remain moving. Inertia is a *property* of matter to behave this way, not some kind of force.

11. The tendency of the ball is to remain at rest. From a point of view outside the wagon, the ball stays in place as the back of the wagon moves toward it. (Because of friction, the ball may roll along the cart surface—without friction the surface would slide beneath the ball.)

13. Your body tends to remain at rest, in accord with Newton's first law. The back of the seat pushes you forward. If there is no support at the back of your head, your head is not pushed forward with your body, likely injuring your neck. Hence, headrests are recommended!

15. The law of inertia applies in both cases. When the bus slows, you tend to keep moving at the previous speed and lurch forward. When the bus picks up speed, you tend to keep moving at the previous (lower) speed and you lurch backward.

17. An object in motion tends to stay in motion, hence the discs tend to compress upon each other just as the hammer head is compressed onto the handle in Figure 2.4. This compression results in people being slightly shorter at the end of the day than in the morning. The discs tend to separate while sleeping in a prone position, so you regain your full height by morning. This is easily noticed if you find a point you can almost reach up to in the evening, and then find it is easily reached in the morning. Try it and see!

19. If there were no force acting on the ball it would continue in motion without slowing. But air drag does act, along with slight friction with the lane, and the ball slows. This doesn't violate the law of inertia because external forces indeed act.

21. In mechanical equilibrium, the vector sum of all forces, the net force, necessarily equals zero: $\Sigma F = 0$.

23. If only a single nonzero force acts on an object, it will not be in mechanical equilibrium. There would have to be another or other forces to result in a zero net force for equilibrium.

25. If the puck moves in a straight line with unchanging speed, the forces of friction are negligible. Then the net force is practically zero, and the puck can be considered to be in dynamic equilibrium.

27. From the equilibrium rule, $\Sigma F = 0$, the upward forces are 400 N + tension in the right scale. This sum must equal the downward forces 250 N + 300 N + 300 N. Arithmetic shows the reading on the right scale is 450 N.

29. In the left figure, Harry is supported by two strands of rope that share his weight (like the little girl in Exercise 28). So each strand supports only 250 N, below the breaking point. Total force up supplied by ropes equals weight acting downward, giving a net force of zero and no acceleration. In the right figure, Harry is now supported by one strand, which for Harry's well-being requires that the tension be 500 N. Since this is above the breaking point of the rope, it breaks. The net force on Harry is then only his weight, giving him a downward acceleration of g. The sudden return to zero velocity changes his vacation plans.

31. The upper limit he can lift is a load equal to his weight. Beyond that he leaves the ground!

33. The force that prevents downward acceleration is the normal force—the table pushing up on the book.

35. Normal force is greatest when the table surface is horizontal, and progressively decreases as the angle of tilt increases. As the angle of tilt approaches 90°, the normal force approaches zero. When the table surface is vertical, it no longer presses on the book, which then freely falls.

37. When standing on a floor, the floor pushes upward against your feet with a force equal to that of your weight. This upward force (called the normal force) and your weight are oppositely directed, and since they both act on the same body, you, they cancel to produce a net force on you of zero—hence, you are not accelerated.

39. Without water, the support force is W. With water, the support force is $W + w$.

41. The friction force is 600 N for constant speed. Only then will $\Sigma F = 0$.

43. The net force on the rope is zero, provided by each person pulling with 300 N in opposite directions.

45. A stone will fall vertically if released from rest. If the stone is dropped from the top of the mast of a moving ship, the horizontal motion is not changed when the stone is dropped—providing air drag on the stone is negligible and the ship's motion is steady and straight. From the frame of reference of the moving ship, the stone falls in a vertical straight-line path, landing at the base of the mast.

47. We aren't swept off because we are traveling just as fast as the Earth, just as in a fast-moving vehicle you move along with the vehicle. Also, there is no atmosphere through which the Earth moves, which would do more than blow our hats off!

49. This is similar to Exercise 45. If the ball is shot while the train is moving at constant velocity (constant speed in a straight line), its horizontal motion before, during, and after being fired is the same as that of the train; so the ball falls back into the chimney as it would have if the train were at rest. If the train changes speed, the ball will miss because the ball's horizontal speed will match the train speed as the ball is fired, but not when the ball lands. Similarly, on a circular track the ball will also miss the chimney because the ball will move along a tangent to the track while the train turns away from this tangent. So the ball returns to the chimney in the first case, and misses in the second and third cases because of the *change* in motion.

ANSWERS TO CHAPTER 3 EXERCISES (Linear Motion)

1. The impact speed will be the relative speed, 2 km/h (100 km/h – 98 km/h = 2 km/h).

3. Your fine for speeding is based on your instantaneous speed; the speed registered on a speedometer or a radar gun.

5. Constant velocity means no acceleration, so the acceleration of light is zero.

7. Although the car moves at the speed limit relative to the ground, it approaches you at twice the speed limit.

9. Yes, again, velocity and acceleration need not be in the same direction. A ball tossed upward, for example, reverses its direction of travel at its highest point while its acceleration g, directed downward, remains constant (this idea will be explained further in Chapter 4). Note that if a ball had zero acceleration at a point where its speed is zero, its speed would *remain* zero. It would sit still at the top of its trajectory!

11. "The dragster rounded the curve at a constant speed of 100 km/h." Constant velocity means not only constant speed but constant direction. A car rounding a curve changes its direction of motion.

13. You cannot say which car underwent the greater acceleration unless you know the times involved.

15. Any object moving in a circle or along a curve is changing velocity (accelerating) even if its speed is constant because direction is changing. Something with constant velocity has both constant direction *and* constant speed, so there is no example of motion with constant velocity and varying speed.

17. (a) Yes. For example, an object sliding or rolling horizontally on a frictionless plane.
    (b) Yes. For example, a vertically thrown ball at the top of its trajectory.

19. Only on the middle hill does the acceleration along the path decrease with time, for the hill becomes less steep as motion progresses. When the hill levels off, acceleration will be zero. On the left hill, acceleration is constant. On the right hill, acceleration increases as the hill becomes steeper. In all three cases, speed increases.

21. The acceleration is zero, for no change in velocity occurs. Whenever the change in velocity is zero, the acceleration is zero. If the velocity is "steady," "constant," or "uniform," the change in velocity is zero. Remember the definition of acceleration!

23. At 90° the acceleration is that of free fall, g. At 0° the acceleration is zero. So the range of accelerations is 0 to g, or 0 to 9.8 m/s².

25. Speed readings would increase by 10 m/s each second.

27. The acceleration of free fall at the end of the 5th, 10th, or any number of seconds will be g. Its *velocity* has different values at different times, but since it is free from the effects of air resistance, its *acceleration* remains a constant g.

29. Whether up or down, the rate of change of speed with respect to time is 10 m/s² (or 9.8 m/s²), so each second while going up the speed decreases by 10 m/s (or 9.8 m/s). Coming down, the speed increases 10 m/s (or 9.8 m/s) each second. So when air resistance can be neglected, the time going up equals the time coming down.

31. When air drag affects motion, the ball thrown upward returns to its starting level with less speed than its initial speed; and also less speed than the ball tossed downward. So the downward thrown ball hits the ground below with a greater speed.

33. Its acceleration would actually be less if the air resistance it encounters at high speed retards its motion. (We will treat this concept in detail in Chapter 4.)

196

35. The acceleration due to gravity remains a constant g at all points along its path as long as no other forces like air drag act on the projectile.

37.

Time (in seconds)	Velocity (in meters/second)	Distance (in meters)
0	0	0
1	10	5
2	20	20
3	30	45
4	40	80
5	50	125
6	60	180
7	70	245
8	80	320
9	90	405
10	100	500

39. Air resistance decreases speed. So a tossed ball will return with less speed than it possessed initially.

41. (a) Average speed is greater for the ball on track B.
(b) The instantaneous speed at the ends of the tracks is the same because the speed gained on the down-ramp for B is equal to the speed lost on the up-ramp side. (Many people get the wrong answer for Exercise 40 because they assume that because the balls end up with the same speed that they roll for the same time. Not so.)

43. As water falls it picks up speed. Since the same amount of water issues from the faucet each second, it stretches out as distance increases. It becomes thinner just as taffy that is stretched gets thinner the more it is stretched. When the water is stretched too far, it breaks up into droplets.

45. Open exercise.

SOLUTIONS TO CHAPTER 3 PROBLEMS

1. From $v = \dfrac{d}{t}$, $t = \dfrac{d}{v}$. We convert 3 m to 3000 mm, and $t = \dfrac{3000\ \text{nm}}{1.5\ \text{mm}/\text{year}} = $ **2000 years.**

3. Since it starts going up at 30 m/s and loses 10 m/s each second, its time going up is 3 seconds. Its time returning is also 3 seconds, so it's in the air for a total of 6 seconds. Distance up (or down) is $1/2gt^2 = 5 \times 3^2 = $ **45 m**. Or from $d = vt$, where average velocity is $(30 + 0)/2 = 15$ m/s, and time is 3 seconds, we also get $d = 15$ m/s $\times$ 3 s = 45 m.

5. Using $g = 10$ m/s^2, we see that $v = gt = (10$ m/s$^2)(10$ s$) = 100$ m/s;
$$v_{av} = \frac{(v_{beginning} + v_{final})}{2} = \frac{(0 + 100)}{2} = \textbf{50 m/s, downward.}$$
We can get "how far" from either $d = v_{av}t = (50$ m/s$)(10$ s$) = $ **500 m,**
or equivalently, $d = 1/2gt^2 = 5(10)^2 = 500$ m.
(Physics is nice...we get the same distance using either formula!)

7. Average speed = total distance traveled/time taken = 1200 km/total time. Time for the first leg of trip = 600 km/200 km/h = 3 h. Time for last leg of trip = 600 km/300 km/h = 2 h. So total time is 5 h. Then average speed = 1200 km/5 h = **240 km/h.** (Note you can't use the formula average speed = beginning speed + end speed divided by two—which applies for constant acceleration only.)

9. Drops would be in free fall and accelerate at g. Gain in speed = gt, so we need to find the time of fall. From $d = 1/2gt^2$, $t = \sqrt{2d/g} = \sqrt{2000\ \text{m}/10\ \text{m/s}^2} = 14.1$ s. So gain in speed = $(10$ m/s$^2)(14.1$ s$) = $ **141 m/s** (more than 300 miles per hour)!

ANSWERS TO CHAPTER 4 EXERCISES (Newton's Second Law of Motion)

1. Yes, as illustrated by a ball thrown vertically into the air. Its velocity is initially up, and finally down, all the while accelerating at a constant g.

3. No. An object can move in a curve only when a force acts. With no force its path would be a straight line.

5. No, inertia involves mass, not weight.

7. Sliding down at constant velocity means acceleration is zero and the net force is zero. This can occur if friction equals the bear's weight, which is 4000 N. Friction = bear's weight = mg = (400 kg)(10 m/ s^2) = 4000 N.

9. Shake the boxes. The box that offers the greater resistance to acceleration is the more massive box, the one containing the sand.

11. A massive cleaver is more effective in chopping vegetables because its greater mass contributes to greater tendency to keep moving as the cleaver chops.

13. Neither the mass nor the weight of a junked car changes when it is crushed. What does change is its volume, not to be confused with mass and weight.

15. A dieting person loses mass. Interestingly, a person can lose weight by simply being farther from the center of the Earth, at the top of a mountain, for example.

17. One kg of mass corresponds to 2.2 pounds of weight at the Earth's surface. As an example for your weight, if you weigh 100 pounds, your mass is 100 lb/2.2 kg/lb= 45 kg. Your weight in newtons, using the relationship weight = mg, is then 45 kg × 9.8 N/kg= 441 N.

19. Friction is the force that keeps the crate picking up the same amount of speed as the truck. With no friction, the accelerating truck would leave the crate behind.

21. To see why the acceleration gains as a rocket burns its fuel, look at the equation $a = F/m$. As fuel is burned, the mass of the rocket becomes less. As m decreases, a increases! There is simply less mass to be accelerated as fuel is consumed.

23. Rate of gain in speed (acceleration), is the ratio force/mass (Newton's second law), which in free fall is just weight/mass. Since weight is proportional to mass, the ratio weight/mass is the same whatever the weight of a body. So all freely falling bodies undergo the same gain in speed—g (illustrated in Figures 4.12 and 4.13). Although weight doesn't affect speed in free fall, weight does affect falling speed when air resistance is present (nonfree fall).

25. The forces acting horizontally are the driving force provided by friction between the tires and the road, and resistive forces—mainly air drag. These forces cancel and the car is in dynamic equilibrium with a net force of zero.

27. Note that 30 N pulls 3 blocks. To pull 2 blocks then requires a 20-N pull, which is the tension in the rope between the second and third block. Tension in the rope that pulls only the third block is therefore 10 N. (Note that the net force on the first block, 30 N – 20 N = 10 N, is the force needed to accelerate that block, having one-third of the total mass.)

29. The velocity of the ascending coin decreases while its acceleration remains constant (in the absence of air resistance).

31. The force vector mg is the same at all locations. Acceleration g is therefore the same at all locations also.

33. At the top of your jump your acceleration is *g*. Let the equation for acceleration via Newton's second law guide your thinking: $a = F/m = mg/m = g$. If you said zero, you're implying the force of gravity ceases to act at the top of your jump—not so.

35. When you stop suddenly, your velocity changes rapidly, which means a large acceleration of stopping. By Newton's second law, this means the force that acts on you is also large. Experiencing a large force is what hurts you.

37. When you drive at constant velocity, the zero net force on the car is the resultant of the driving force that your engine supplies against the friction drag force. You continue to apply a driving force to offset the drag force that otherwise would slow the car.

39. When held at rest the upward support force equals the gravitational force on the apple and the net force is zero. When released, the upward support force is no longer there and the net force is the gravitational force, 1 N. (If the apple falls fast enough for air resistance to be important, then the net force will be less than 1 N, and eventually can reach zero if air resistance builds up to 1 N.)

41. Both forces have the same magnitude. This is easier to understand if you visualize the parachutist at rest in a strong updraft—static equilibrium. Whether equilibrium is static or dynamic, the net force is zero.

43. The net force is *mg*, 10 N (or more precisely, 9.8 N).

45. Agree with your friend. Although acceleration decreases, the ball is nevertheless gaining speed. It will do so until it reaches terminal speed. Only then will it not continue gaining speed.

47. In each case the paper reaches terminal speed, which means air drag equals the weight of the paper. So air resistance will be the same on each! Of course the wadded paper falls faster for air resistance to equal the weight of the paper.

49. When anything falls at constant velocity, air drag and gravitational force are equal in magnitude. Raindrops are merely one example.

51. When a parachutist opens her chute she slows down. That means she accelerates upward.

53. Just before a falling body attains terminal velocity, there is still a downward acceleration because gravitational force is still greater than air resistance. When the air resistance builds up to equal the gravitational force, terminal velocity is reached. Then air resistance is equal and opposite to gravitational force.

55. The sphere will be in equilibrium when it reaches terminal speed—which occurs when the gravitational force on it is balanced by an equal and opposite force of fluid drag.

57. The heavier tennis ball will strike the ground first for the same reason the heavier parachutist in Figure 4.15 strikes the ground first. Note that although the air resistance on the heavier ball is smaller relative to the weight of the ball, it is actually greater than the air resistance that acts on the other ball. Why? Because the heavier ball falls faster, and air resistance is greater for greater speed.

59. The ball rises in less time than it falls. By exaggerating the circumstance and considering the feather example in the answer to Exercise 58, the time for the feather to flutter from its maximum altitude is clearly longer than the time it took to attain that altitude. The same is true for the not-so-obvious case of the ball.

SOLUTIONS TO CHAPTER 4 PROBLEMS

1. Acceleration = F/m = 0.9 mg/m = **0.9 g**.

3. Weight of the pail is mg = 20 kg × 10 m/s² = 200 N.
   So $a = F/m$ = (300 N – 200 N)/(20 kg) = **5 m/s²**.

5. For the jumbo jet: $a = F/m$ = 4(30,000 N)/30,000 kg = **4 m/s²**.

7. Net force (downward) = ma = (80 kg)(4 m/s²) = 320 N. Gravity is pulling him downward with a force of (80 kg)(10 m/s²) = 800 N, so the upward force of friction is 800 N – 320 N = **480 N**.

9. (a) a = (change of v)/t = (1 m/s)/(2 s) = **0.5 m/s²**.

   (b) $F = ma$ = (60 kg)(0.5 m/s²) = **30 N**.

ANSWERS TO CHAPTER 5 EXERCISES (Newton's Third Law of Motion)

1. When pushing backward on the floor your foot tends to move backward. Friction opposes this motion and acts in the opposite direction—forward. Hence friction against your foot moves you forward.

3. No, for each hand pushes equally on the other in accord with Newton's third law—you cannot push harder on one hand than the other.

5. (a) Two force pairs act; Earth's pull on the apple (action), and the apple's pull on the Earth (reaction). Hand pushes apple upward (action), and apple pushes hand downward (reaction). (b) If air drag can be neglected, one force pair acts; Earth's pull on apple, and apple's pull on Earth. If air drag counts, then air pushes upward on apple (action) and apple pushes downward on air (reaction).

7. (a) Action; bat hits ball. Reaction; ball hits bat. (b) While in flight there are two interactions, one with the Earth's gravity and the other with the air. Action; Earth pulls down on ball (weight). Reaction; ball pulls up on Earth. And, action; air pushes ball, and reaction; ball pushes air.

9. When the ball exerts a force on the floor, the floor exerts an equal and opposite force on the ball—hence bouncing. The force of the floor on the ball provides the bounce.

11. Yes, it's true. The Earth can't pull you downward without you simultaneously pulling Earth upward. The acceleration of Earth is negligibly small, and not noticed, due to its enormous mass.

13. The scale will read 100 N, the same it would read if one of the ends were tied to a wall instead of tied to the 100-N hanging weight. Although the net force on the system is zero, the tension in the rope within the system is 100 N, as shown on the scale reading.

15. The forces must be equal and opposite because they are the only forces acting on the person, who obviously is not accelerating. Note that the pair of forces do *not* comprise an action-reaction pair, however, for they act on the *same* body. The downward force, the man's weight, *Earth pulls down on man*; has the reaction *man pulls up on Earth*, not the floor pushing up on him. And the upward force of the floor on the man has the reaction of man against the floor, not the interaction between the man and Earth. (If you find this confusing, you may take solace in the fact that Newton himself had trouble applying his 3rd law to certain situations. Apply the rule, A on B reacts to B on A, as in Figure 5.7.)

17. Yes, a baseball exerts an external force on the bat, opposite to the bat's motion. This external force decelerates the oncoming bat.

19. When you push the car, you exert a force on the car. When the car simultaneously pushes back on you, that force is on you—not the car. You don't cancel a force on the car with a force on you. For cancellation, the forces have to be equal and opposite and act on the same object.

21. The strong man can exert only equal forces on both cars, just as your push against a wall equals the push of the wall on you. Likewise for two walls, or two freight cars. Since their masses are equal, they will undergo equal accelerations and move equally.

23. The friction on the crate is 200 N, which cancels your 200-N push on the crate to yield the zero net force that accounts for the constant velocity (zero acceleration). Although the friction force is equal and oppositely directed to the applied force, the two do *not* make an action-reaction pair of forces. That's because both forces *do* act on the same object—the crate. The reaction to your push on the crate is the crate's push back on you. The reaction to the frictional force of the floor on the crate is the opposite friction force of the crate on the floor.

25. Both will move. Ken's pull on the rope is transmitted to Joanne, causing her to accelerate toward him. By Newton's third law, the rope pulls back on Ken, causing him to accelerate toward Joanne.

27. The tension in the rope is 250 N. Since they aren't accelerating, each must experience a 250-N force of friction via the ground. This is provided by pushing against the ground with 250 N.

29. The forces on each are the same in magnitude, and their masses are the same, so their accelerations will be the same. They will slide equal distances of 6 meters to meet at the midpoint.

31. Vector quantities are velocity and acceleration. All others are scalars.

33. A pair of vectors can cancel only if they are equal in magnitude and opposite in direction. But three unequal vectors can combine to equal zero—the vectors comprising the tensions in the ropes that support Nellie in Figure 5.26, for example.

35. No, no, no. A vector quantity and scalar quantity can never be added.

37. Tension will be greater for a small sag. That's because large vectors in each side of the rope supporting the bird are needed for a resultant that is equal and opposite to the bird's weight.

39. By the parallelogram rule, the tension is greater than 50 N.

41. To climb upward means pulling the rope downward, which moves the balloon downward as the person climbs.

43. (a) The other vector is upward as shown.

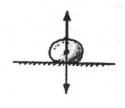

    (b) It is called the normal force.

45. (a) As shown.

    (b) Upward tension force is greater resulting in an upward net force.

47. The acceleration of the stone at the top of its path, or anywhere where the net force on the stone is *mg*, is *g*.

49. (a) As shown.

    (b) Note the resultant of the normals is equal and opposite to the stone's weight.

SOLUTIONS TO CHAPTER 5 PROBLEMS

1. $F = ma = m\Delta v/\Delta t = (0.003\text{ kg})(25\text{ m/s})/(0.05\text{ s}) = \textbf{1.5 N}$, which is about $^1/_3$ pound.

3. They hit your face with the resultant of the horizontal and vertical components:
   $R = \sqrt{[(3.0\text{ m/s})^2 + (4.0\text{ m/s})^2]} = \textbf{5 m/s}$.

5. Ground velocity $V = \sqrt{[(100\text{ km/h})^2 + (100\text{ km/h})^2]} = \textbf{141 km/h, 45° northeast}$ (45° from the direction of the wind). The velocity relative to the ground makes the diagonal of a 45°-45°-90° triangle.

ANSWERS TO CHAPTER 6 EXERCISES (Momentum)

1. Supertankers are so massive, that even at modest speeds their motional inertia, or *momenta*, are enormous. This means enormous impulses are needed for changing motion. How can large impulses be produced with modest forces? By applying modest forces over long periods of time. Hence the force of the water resistance over the time it takes to coast 25 kilometers sufficiently reduces the momentum.

3. Air bags lengthen the time of impact thereby reducing the force of impact.

5. This illustrates the same point as Exercise 4. The time during which momentum decreases is lengthened, thereby decreasing the jolting force of the rope. Note that in this and other examples that bringing a person to a stop more gently does *not* reduce the impulse. It only reduces the force.

7. Bent knees will allow more time for momentum to decrease, therefore reducing the force of landing.

9. Extended hands allow more time for reducing the momentum of the ball to zero, resulting in a smaller force of impact on your hands.

11. The blades impart a downward impulse to the air and produce a downward change in the momentum of the air. The air at the same time exerts an upward impulse on the blades, providing lift. (Newton's third law applies to impulses as well as forces.)

13. The impulse required to stop the heavy truck is considerably more than the impulse required to stop a skateboard moving with the same speed. The *force* required to stop either, however, depends on the time during which it is applied. Stopping the skateboard in a split second results in a certain force. Apply less than this amount of force on the moving truck and given enough time, the truck will come to a halt.

15. The large momentum of the spurting water is met by a recoil that makes the hose difficult to hold, just as a shotgun is difficult to hold when it fires birdshot.

17. Impulse is force × time. The forces are equal and opposite, by Newton's third law, and the times are the same, so the impulses are equal and opposite.

19. The momentum of the falling apple is transferred to the Earth. Interestingly enough, when the apple is released, the Earth and the apple move toward each other with equal and oppositely directed momenta. Because of the Earth's enormous mass, its motion is imperceptible. When the apple and Earth hit each other, their momenta are brought to a halt—zero, the same value as before.

21. The lighter gloves have less padding, and less ability to extend the time of impact, and therefore result in greater forces of impact for a given punch.

23. Without this slack, a locomotive might simply sit still and spin its wheels. The loose coupling enables a longer time for the entire train to gain momentum, requiring less force of the locomotive wheels against the track. In this way, the overall required impulse is broken into a series of smaller impulses. (This loose coupling can be very important for braking as well.)

25. In jumping, you impart the same momentum to both you and the canoe. This means you jump from a canoe that is moving away from the dock, reducing your speed relative to the dock, so you don't jump as far as you expected to.

27. To get to shore, the person may throw keys, coins or an item of clothing. The momentum of what is thrown will be accompanied by the thrower's oppositely-directed momentum. In this way, one can recoil towards shore. (One can also inhale facing the shore and exhale facing away from the shore.)

29. Regarding Exercise 27; If one throws clothing, the force that accelerates the clothes will be paired with an equal and opposite force on the thrower. This force can provide recoil toward

shore. Regarding Exercise 28; According to Newton's third law, whatever forces you exert on the ball, first in one direction, then in the other, are balanced by equal forces that the ball exerts on you. Since the forces on the ball give it no final momentum, the forces it exerts on you also give no final momentum.

31. When two objects interact, the forces they exert on each other are equal and opposite and these forces act for the same time, so the impulses are equal and opposite. Therefore their changes of momenta are equal and opposite, and the total change of momentum of the two objects is zero.

33. Momentum is not conserved for the ball itself because an impulse is exerted on it (gravitational force × time). So the ball gains momentum. It is in the *absence* of an external force that momentum doesn't change. If the whole Earth and the rolling ball are taken together as a system, then the gravitational interaction between the Earth and the ball are internal forces and no external impulse acts. Then the momentum of the ball is accompanied by an equal and opposite momentum of the Earth, which results in no change in momentum.

35. A system is any object or collection of objects. Whatever momentum such a system has, in the absence of external forces, that momentum remains unchanged—what the conservation of momentum is about.

37. For the system comprised of ball + Earth, momentum is conserved for the impulses acting are internal impulses. The momentum of the falling apple is equal in magnitude to the momentum of the Earth toward the apple.

39. Let the system be the car and the Earth together. As the car gains downward momentum during its fall, the Earth gains equal upward momentum. When the car crashes and its momentum is reduced to zero, the Earth stops its upward motion, also reducing its momentum to zero.

41. The craft moves to the right. This is because there are two impulses that act on the craft: One is that of the wind against the sail, and the other is that of the fan recoiling from the wind it produces. These impulses are oppositely directed, but are they equal in magnitude? No, because of bouncing. The wind bounces from the sail and produces a greater impulse than if it merely stopped. This greater impulse on the sail produces a net impulse in the forward direction, toward the right. We can see this in terms of forces as well. Note in the sketch there are two force pairs to consider: (1) the fan-air force pair, and (2) the air-sail force pair. Because of bouncing, the air-sail pair is greater. Solid vectors show forces exerted on the craft; dashed vectors show forces exerted on the air. The net force on the craft is forward, to the right. The principle described here is applied in thrust reversers used to slow jet planes after they land. Also, you can see that after the fan is turned on, there is a net motion of air to the left, so the boat, to conserve momentum, will move to the right.

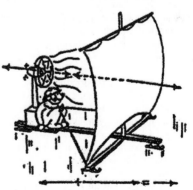

43. Removing the sail and turning the fan around is the best means of propelling the boat! Then maximum impulse is exerted on the craft. If the fan is not turned around, the boat is propelled backward, to the left. (Such propeller-driven boats are used where the water is very shallow, as in the Florida Everglades.)

45. Yes, because you push upward on the ball you toss, which means the ball pushes downward on you, which is transmitted to the ground. So normal force increases as the ball is thrown (and goes back to equal *mg* after the ball is released).

47. In accord with Newton's third law, the forces on each are equal in magnitude, which means the impulses are likewise equal in magnitude, which means both undergo equal changes in momentum.

49. Cars brought to a rapid halt experience a change in momentum, and a corresponding impulse. But greater momentum change occurs if the cars bounce, with correspondingly greater impulse and therefore greater damage. Less damage results if the cars stick upon impact than if they bounce apart.

51. In terms of force: When the sand lands on the cart it is brought up to the cart's speed. This means a horizontal force provided by the cart acts on the sand. By action-reaction, the sand exerts a force on the cart in the opposite direction—which slows the cart. In terms of momentum conservation: Since no external forces act in the horizontal direction, the momentum after the cart catches sand equals the momentum before. Since mass is added, velocity must decrease.

53. We assume the equal strengths of the astronauts means that each throws with the same speed. Since the masses are equal, when the first throws the second, both the first and second move away from each other at equal speeds. Say the thrown astronaut moves to the right with velocity V, and the first recoils with velocity $-V$. When the third makes the catch, both she and the second move to the right at velocity $V/2$ (twice the mass moving at half the speed, like the freight cars in Figure 6.11). When the third makes her throw, she recoils at velocity V (the same speed she imparts to the thrown astronaut) which is added to the $V/2$ she acquired in the catch. So her velocity is $V + V/2 = 3V/2$, to the right—too fast to stay in the game. Why? Because the velocity of the second astronaut is $V/2 - V = -V/2$, to the left—too slow to catch up with the first astronaut who is still moving at $-V$. The game is over. Both the first and the third got to throw the second astronaut only once!

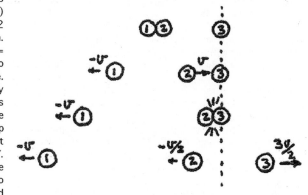

55. The impulse will be greater if the hand is made to bounce because there is a greater change in the momentum of hand and arm, accompanied by a greater impulse. The force exerted on the bricks is equal and opposite to the force of the bricks on the hand. Fortunately, the hand is resilient and toughened by long practice.

57. Their masses are the same; half speed for the coupled particles means equal masses for the colliding and the target particles. This is like the freight cars of equal mass shown in Figure 6.14.

59. If a ball does not hit straight on, then the target ball flies off at an angle (to the left, say) and has a component of momentum sideways to the initial momentum of the moving ball. To offset this, the striking ball cannot be simply brought to rest, but must fly off in the other direction (say, the right). It will do this in such a way that its sideways component of momentum is equal and opposite to that of the target ball. This means the total sideways momentum is zero—what it was before collision. (See how the sideways components of momentum cancel to zero in Figure 6.19.)

SOLUTIONS TO CHAPTER 6 PROBLEMS

1. $Ft = \Delta mv$, $F = \Delta mv/t$ = (50 kg)(4 m/s)/3 s = **66.7 N**.

3. From $Ft = \Delta mv$, $F = \dfrac{\Delta mv}{t}$ $\quad$ = [(75 kg)(25 m/s)]/0.1 s = **18,750 N**.

5. Momentum of the caught ball is (0.15 kg)(40 m/s) = 6.0 kg·m/s.

   (a) The impulse to produce this change of momentum has the same magnitude, **6.0 N·s**.

   (b) From $Ft = \Delta mv$, $F = \Delta mv/t$ = [(0.15 kg)(40 m/s)]/0.03 s = **200 N**.

7. The answer is 4 km/h. Let m be the mass of the freight car, and $4m$ the mass of the diesel engine, and v the speed after both have coupled together. Before collision, the total momentum is due only to the diesel engine, $4m$(5 km/h), because the momentum of the freight car is 0. After collision, the combined mass is ($4m + m$), and combined momentum is ($4m + m$)v. By the conservation of momentum equation:

   Momentum$_{before}$ = momentum$_{after}$
   $4m$(5 km/h) + 0 = ($4m + m$)v
   $v = \dfrac{(20m\text{·km/h})}{5m}$ $\quad$ = **4 km/h**
   (Note that you don't have to know m to solve the problem.)

9. By momentum conservation,
   asteroid mass × 800 m/s = Superman's mass × v.
   Since asteroid's mass is 1000 times Superman's,
   ($1000m$)(800 m/s) = mv
   v = **800,000 m/s**. This is nearly 2 million miles per hour!

ANSWERS TO CHAPTER 7 EXERCISES (Energy)

1. It is easier to stop a lightly loaded truck than a heavier one moving at the same speed because it has less KE and will therefore require less work to stop. (An answer in terms of impulse and momentum is also acceptable.)

3. Zero work, for negligible horizontal force acts on the backpack.

5. Although no work is done on the wall, work is nevertheless done on internal parts of your body (which generate heat).

7. Work done by each is the same, for they reach the same height. The one who climbs in 30 s uses more power because work is done in a shorter time.

9. The PE of the drawn bow as calculated would be an overestimate, (in fact, about twice its actual value) because the force applied in drawing the bow begins at zero and increases to its maximum value when fully drawn. It's easy to see that less force and therefore less work is required to draw the bow halfway than to draw it the second half of the way to its fully-drawn position. So the work done is not *maximum force × distance drawn*, but *average force × distance drawn*. In this case where force varies almost directly with distance (and not as the square or some other complicated factor) the average force is simply equal to the initial force + final force, divided by 2. So the PE is equal to the average force applied (which would be approximately half the force at its full-drawn position) multiplied by the distance through which the arrow is drawn.

11. When a rifle with a long barrel is fired, more work is done as the bullet is pushed through the longer distance. A greater KE is the result of the greater work, so of course, the bullet emerges with a greater velocity. (It might be mentioned that the force acting on the bullet is not constant, but decreases with increasing distance inside the barrel.)

13. The KE of the tossed ball relative to occupants in the airplane does not depend on the speed of the airplane. The KE of the ball relative to observers on the ground below, however, is a different matter. KE, like velocity, is relative. See the answer to the Check Yourself question 2 in the textbook following Figure 7.11.

15. The energies go into frictional heating of the tires, the runway, and the air.

17. For the same KE, the baseball is traveling very fast compared with the bowling ball, whose KE has more to do with its mass. The bowling ball is therefore safer to catch. Exaggerate: Which is safer, being hit with a bullet or being bumped by a car with the same KE?

19. The KE of a pendulum bob is maximum where it moves fastest, at the lowest point; PE is maximum at the uppermost points. When the pendulum bob swings by the point that marks half its maximum height, it has half its maximum KE, and its PE is halfway between its minimum and maximum values. If we define PE = 0 at the bottom of the swing, the place where KE is half its maximum value is also the place where PE is half its maximum value, and KE = PE at this point. (In accordance with energy conservation: Total energy = KE + PE.)

21. Yes to both, relative to Earth, because work was done to lift it in Earth's gravitational field and to impart speed to it.

23. According to the work-energy theorem, twice the speed corresponds to 4 times the energy, and therefore 4 times the driving distance. At 3 times the speed, driving distance is 9 times as much.

25. On the hill there is a component of gravitational force in the direction of the car's motion. This component of force does work on the car. But on the level, there is no component of gravitational force along the direction of the car's motion, so the force of gravity does no work in this case.

27. The fact that the crate pulls back on the rope in action-reaction fashion is irrelevant. The work done on the crate by the rope is the horizontal component of rope force that acts on the crate

multiplied by the distance the crate is moved by that force—period. How much of this work produces KE or thermal energy depends on the amount of friction acting.

29. A Superball will bounce higher than its original height if thrown downward, but if simply dropped, no way. Such would violate the conservation of energy.

31. Kinetic energy is a maximum as soon as the ball leaves the hand. Potential energy is a maximum when the ball has reached its zenith.

33. You agree with your second classmate. The coaster could just as well encounter a low summit before or after a higher one, so long as the higher one is enough lower than the initial summit to compensate for energy dissipation by friction.

35. Except for the very center of the plane, the force of gravity acts at an angle to the plane, with a component of gravitational force along the plane—along the block's path. Hence the block goes somewhat against gravity when moving away from the central position, and moves somewhat with gravity when coming back. As the object slides farther out on the plane, it is effectively traveling "upward" against Earth's gravity, and slows down. It finally comes to rest and then slides back and the process repeats itself. The block slides back and forth along the plane. From a flat-Earth point of view the situation is equivalent to that shown in the sketch.

37. Yes, a car burns more gasoline when its lights are on. The overall consumption of gasoline does not depend on whether or not the engine is running. Lights and other devices run off the battery, which "run down" the battery. The energy used to recharge the battery ultimately comes from the gasoline.

39. Sufficient work occurs because with each pump of the jack handle, the force she exerts acts over a much greater distance than the car is. A small force acting over a long distance can do significant work.

41. Your friend may not realize that mass itself is congealed energy, so you tell your friend that much more energy in its congealed form is put into the reactor than is taken out from the reactor. Almost 1% of the mass of fission fuel is converted to energy of other forms.

43. The work that the rock does on the ground is equal to its PE before being dropped, $mgh = 100$ joules. The force of impact, however, depends on the distance that the rock penetrates into the ground. If we do not know this distance we cannot calculate the force. (If we knew the time during which the impulse occurs we could calculate the force from the impulse-momentum relationship—but not knowing the distance or time of the rock's penetration into the ground, we cannot calculate the force.)

45. When air resistance is a factor, the ball will return with less speed (discussed in Exercise 49 in Chapter 4). It therefore will have less KE. You can see this directly from the fact that the ball loses mechanical energy to the air molecules it encounters, so when it returns to its starting point and to its original PE, it will have less KE. This does not contradict energy conservation, for energy is dissipated, not destroyed.

47. The other 15 horsepower is supplied by electric energy from the batteries.

49. The question can be restated; Is $(30^2 - 20^2)$ greater or less than $(20^2 - 10^2)$? We see that $(30^2 - 20^2) = (900 - 400) = 500$, which is considerably greater than $(20^2 - 10^2) = (400 - 100) = 300$. So KE changes more for a given Δv at the higher speed.

51. When the mass is doubled with no change in speed, both momentum and KE are doubled.

53. Both have the same momentum, but the 1-kg one, the faster one, has the greater KE.

55. Zero KE means zero speed, so momentum is also zero.

57. Not at all. A low-mass object moving at high speed can have the same KE as a high-mass object moving at low speed.

59. The two skateboarders have equal momenta, but the lighter one has twice the KE and can do twice as much work on you. So choose the collision with the heavier, slower-moving kid and you'll endure less damage.

61. Exaggeration makes the fate of teacher Paul Robinson easier to assess: Paul would not be so calm if the cement block were replaced with the inertia of a small stone, for inertia plays a role in this demonstration. If the block were unbreakable, the energy that busts it up would instead be transferred to the beds of nails. So it is desirable to use a block that will break upon impact. If the bed consisted of a single nail, finding a successor to Paul would be very difficult, so it is important that the bed have plenty of nails!

63. Energy is dissipated into nonuseful forms in an inefficient machine, and is "lost" only in the loose sense of the word. In the strict sense, it can be accounted for and is therefore not lost.

65. In the popular sense, conserving energy means not wasting energy. In the physics sense energy conservation refers to a law of nature that underlies natural processes. Although energy can be wasted (which really means transforming it from a more useful to a less useful form), it cannot be destroyed. Nor can it be created. Energy is transferred or transformed, without gain or loss. That's what a physicist means in saying energy is conserved.

67. Your friend is correct, for changing KE requires work, which means more fuel consumption and decreased air quality.

69. Once used, energy cannot be regenerated, for it dissipates in the environment—inconsistent with the term "renewable energy." Renewable energy refers to energy derived from renewable resources—trees, for example.

SOLUTIONS TO CHAPTER 7 PROBLEMS

1. $W = \Delta E = \Delta mgh = 300$ kg $\times$ 10 N/k $\times$ 6 m = **18,000 J**.

3. The work done by 10 N over a distance of 5 m = 50 J. That by 20 N over 2 m = 40 J. So the 10-N force over 5 m does more work and could produce a greater change in KE.

5. $(F \times d)_{in} = (F \times d)_{out}$.
   50 N $\times$ 1.2 m = W $\times$ 0.2 m.
   $W = [(50$ N$)(1.2$ m$)]/0.2$ m = **300 N**.

7. $(Fd)_{input} = (Fd)_{output}$.
   $(100$ N x 10 cm$)_{input} = ($? x 1 cm$)_{output}$.
   So we see that the output force is **1000 N** (or less if the efficiency is less than 100%).

9. The freight cars have only **half the KE** possessed by the single car before collision. Here's how to figure it:
   $KE_{before} = 1/2\ m\ v^2$.
   $KE_{after} = 1/2\ (2m)(v/2)^2 = 1/2\ (2m)\ v^2/4 = 1/4\ m\ v^2$.
   What becomes of this energy? Most of it goes into nature's graveyard—thermal energy.

11. At 25% efficiency, only $1/4$ of the 40 megajoules in one liter, or 10 MJ, will go into work. This work is
    $F \times d = 500$ N $\times d = 10$ MJ.
    Solve this for d and convert MJ to J, to get
    $d = 10$ MJ/500 N = 10,000,000 J/500 N = 20,000 m = **20 km**.
    So under these conditions, the car gets 20 kilometers per liter (which is 47 miles per gallon).

ANSWERS TO CHAPTER 8 EXERCISES   (Rotational   Motion)

1. Tape moves faster when r is greater, in accord with $v = r\omega$. So the reel with the most-filled reel corresponds to the tape with the greatest linear speed v.

3. Large diameter tires mean you travel farther with each revolution of the tire. So you'll be moving faster than your speedometer indicates. (A speedometer actually measures the RPM of the wheels and displays this as mi/h or km/h. The conversion from RPM to the mi/h or km/h reading assumes the wheels are a certain size.) Oversize wheels give too low a reading because they really travel farther per revolution than the speedometer indicates, and undersize wheels give too high a reading because the wheels do not go as far per revolution.

5. The amount of taper is related to the amount of curve the railroad tracks take. On a curve where the outermost track is say 10% longer than the inner track, the wide part of the wheel will also have to be at least 10% wider than the narrow part. If it's less than this, the outer wheel will rely on the rim to stay on the track, and scraping will occur as the train makes the curve. The "sharper" the curve, the more the taper needs to be on the wheels.

7. The CM is directly above the bird's foot.

9. Rotational inertia and torque are most predominantly illustrated here, and the conservation of angular momentum also plays a role. The long distance to the front wheels increases the rotational inertia of the vehicle relative to the back wheels and also increases the lever arm of the front wheels without appreciably adding to the vehicle's weight. As the back wheels are driven clockwise, the chassis tends to rotate counterclockwise (conservation of angular momentum) and thereby lift the front wheels off the ground. The greater rotational inertia and the increased clockwise torque of the more distant front wheels counter this effect.

11. Friction by the road on the tires produces a torque about the car's CM. When the car accelerates forward, the friction force points forward and rotates the car upward. When braking, the direction of friction is rearward, and the torque rotates the car in the opposite direction so the rear end rotates upward (and the nose downward).

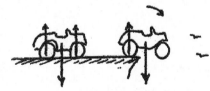

13. The ball to reach the bottom first is the one with the least rotational inertia compared with its mass—that's the hollow basketball.

15. Don't say the same, for the water slides inside the can while the ice is made to roll along with the can. When the water inside slides, it contributes weight rather than rotational inertia to the can. So the can of water will roll faster. (It will even beat a hollow can.)

17. Advise the youngster to use wheels with the least rotational inertia—lightweight solid ones without spokes.

19. In the horizontal position the lever arm equals the length of the sprocket arm, but in the vertical position, the lever arm is zero because the line of action of forces passes right through the axis of rotation. (With cycling cleats, a cyclist pedals in a circle, which means they push their feet over the top of the spoke and pull around the bottom and even pull up on the recovery. This allows torque to be applied over a greater portion of the revolution.)

21. No, because there is zero lever arm about the CM. Zero lever arm means zero torque.

23. Friction between the ball and the lane provides a torque, which rotates the ball.

25. With your legs straight out, your CG is farther away and you exert more torque sitting up. So sit-ups are more difficult with legs straight out.

27. The wobbly motion of a star is an indication that it is revolving about a center of mass that is not at its geometric center, implying that there is some other mass nearby to pull the center of

mass away from the star's center. This is the way in which astronomers have discovered that planets exist around stars other than our own.

29. Two buckets are easier because you may stand upright while carrying a bucket in each hand. With two buckets, the CG will be in the center of the support base provided by your feet, so there is no need to lean. (The same can be accomplished by carrying a single bucket on your head.)

31. The CG of a ball is not above a point of support when the ball is on an incline. The weight of the ball therefore acts at some distance from the point of support which behaves like a fulcrum. A torque is produced and the ball rotates. This is why a ball rolls down a hill.

33. The Earth's atmosphere is a nearly spherical shell, which like a basketball, has its center of mass at its center, i.e., at the center of the Earth.

35. An object is stable when its PE must be raised in order to tip it over, or equivalently, when its PE must be increased before it can topple. By inspection, the first cylinder undergoes the least change in PE compared to its weight in tipping. This is because of its narrow base.

37. The track will remain in equilibrium as the balls roll outward. This is because the CG of the system remains over the fulcrum. For example, suppose the billiard ball has twice the mass of the golf ball. By conservation of momentum, the twice-as-massive ball will roll outward at half the speed of the lighter ball, and at any time be half as far from the starting point as the lighter ball. So there is no CG change in the system of the two balls. We can see also that the torques produced by the weights of the balls multiplied by their relative distances from the fulcrum are equal at all points—because at any time the less massive ball has a correspondingly larger lever arm.

39. In accord with the equation for centripetal force, twice the speed corresponds to four times the force.

41. Newton's first and third laws provide a straight-forward explanation. You tend to move in a straight line (Newton's first law) but are intercepted by the door. You press against the door because the door is pressing against you (Newton's third law). The push by the door provides the centripetal force that keeps you moving in a curved path. Without the door's push, you wouldn't turn with the car—you'd move along a straight line and be "thrown out." No need to invoke centrifugal force.

43. Yes, in accord with $F_c = mv^2/r$. Force is directly proportional to the square of speed.

45. Centripetal force will be adequate when only the radial component of the normal force equals the mass of the car times the square of its speed divided by an appropriate radial distance from the center of the curve.

47.

49. (a) Except for the vertical force of friction, no other vertical force except the weight of the motorcycle + rider exists. Since there is no change of motion in the vertical direction, the force of friction must be equal and opposite to the weight of motorcycle + rider.
(b) The horizontal vector indeed represents the normal force. Since it is the only force acting in the radial direction, horizontally, it is also the centripetal force. So it's both.

51. The rotational inertia of you and the rotating turntable is least when you are at the rotational axis. As you crawl outward, the rotational inertia of the system increases (like the masses held outward in Figure 8.53). In accord with the conservation of angular momentum, as you crawl toward the outer rim, you increase the rotational inertia of the spinning system and decrease

the angular speed. You can also see that if you don't slip as you crawl out, you exert a friction force on the turntable opposite to its direction of rotation, thereby slowing it down.

53. In accord with the conservation of angular momentum, as the radial distance of mass increases, the angular speed decreases. The mass of material used to construct skyscrapers is lifted, slightly increasing the radial distance from the Earth's spin axis. This would tend to slightly decrease the Earth's rate of rotation, which in turn tends to make the days a bit longer. The opposite effect occurs for falling leaves, as their radial distance from the Earth's axis decreases. As a practical matter, these effects are entirely negligible!

55. In accord with the conservation of angular momentum, if mass moves closer to the axis of rotation, rotational speed increases. So the day would be ever so slightly shorter.

57. The angular momentum of the wheel-train system will not change in the absence of an external torque. So when the train moves clockwise, the wheel moves counterclockwise with an equal and opposite angular momentum. When the train stops, the wheel stops. When the train backs up, the wheel moves clockwise. If masses of the train and wheel are equal, they will move with equal speeds (since the mass of the wheel is as far from the axis as the mass of the train—equal masses at equal radial distances having equal rotational inertias). If the train is more massive than the wheel, the wheel will "recoil" with more speed than the train, and vice versa. (This is a favorite demonstration of Paul Robinson, whose children David and Kristen are shown in the photo.)

59. Gravitational force acting on every particle by every other particle causes the cloud to condense. The decreased radius of the cloud is then accompanied by an increased angular speed because of angular momentum conservation. The increased speed results in many stars being thrown out into a dish-like shape.

SOLUTIONS TO CHAPTER 8 PROBLEMS

1. Since the bicycle moves 2 m with each turn of the wheel, and the wheel turns once each second, the linear speed of the bicycle is **2 m/s**.

3. The center of mass of the two weights is where a fulcrum would balance both—where the torques about the fulcrum would balance to zero. Call the distance (lever arm) from the 1-kg weight to the fulcrum x. Then the distance (lever arm) from the fulcrum to the 3-kg weight is (100 – x). Equating torques:

   1x = (100 – x)3
   x = 300 – 3x
   x = 75.

   So the center of mass of the system is just below the **75-cm** mark. Then the three-times-as-massive weight is one-third as far from the fulcrum.

5. The mass of the stick is **1 kg**. (This is a "freebie"; see the Check Yourself question and answer that follows Figure 8.28.)

7. Centripetal force (and "weight" and "g" in the rotating habitat) is directly proportional to radial distance from the hub. At half the radial distance, the g force will be **half** that at his feet. The man will literally be "light-headed." (Gravitational variations of greater than 10% head-to-toe are uncomfortable for most people.)

9. The artist will rotate **3 times per second**. By the conservation of angular momentum, the artist will increase rotation rate by 3. That is

   $I\omega_{before} = I\omega_{after}$
   $I\omega_{before} = [(1/3)I(3\omega)]_{after}$

ANSWERS TO CHAPTER 9 EXERCISES (Gravity)

1. Nothing to be concerned about on this consumer label. It simply states the universal law of gravitation, which applies to *all* products. It looks like the manufacturer knows some physics and has a sense of humor.

3. In accord with the law of inertia, the Moon would move in a straight-line path instead of circling both the Sun and Earth.

5. The force of gravity is the same on each because the masses are the same, as Newton's equation for gravitational force verifies. When dropped the crumpled paper falls faster only because it encounters less air drag than the sheet.

7. Newton didn't know the mass of the Earth, so he couldn't find *G* from the weights of objects, and he didn't have any equipment sensitive enough to measure the tiny forces of gravity between two objects of known mass. This measurement eventually occurred more than a century after Newton with the experiments of Cavendish and Philipp Von Jolly.

9. If gravity between the Moon and its rocks vanished, the rocks, like the Moon, would continue in their orbital path around the Earth. The assumption ignores the law of inertia.

11. Nearer the Moon.

13. In accord with Newton's 3rd law, the weight of the Earth in the gravitational field of the apple is 1 N; the same as the weight of the apple in the Earth's gravitational field.

15. Although the forces are equal, the accelerations are not. The much more massive Earth has much less acceleration than the Moon. Actually Earth and Moon *do* rotate around a common point, but it's not midway between them (which would require both Earth and Moon to have the same mass). The point around which Earth and Moon rotate (called the *barycenter*) is within the Earth about 4600 km from the Earth's center.

17. Letting the equation for gravitation guide your thinking, twice the diameter is twice the radius, which corresponds to $^1/4$ the astronaut's weight at the planet's surface.

19. Your weight would decrease if the Earth expanded with no change in its mass and would increase if the Earth contracted with no change in its mass. Your mass and the Earth's mass don't change, but the distance between you and the Earth's center does change. Force is proportional to the inverse square of this distance.

21. By the geometry of Figure 9.5, tripling the distance from the small source spreads the light over 9 times the area, or 9 m². Five times the distance spreads the light over 25 times the area or 25 m², and for 10 times as far, 100 m².

23. The high-flying jet plane is not in free fall. It moves at approximately constant velocity so a passenger experiences no net force. The upward support force of the seat matches the downward pull of gravity, providing the sensation of weight. The orbiting space vehicle, on the other hand, is in a state of free fall. No support force is offered by a seat, for it falls at the same rate as the passenger. With no support force, the force of gravity on the passenger is not sensed as weight.

25. In a car that drives off a cliff you "float" because the car no longer offers a support force. Both you and the car are in the same state of free fall. But gravity is still acting on you, as evidenced by your acceleration toward the ground. So, by definition, you would be weightless (until air resistance becomes important).

27. The two forces are the normal force and *mg*, which are equal when the elevator doesn't accelerate, and unequal when the elevator accelerates.

29. The jumper is weightless due to the absence of a support force.

31. You disagree, for the force of gravity on orbiting astronauts is almost as strong as at Earth's surface. They feel weightless because of the absence of a support force.

33. The gravitational force varies with distance. At noon you are closer to the Sun. At midnight you are an extra Earth diameter farther away. Therefore the gravitational force of the Sun on you is greater at noon.

35. The gravitational pull of the Sun on the Earth is greater than the gravitational pull of the Moon. The tides, however, are caused by the *differences* in gravitational forces by the Moon on opposite sides of the Earth. The difference in gravitational forces by the Moon on opposite sides of the Earth is greater than the corresponding difference in forces by the stronger pulling but much more distant Sun.

37. No. Tides are caused by differences in gravitational pulls. If there are no differences in pulls, there are no tides.

39. Lowest tides occur along with highest tides—spring tides. So the spring tide cycle consists of higher-than-average high tides followed by lower-than-average low tides (best for digging clams).

41. Because of its relatively small size, different parts of the Mediterranean Sea are essentially equidistant from the Moon (or from the Sun). As a result, one part is not pulled with any appreciably different force than any other part. This results in extremely tiny tides. The same argument applies, with even more force, to smaller bodies of water, such as lakes, ponds, and puddles. In a glass of water under a full Moon you'll detect no tides because no part of the water surface is closer to the Moon than any other part of the surface. Tides are caused by appreciable differences in pulls.

43. Yes, the Earth's tides would be due only to the Sun. They would occur twice per day (every 12 hours instead of every 12.5 hours) due to the Earth's daily rotation.

45. From the nearest body, the Earth.

47. In accord with the inverse-square law, twice as far from the Earth's center diminishes the value of g to $1/4$ its value at the surface or 2.45 m/s^2.

49. Your weight would be less in the mine shaft. One way to explain this is to consider the mass of the Earth above you which pulls upward on you. This effect reduces your weight, just as your weight is reduced if someone pulls upward on you while you're weighing yourself. Or more accurately, we see that you are effectively within a spherical shell in which the gravitational field contribution is zero; and that you are being pulled only by the spherical portion below you. You are lighter the deeper you go, and if the mine shaft were to theoretically continue to the Earth's center, your weight moves closer to zero.

51. More fuel is required for a rocket that leaves the Earth to go to the Moon than the other way around. This is because a rocket must move against the greater gravitational field of the Earth most of the way. (If launched from the Moon to the Earth, then it would be traveling with the Earth's field most of the way.)

53. $F \sim m_1 \, m_2/d^2$, where m_2 is the mass of the Sun (which doesn't change when forming a black hole), m_1 is the mass of the orbiting Earth, and d is the distance between the center of mass of the Earth and the Sun. None of these terms change, so the force F that holds the Earth in orbit does not change. (There may in fact be black holes in the galaxy around which stars or planets orbit.)

55. The misunderstanding here is not distinguishing between a theory and a hypothesis or conjecture. A theory, such as the theory of universal gravitation, is a synthesis of a large body of information that encompasses well-tested and verified hypothesis about nature. Any doubts about the theory have to do with its applications to yet untested situations, not with the theory itself. One of the features of scientific theories is that they undergo refinement with new knowledge. (Einstein's general theory of relativity has taught us that in fact there are limits to the validity of Newton's theory of universal gravitation.)

57. You weigh a tiny bit less in the lower part of a massive building because the mass of the building above pulls upward on you.

59. There is no gravitational field change at the spaceship's location as evidenced by no changes in the terms of the gravitational equation. The mass of the black hole is the same before and after collapse.

SOLUTIONS TO CHAPTER 9 PROBLEMS

1. From $F = GmM/d^2$, $^1/_5$ of d squared is $^1/_{25}$th d^2, which means the force is **25 times** greater.

3. $a = \dfrac{F}{m} = G\dfrac{mM/d^2}{m} = G\dfrac{M}{d^2}$.

5. $g = \dfrac{GM}{d^2} = \dfrac{(6.67 \times 10^{-11})(6.0 \times 10^{24})}{[(6380 + 200) \times 10^3]^2}$ = 9.24 N/kg or 9.24 m/s^2; 9.24/9.8 = 0.94 or **94%.**

ANSWERS TO CHAPTER 10 EXERCISES   (Projectile   and   Satellite   Motion)

1. The divers are in near-free-fall, and as Figure 4.15 back in Chapter 4 shows, falling speed is independent of mass (or weight).

3. Yes, it will hit with a higher speed in the same time because the horizontal (not the vertical) component of motion is greater.

5. The crate will not hit the Porsche, but will crash a distance beyond it determined by the height and speed of the plane.

7. (a) The paths are parabolas. (b) The paths would be straight lines.

9. Minimum speed occurs at the top, which is the same as the horizontal component of velocity anywhere along the path.

11. Kicking the ball at angles greater than 45° sacrifices some distance to gain extra time. A kick greater than 45° doesn't go as far, but stays in the air longer, giving players on the kicker's team a chance to run down field and be close to the player on the other team who catches the ball.

13. The bullet falls beneath the projected line of the barrel. To compensate for the bullet's fall, the barrel is elevated. How much elevation depends on the velocity and distance to the target. Correspondingly, the gunsight is raised so the line of sight from the gunsight to the end of the barrel extends to the target. If a scope is used, it is tilted downward to accomplish the same line of sight

15. Any vertically projected object has zero speed at the top of its trajectory. But if it is fired at an angle, only its vertical component of velocity is zero and the velocity of the projectile at the top is equal to its horizontal component of velocity. This would be 100 m/s when the 141-m/s projectile is fired at 45°.

17. The hang time will be the same, in accord with the answer to Exercise 16. Hang time is related to the vertical height attained in a jump, not on horizontal distance moved across a level floor.

19. Yes, the shuttle is accelerating, as evidenced by its continual change of direction. It accelerates due to the gravitational force between it and the Earth. The acceleration is toward the Earth's center.

21. Neither the speed of a falling object (without air resistance) nor the speed of a satellite in orbit depends on its mass. In both cases, a greater mass (greater inertia) is balanced by a correspondingly greater gravitational force, so the acceleration remains the same ($a = F/m$, Newton's 2nd law).

23. Gravitation supplies the centripetal force on satellites.

25. The initial vertical climb lets the rocket get through the denser, retarding part of the atmosphere most quickly, and is also the best direction at low initial speed, when a large part of the rocket's thrust is needed just to support the rocket's weight. But eventually the rocket must acquire enough tangential speed to remain in orbit without thrust, so it must tilt until finally its path is horizontal.

27. The Moon has no atmosphere (because escape velocity at the Moon's surface is less than the speeds of any atmospheric gases). A satellite 5 km above the Earth's surface is still in considerable atmosphere, as well as in range of some mountain peaks. Atmospheric drag is the factor that most determines orbiting altitude.

29. Consider "Newton's cannon" fired from a tall mountain on Jupiter. To match the wider curvature of much larger Jupiter, and to contend with Jupiter's greater gravitational pull, the cannonball would have to be fired significantly faster. (Orbital speed about Jupiter is about 5 times that for Earth.)

31. Upon slowing it spirals in toward the Earth and in so doing has a component of gravitational force in its direction of motion which causes it to gain speed. Or put another way, in circular orbit the perpendicular component of force does no work on the satellite and it maintains constant speed. But when it slows and spirals toward Earth there is a component of gravitational force that does work to increase the KE of the satellite.

33. A satellite travels faster when closest to the body it orbits. Therefore Earth travels faster about the Sun in December than in June.

35. When descending, a satellite meets the atmosphere at almost orbital speed. When ascending, its speed through the air is considerably less and it attains orbital speed well above air drag.

37. The component along the direction of motion does work on the satellite to change its speed. The component perpendicular to the direction of motion changes its direction of motion.

39. When the velocity of a satellite is everywhere perpendicular to the force of gravity, the orbital path is a circle (see Figure 10.18).

41. No way, for the Earth's center is a focus of the elliptical path (including the special case of a circle), so an Earth satellite orbits the center of the Earth. The plane of a satellite coasting in orbit always intersects the Earth's center.

43. The plane of a satellite coasting in orbit intersects the Earth's center. If its orbit were tilted relative to the equator, it would be sometimes over the Northern Hemisphere, sometimes over the Southern Hemisphere. To stay over a fixed point off the equator, it would have to be following a circle whose center is not at the center of the Earth.

45. Period is greater for satellites farthest from Earth.

47. It could be dropped by firing it straight backward at the same speed of the satellite. Then its speed relative to Earth would be zero, and it would fall straight downward.

49. If the speed of the probe relative to the satellite is the same as the speed of the satellite relative to the Moon, then, like the projected capsule that fell to Earth in Exercise 48, it will drop vertically to the Moon. If fired at twice the speed, it and the satellite would have the same speed relative to the Moon, but in the opposite direction, and might collide with the satellite after half an orbit.

51. Communication satellites only appear motionless because their orbital period coincides with the daily rotation of the Earth. If they were at rest and not orbiting, they would crash to Earth.

53. The design is a good one. Rotation would provide a centripetal force on the occupants. Watch for this design in future space faring.

55. The escape speeds from various planets refer to "ballistic speeds"—to the speeds attained *after* the application of an applied force at low altitude. If the force is sustained, then a space vehicle could escape the Earth at any speed, so long as the force is applied sufficiently long.

57. This is similar to Exercise 56. In this case, Pluto's maximum speed of impact on the Sun, by virtue of only the Sun's gravity, would be the same as the escape speed from the surface of the Sun, which according to Table 10.1 in the text is 620 km/s.

59. The satellite experiences the greatest gravitational force at A, where it is closest to the Earth; and the greatest speed and the greatest velocity at A, and by the same token the greatest momentum and greatest kinetic energy at A, and the greatest gravitational potential energy at the farthest point C. It would have the same total energy (KE + PE) at all parts of its orbit, likewise the same angular momentum because it's conserved. It would have the greatest acceleration at A, where F/m is greatest.

SOLUTIONS TO CHAPTER 10 PROBLEMS

1. One second after being thrown, its horizontal component of velocity is 10 m/s, and its vertical component is also 10 m/s. By the Pythagorean theorem, V = √(10² + 10²) = **14.1 m/s.** (It is moving at a 45° angle.)

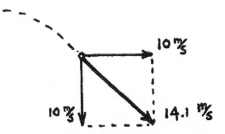

3. **100 m/s.** At the top of its trajectory, the vertical component of velocity is zero, leaving only the horizontal component. The horizontal component at the top or anywhere along the path is the same as the initial horizontal component, 100 m/s (the side of a square where the diagonal is 141).

5. John and Tracy's horizontal jumping velocity will be the horizontal distance traveled divided by the time of the jump. The horizontal distance will be a minimum of 20 m, but what will be the time? Aha, the same time it would take John and Tracy to fall straight down! From Table 3.3 we see such a fall would take 4 seconds. Or we can find the time from

$d = 5t^2$, where rearrangement gives $t = \sqrt{\dfrac{d}{5}}$ $= \sqrt{\dfrac{80}{5}}$ $= 4$ s.

So to travel 20 m horizontally in this time means John and Tracy should jump horizontally with a velocity of 20 m/4 s = 5 m/s. But this would put them at the edge of the pool, so they should jump a little faster. If we knew the length of the pool, we could calculate how much faster without hitting the far end of the pool. (John and Tracy would be better advised to take the elevator.) So the answer is **slightly faster than 5 m/s.**

7. Hang time depends only on the vertical component of initial velocity and the corresponding vertical distance attained. From $d = 5t^2$ a vertical 1.25 m drop corresponds to 0.5 s ($t = \sqrt{2d/g} = \sqrt{2(1.25)/10} = 0.5$ s). Double this (time up and time down) for a hang time of 1 s. Hang time is the **same** whatever the horizontal distance traveled.

9. $v = \sqrt{\dfrac{GM}{d}}$ $= \sqrt{\dfrac{(6.67 \times 10^{-11})(6 \times 10^{24})}{3.8 \times 10^8}}$ $= \mathbf{1026 \ m/s.}$

ANSWERS TO CHAPTER 11 EXERCISES (The Atomic Nature of Matter)

1. One.

3. The average speed of molecules increases.

5. The cat leaves a trail of molecules and atoms on the grass. These in turn leave the grass and mix with the air, where they enter the dog's nose, activating its sense of smell.

7. The atoms that make up a newborn baby or anything else in this world originated in the explosions of ancient stars. (See Figure 11.8, my daughter Leslie.) The *molecules* that make up the baby, however, were formed from atoms ingested by the mother and transferred to her womb.

9. Agree partially. It's better to say an element is defined by the number of protons in the nucleus. The number of protons and electrons are equal only when the element is not ionized.

11. Brownian motion is the result of more atoms or molecules bumping against one side of a tiny particle than the other. This produces a net force on the particle, which it is set in motion. Such doesn't occur for larger particles because the numbers of bumps on opposite sides is more likely equal, producing no net force. The number of bumps on a baseball is practically the same on all sides, with no net force and no change in the baseball's motion.

13. Individual Ping-Pong balls are less massive than individual golf balls, so equal masses of each means more Ping-Pong balls than golf balls.

15. Since aluminum atoms are less massive than lead atoms, more aluminum atoms than lead atoms compose a 1-kg sample.

17. Nine.

19. The element is copper, atomic number 29. Any atom having 29 protons is by definition copper.

21. Carbon in trees is extracted from carbon dioxide in the air. In a loose sense, we can view a tree as solidified air!

23. Check the periodic table and see that gold is atomic number 79. Taking a proton from the nucleus leaves the atomic number 78, platinum—much more valuable than adding a proton to get mercury, atomic number 80.

25. Lead.

27. In an electrically neutral atom the number of protons in the nucleus equals the number of orbiting electrons. In an ion, the number of electrons differs from the number of nuclear protons.

29. An atom loses an electron to become a positive ion. Then it has more protons than electrons.

31. The capsule would be arsenic.

33. Sodium and chlorine atoms combine to form a molecule with completely different characteristics—the molecules of common table salt.

35. Neon, argon, krypton, xenon, and radon (the noble gases).

37. Germanium has properties most like silicon, as it is in the same column, Group XIV, as silicon in the periodic table.

39. Protons contribute more to an atom's mass, and electrons more to an atom's size.

41. The hydrogen molecules, having less mass, move faster than the heavier oxygen molecules.

43. The water and alcohol molecules actually fit into one another and occupy less space when combined than they do individually. Hence, when water and alcohol are mixed, their combined volume is less than the sum of their volumes separately.

45. You really are a part of every person around you in the sense that you are composed of atoms not only from every person around you, but from every person who ever lived on Earth! The child's statement in the Part 2 photo opener is indisputable. And the atoms that now compose you will make up the atomic pool that others will draw upon.

47. They assumed hydrogen and oxygen were single-atom molecules with water's formula being H_8O.

49. The amount of matter that a given amount of antimatter would annihilate is the same as the amount of antimatter, a pair of particles at a time. The whole world could not be annihilated by antimatter unless the mass of antimatter were at least equal to the mass of the world.

SOLUTIONS TO CHAPTER 11 PROBLEMS

1. There are **16 grams of oxygen** in 18 grams of water. We can see from the formula for water, H_2O, there are twice as many hydrogen atoms (each of atomic mass 1) as oxygen atoms (each of atomic mass 16). So the molecular mass of H_2O is 18, with 16 parts oxygen by mass.

3. The atomic mass of element A is $3/2$ **the mass of element B**. Why? Gas A has three times the mass of Gas B. If the equal number of molecules in A and B had equal numbers of atoms, then the atoms in Gas A would simply be three times as massive. But there are twice as many atoms in A, so the mass of each atom must be half of three times as much—$3/2$.

5. (a) **10^4 atoms** (length 10^{-6} m divided by size 10^{-10} m).

   (b) **10^8 atoms** ($10^4 \times 10^4$).

   (c) **10^{12} atoms** ($10^4 \times 10^4 \times 10^4$).

   (d) $10,000 buys a good used car, for instance. $100 million buys a few jet aircraft and an airport on which to store them, for instance. $1 trillion buys a medium-sized country, for instance. (Answers limited only by the imagination of the student.)

7. There are 10^{22} **breaths of air** in the world's atmosphere, which is the **same number of** atoms in a single breath. So for any one breath evenly mixed in the atmosphere, we sample **one of Julius Caesar's atoms** at any place or any time in the atmosphere.

ANSWERS TO CHAPTER 12 EXERCISES (Solids)

1. Both the same, for 1000 mg = 1 g.

3. The carbon that comprises most of the mass of a tree originates from CO_2 extracted from the air.

5. Evidence for crystalline structure include the symmetric diffraction patterns given off by various materials, micrographs such as the one shown by Professor Hubisz in the chapter-opener photo, and even brass doorknobs that have been etched by the perspiration of hands.

7. Iron is denser than cork, but not necessarily heavier. A common cork from a wine bottle, for example, is heavier than an iron thumbtack—but it wouldn't be heavier if the volumes of each were the same.

9. Ice is less dense than water.

11. Density has not only to do with the mass of the atoms that make up a material, but with the spacing between the atoms as well. The atoms of the metal osmium, for example, are not as massive as uranium atoms, but due to their close spacing they make up the densest of the metals. Uranium atoms are not as closely spaced as osmium atoms.

13. Water is denser, so a liter of water weighs more than a liter of ice. (Once a liter of water freezes, its volume is greater than 1 liter.)

15. The top part of the spring supports the entire weight of the spring and stretches more than, say the middle, which only supports half the weight and stretches half as far. Parts of the spring toward the bottom support very little of the spring's weight and hardly stretch at all.

17. A twice-as-thick rope has four times the cross-section and is therefore four times as strong. The length of the rope does not contribute to its strength. (Remember the old adage, a chain is only as strong as its weakest link—the strength of the chain has to do with the thickness of the links, not the length of the chain.)

19. Case 1: Tension at the top and compression at the bottom.   Case 2: Compression at the top and tension at the bottom.

21. A horizontal I-beam is stronger when the web is vertical because most of the material is where it is needed for the most strength, in the top and bottom flanges. When supporting a load, one flange will be under tension and the other flange under compression. But when the web is horizontal, only the edges of the flanges, much smaller than the flanges themselves, play these important roles.

23. Like the dams in Exercise 22, the ends should be concave as on the left. Then the pressure due to the wine inside produces compression on the ends that strengthens rather than weakens the barrel. If the ends are convex as on the right, the pressure due to the wine inside produces tension, which tends to separate the boards that make up the ends.

25. Scale a beam up to twice its linear dimensions, I-beam or otherwise, and it will be four times as thick. Along its cross-section then, it will be four times as strong. But it will be eight times as heavy. Four times the strength supporting eight times the weight results in a beam only half as strong as the original beam. The same holds true for a bridge that is scaled up by two. The larger bridge will be only half as strong as the smaller one. (Larger bridges have different designs than smaller bridges. How they differ is what architects and engineers get paid for!)

Interestingly, how strength depends on size was one of Galileo's "two new sciences," published in 1683.

27. Since each link in a chain is pulled by its neighboring links, tension in the hanging chain is exactly along the chain—parallel to the chain at every point. If the arch takes the same shape, then compression all along the arch will similarly be exactly along the arch—parallel to the arch at every point. There will be no internal forces tending to bend the arch. This shape is a catenary, and is the shape of modern-day arches such as the one that graces the city of St. Louis.

29. The candymaker needs less taffy for the larger apples because the surface area is less per kilogram. (This is easily noticed by comparing the peelings of the same number of kilograms of small and large apples.)

31. The answer to this question uses the same principle as the answer to Exercise 30. The greater surface area of the coal in the form of dust insures an enormously greater proportion of carbon atoms in the coal having exposure to the oxygen in the air. The result is very rapid combustion.

33. An apartment building has less area per dwelling unit exposed to the weather than a single-family unit of the same volume. The smaller area means less heat loss per unit. (It is interesting to see the nearly cubical shapes of apartment buildings in northern climates—a cube has the least surface area for a solid with rectangular sides.)

35. The surface area of crushed ice is greater which provides more melting surface to the surroundings.

37. Rusting is a surface phenomenon. For a given mass, iron rods present more surface area to the air than thicker piles.

39. The wider, thinner burger has more surface area for the same volume. The greater the surface area, the greater will be the heat transfer from the stove to the meat.

41. Mittens have less surface than gloves. Anyone who has made mittens and gloves will tell you that much more material is required to make gloves. Hands in gloves will cool faster than hands in mittens. Fingers, toes, and ears have a disproportionately large surface area relative to other parts of the body and are therefore more prone to frostbite.

43. Small animals radiate more energy per bodyweight, so the flow of blood is correspondingly greater, and the heartbeat faster.

45. The inner surface of the lungs is not smooth, but is sponge-like. As a result, there is an enormous surface exposed to the air that is breathed. This is nature's way of compensating for the proportional decrease in surface area for large bodies. In this way, the adequate amount of oxygen vital to life is taken in.

47. Large raindrops fall faster than smaller raindrops for the same reason that heavier parachutists fall faster than lighter parachutists. Both larger things have less surface area and therefore less air resistance relative to their weights.

49. Scaling plays a significant role in the design of the hummingbird and the eagle. The wings of a hummingbird are smaller than those of the eagle relative to the size of the bird, but are larger relative to the mass of the bird. The hummingbird's swift maneuvers are possible because the small rotational inertia of the short wings permits rapid flapping that would be impossible for wings as large as those of an eagle. If a hummingbird were scaled up to the size of an eagle, its wings would be much shorter than those of an eagle, so it couldn't soar. Its customary rate of flapping would be insufficient to provide lift for its disproportionately greater weight. Such a giant hummingbird couldn't fly, and unless its legs were disproportionately thicker, it would have great difficulty walking. The great difference in the design of hummingbirds and eagles is a natural consequence of the area to volume ratio of scaling. Interesting?

SOLUTIONS TO CHAPTER 12 PROBLEMS

1. Density = $\dfrac{\text{mass}}{\text{volume}}$ = $\dfrac{5 \text{ kg}}{V}$. Now the volume of a cylinder is its (round area) × (its height) ($\pi r^2 h$).

   So density = $\dfrac{5 \text{ kg}}{\pi r^2 h}$ = $\dfrac{5000 \text{ g}}{(3.14)(3^2)(10)\text{cm}^3}$ = **17.7 g/cm³**.

3. 45 N is 2.25 times 20 N, so the spring will stretch 2.25 times as far, **9 cm**. Or from Hooke's law; $F = kx$, $x = F/k = 45$ N/(20 N/4 cm) = 9 cm. (The spring constant $k = 5$ N/cm.)

5. If the spring is cut in half, it will stretch as far as half the spring stretched before it was cut—half as much. This is because the tension in the uncut spring is the same everywhere, equal to the full load at the middle as well as the end. So the 10 N load will stretch it **2 cm**. (Cutting the spring in half doubles the spring constant k. Initially $k = 10$ N/4 cm = 2.5 N/cm; when cut in half, $k = 10$ N/2 cm = 5 N/cm.)

7. (a) **Eight** smaller cubes (see Figure 12.16).

   (b) Each face of the original cube has an area of 4 cm² and there are 6 faces, so the total area is **24 cm²**. Each of the smaller cubes has an area of 6 cm² and there are eight of them, so their total surface area is **48 cm²**, twice as great.

   (c) The surface-to-volume ratio for the original cube is (24 cm²)/(8 cm³) = **3 cm⁻¹**. For the set of smaller cubes, it is (48 cm²)/(8 cm³) = **6 cm⁻¹**, twice as great. (Notice that the surface-to-volume ratio has the unit inverse cm.)

9. The big cube will have the **same combined volume** of the eight little cubes, but **half their combined area**. The area of each side of the little cubes is 1 cm², and for its six sides the total area of each little cube is 6 cm². So all eight individual cubes have a total surface area 48 cm². The area of each side of the big cube, on the other hand, is 2² or 4 cm²; for all six sides its total surface area is 24 cm², half as much as the separate small cubes.

ANSWERS TO CHAPTER 13 EXERCISES (Liquids)

1. Water.

3. A woman with spike heels exerts considerably more pressure on the ground than an elephant! Example: A 500-N woman with 1-cm² spike heels puts half her weight on each foot, distributed (let's say) half on her heel and half on her sole. So the pressure exerted by each heel will be (125 N/1 cm²) = 125 N/cm². A 20,000-N elephant with 1000 cm² feet exerting ¹/4 its weight on each foot produces (5000N/1000 cm²) = 5N/cm²; about 25 times less pressure. (So a woman with spike heels will make greater dents in a new linoleum floor than an elephant will.)

5. There is less pressure with a waterbed due to the greater contact area.

7. More water will flow from the downstairs faucet due to greater water pressure there.

9. Your body gets more rest when lying than when sitting or standing because when lying, the heart does not have to pump blood to the heights that correspond to standing or sitting. Blood pressure is normally greater in the lower parts of your body simply because the blood is "deeper" there. Since your upper arms are at the same level as your heart, the blood pressure in your upper arms will be the same as the blood pressure in your heart.

11. Both are the same, for pressure depends on depth.

13. (a) The reservoir is elevated so as to produce suitable water pressure in the faucets that it serves. (b) The hoops are closer together at the bottom because the water pressure is greater at the bottom. Closer to the top, the water pressure is not as great, so less reinforcement is needed there.

15. A one-kilogram block of aluminum is larger than a one-kilogram block of lead. The aluminum therefore displaces more water.

17. The smaller the window area, the smaller the crushing force of water on it.

19. From a physics point of view, the event was quite reasonable, for the force of the ocean on his finger would have been quite small. This is because the pressure on his finger has only to do with the depth of the water, specifically the distance of the leak below the sea level—not the weight of the ocean. For a numerical example, see Problem 4.

21. Water seeking its own level is a consequence of pressure depending on depth. In a bent U-tube full of water, for example, the water in one side of the tube tends to push water up the other side until the pressures at the same depth in each tube are equal. If the water levels were not the same, there would be more pressure at a given level in the fuller tube, which would move the water until the levels were equal.

23. In deep water, you are buoyed up by the water displaced and as a result, you don't exert as much pressure against the stones on the bottom. When you are up to your neck in water, you hardly feel the bottom at all.

25. The diet drink is less dense than water, whereas the regular drink is denser than water. (Water with dissolved sugar is denser than pure water.) Also, the weight of the can is less than the buoyant force that would act on it if totally submerged. So it floats, where buoyant force equals the weight of the can.

27. Mountain ranges are very similar to icebergs: both float in a denser medium, and extend farther down into that medium than they extend above it. Mountains, like icebergs, are bigger than they appear to be. The concept of floating mountains is *isostacy*—Archimedes' principle for rocks.

29. The force needed will be the weight of 1 L of water, which is 9.8 N. If the weight of the carton is not negligible, then the force needed would be 9.8 N minus the carton's weight, for then the carton would be "helping" to push itself down.

31. The buoyant force on the ball beneath the surface is much greater than the force of gravity on the ball, producing a large net force and large acceleration.

33. While floating, BF equals the weight of the submarine. When submerged, BF equals the submarine's weight *plus* the weight of water taken into its ballast tanks. Looked at another way, the submerged submarine displaces a greater weight of water than the same submarine floating.

35. When a ship is empty its weight is least and it displaces the least water and floats highest. Carrying a load of anything increases its weight and makes it float lower. It will float as low carrying a few tons of Styrofoam as it will carrying the same number of tons of iron ore. So the ship floats lower in the water when loaded with Styrofoam than when empty. If the Styrofoam were outside the ship, below water line, then the ship would float higher as a person would with a life preserver.

37. The water level will fall. This is because the iron will displace a greater amount of water while being supported than when submerged. A floating object displaces its weight of water, which is more than its own volume, while a submerged object displaces only its volume. (This may be illustrated in the kitchen sink with a dish floating in a dishpan full of water. Silverware in the dish takes the place of the scrap iron. Note the level of water at the side of the dishpan, and then throw the silverware overboard. The floating dish will float higher and the water level at the side of the dishpan will fall. Will the volume of the silverware displace enough water to bring the level to its starting point? No, not as long as it is denser than water.)

39. Buoyant force will remain unchanged on the sinking rock because it displaces the same weight of water at any depth.

41. The balloon will sink to the bottom because its density increases with depth. The balloon is compressible, so the increase in water pressure beneath the surface compresses it and reduces its volume, thereby increasing its density. Density is further increased as it sinks to regions of greater pressure and compression. This sinking is understood also from a buoyant force point of view. As its volume is reduced by increasing pressure as it descends, the amount of water it displaces becomes less. The result is a decrease in the buoyant force that initially was sufficient to barely keep it afloat.

43. A body floats higher in denser fluid because it does not have to sink as far to displace a weight of fluid equal to its own weight. A smaller volume of the displaced denser fluid is able to match the weight of the floating body.

45. Since both preservers are the same size, they will displace the same amount of water when submerged and be buoyed up with equal forces. Effectiveness is another story. The amount of buoyant force exerted on the heavy gravel-filled preserver is much less than its weight. If you wear it, you'll sink. The same amount of buoyant force exerted on the lighter Styrofoam preserver is greater than its weight and it will keep you afloat. The *amount* of the force and the *effectiveness* of the force are two different things.

47. Ice cubes will float lower in a mixed drink because the mixture of alcohol and water is less dense than water. In a less dense liquid a greater volume of liquid must be displaced to equal the weight of the floating ice. In pure alcohol, the volume of alcohol equal to that of the ice cubes weighs less than the ice cubes, and buoyancy is less than weight and ice cubes will sink. Submerged ice cubes in a cocktail indicate that it is predominantly alcohol.

49. The total weight on the scale is the same either way, so the scale reading will be the same whether or not the wooden block is outside or floating in the beaker. Likewise for an iron block, where the scale reading shows the total weight of the system.

51. When the ball is submerged (but not touching the bottom of the container), it is supported partly by the buoyant force on the left and partly by the string connected to the right side. So the left pan must increase its upward force to provide the buoyant force in addition to whatever force it provided before, and the right pan's upward force decreases by the same amount, since it now supports a ball lighter by the amount of the buoyant force. To bring the scale back to balance, the additional weight that must be put on the right side will equal twice

the weight of water displaced by the submerged ball. Why twice? Half of the added weight makes up for the loss of upward force on the right, and the other half for the equal gain in upward force on the left. (If each side initially weighs 10 N and the left side gains 2 N to become 12 N, the right side loses 2 N to become 8 N. So an additional weight of 4 N, not 2 N, is required on the right side to restore balance.) Because the density of water is less than half the density of the iron ball, the restoring weight, equal to twice the buoyant force, will still be less than the weight of the ball.

53. Both you and the water would have half the weight density as on Earth, and you would float with the same proportion of your body above the water as on Earth. Water splashed upward with a certain initial speed would rise twice as high, since it would be experiencing only half the "gravity force." Waves on the water surface would move more slowly than on Earth (at about 70% as fast since $v_{wave} \sim \sqrt{g}$).

55. A Ping-Pong ball in water in a zero-g environment would experience no buoyant force. This is because buoyancy depends on a pressure difference on different sides of a submerged body. In this weightless state, no pressure difference would exist because no water pressure exists. (See the answer to Exercise 24, and Home Project 2.)

57. The strong man will be unsuccessful. He will have to push with 50 times the weight of the 10 kilograms. The hydraulic arrangement is arranged to his disadvantage. Ordinarily, the input force is applied against the smaller piston and the output force is exerted by the large piston—this arrangement is just the opposite.

59. When water is hot, the molecules are moving more rapidly and do not cling to one another as well as when they are slower moving, so the surface tension is less. The lesser surface tension of hot water allows it to pass more readily through small openings.

SOLUTIONS TO CHAPTER 13 PROBLEMS

1. Pressure = weight density × depth = 10,000 N/m³ × 220 m = 2,200,000 N/m² = **2200 kPa** (or using density of 9800 N/m³, pressure = 2160 kPa).

3. (a) The volume of the extra water displaced will weigh as much as the 400-kg horse. And the volume of extra water displaced will also equal the area of the barge times the extra depth. That is,

   $V = Ah$, where A is the horizontal area of the barge; Then $h = \dfrac{V}{A}$.

   Now $A = 5m \times 2m = 10 \ m^2$; to find the volume V of barge pushed into the water by the horse's weight, which equals the volume of water displaced, we know that

   $\text{density} = \dfrac{m}{V}$. Or from this, $V = \dfrac{m}{\text{density}} = \dfrac{400kg}{1000kg/m^3} = 0.4 \ m^3$.

   So $h = \dfrac{V}{A} = \dfrac{0.4 \ m^3}{10 \ m^2} =$ **0.04 m**, which is 4 cm deeper.

   (b) If each horse will push the barge 4 cm deeper, the question becomes: How many 4-cm increments will make 15 cm? 15/4 = 3.75, so 3 horses can be carried without sinking. **4 horses** will sink the barge.

5. From Table 12.1 the density of gold is 19.3 g/cm³. Your gold has a mass of 1000 grams, so $\dfrac{1000 \ g}{V} = 19.3$ g/cm³. Solving for V,

   $V = \dfrac{1000 \ g}{19.3 \ g/cm^3} =$ **51.8 cm³**.

7. 10% of ice extends above water. So 10% of the 9-cm thick ice would float above the water line; **0.9 cm**. So the ice pops up. Interestingly, when mountains erode they become lighter and similarly pop up! Hence it takes a long time for mountains to wear away.

9. The displaced water, with a volume 90 percent of the vacationer's volume, weighs the same as the vacationer (to provide a buoyant force equal to his weight). Therefore his density is 90 percent of the water's density. Vacationer's density = (0.90)(1,025 kg/m³) = **923 kg/m³**.

ANSWERS TO CHAPTER 14 EXERCISES (Gases and Plasmas)

1. Some of the molecules in the Earth 's atmosphere *do* go off into outer space—those like helium with speeds greater than escape speed. But the average speeds of most molecules in the atmosphere are well below escape speed, so the atmosphere is held to Earth by Earth gravity.

3. The weight of a truck is distributed over the part of the tires that make contact with the road. Weight/surface area = pressure, so the greater the surface area, or equivalently, the greater the number of tires, the greater the weight of the truck can be for a given pressure. What pressure? The pressure exerted by the tires on the road, which is determined by (but is somewhat greater than) the air pressure in its tires. Can you see how this relates to Home Project 1?

5. The tires heat, giving additional motion to the gas molecules within.

7. The ridges near the base of the funnel allow air to escape from a container it is inserted into. Without the ridges, air in the container would be compressed and would tend to prevent filling as the level of liquid rises.

9. The bubble's mass does not change. Its volume increases because its pressure decreases (Boyle's law), and its density decreases (same mass, more volume).

11. If the item is sealed in an airtight package at sea level, then the pressure in the package is about 1 atmosphere. Cabin pressure is reduced somewhat for high altitude flying, so the pressure in the package is greater than the surrounding pressure and the package therefore puffs outwards.

13. The can collapses under the weight of the atmosphere. When water was boiling in the can, much of the air inside was driven out and replaced by steam. Then, with the cap tightly fastened, the steam inside cooled and condensed back to the liquid state, creating a partial vacuum in the can which could not withstand the crushing force of the atmosphere outside.

15. A vacuum cleaner wouldn't work on the Moon. A vacuum cleaner operates on Earth because the atmospheric pressure pushes dust into the machine's region of reduced pressure. On the Moon there is no atmospheric pressure to push the dust anywhere.

17. If barometer liquid were half as dense as mercury, then to weigh as much, a column twice as high would be required. A barometer using such liquid would therefore have to be twice the height of a standard mercury barometer, or about 152 cm instead of 76 cm.

19. Mercury can be drawn a maximum of 76 cm with a siphon. This is because 76 vertical cm of mercury exert the same pressure as a column of air that extends to the top of the atmosphere. Or looked at another way; water can be lifted 10.3 m by atmospheric pressure. Mercury is 13.6 times denser than water, so it can only be lifted only $1/13.6$ times as high as water.

21. Drinking through a straw is slightly more difficult atop a mountain. This is because the reduced atmospheric pressure is less effective in pushing soda up into the straw.

23. You agree with your friend, for the elephant displaces far more air than a small helium-filled balloon, or small anything. The *effects* of the buoyant forces, however, is a different story. The large buoyant force on the elephant is insignificant relative to its enormous weight. The tiny buoyant force acting on the balloon of tiny weight, however, is significant.

25. No, assuming the air is not compressed. The air filled bag is heavier, but buoyancy negates the extra weight and the reading is the same. The buoyant force equals the weight of the displaced air, which is the same as the weight of the air inside the bag (if the pressures are the same).

27. Weight is the force with which something presses on a supporting surface. When the buoyancy of air plays a role, the net force against the supporting surface is less, indicating a smaller weight. Buoyant force is more appreciable for larger volumes, like feathers. So the mass of feathers that weigh 1 pound is more than the mass of iron that weighs 1 pound.

29. The air tends to pitch toward the rear (law of inertia), becoming momentarily denser at the rear of the car, less dense in the front. Because the air is a gas obeying Boyle's law, its pressure is greater where its density is greater. Then the air has both a vertical and a horizontal "pressure gradient." The vertical gradient, arising from the weight of the atmosphere, buoys the balloon up. The horizontal gradient, arising from the acceleration, buoys the balloon forward. So the string of the balloon makes an angle. The pitch of the balloon will always be in the direction of the acceleration. Step on the brakes and the balloon pitches backwards. Round a corner and the balloon noticeably leans radially towards the center of the curve. Nice! (Another way to look at this involves the effect of two accelerations, g and the acceleration of the car. The string of the balloon will be parallel to the resultant of these two accelerations. Nice again!)

31. The buoyant force does not change, because the volume of the balloon does not change. The buoyant force is the weight of air displaced, and doesn't depend on what is doing the displacing.

33. A moving molecule encountering a surface imparts force to the surface. The greater the number of impacts, the greater the pressure.

35. The pressure increases, in accord with Boyle's law.

37. The shape would be a catenary. It would be akin to Gateway Arch in St. Louis and the hanging chain discussed in Chapter 12.

39. The end supporting the punctured balloon tips upwards as it is lightened by the amount of air that escapes. There is also a loss of buoyant force on the punctured balloon, but that loss of upward force is less than the loss of downward force, since the density of air in the balloon before puncturing was greater than the density of surrounding air.

41. The force of the atmosphere is on both sides of the window; the net force is zero, so windows don't normally break under the weight of the atmosphere. In a strong wind, however, pressure will be reduced on the windward side (Bernoulli's Principle) and the forces no longer cancel to zero. Many windows are blown *outward* in strong winds.

43. As speed of water increases, internal pressure of the water decreases.

45. Air moves faster over the spinning top of the Frisbee and pressure against the top is reduced. A Frisbee, like a wing, needs an "angle of attack" to ensure that the air flowing over it follows a longer path than the air flowing under it. So as with the beach ball in Exercise 44, there is a difference in pressures against the top and bottom of the Frisbee that produces an upward lift.

47. The helium-filled balloon will be buoyed from regions of greater pressure to regions of lesser pressure, and will "rise" in a rotating air-filled habitat.

49. Spacing of airstreams on opposite sides of a non-spinning ball is the same. For a spinning ball, airstream spacings are less on the side where airspeed is increased by spin action.

51. Greater wing area produces greater lift, important for low speeds where lift is less. Flaps are pulled in to reduce area at cruising speed, reducing lift to equal the weight of the aircraft.

53. The thinner air at high-altitude airports produces less lift for aircraft. This means aircraft need longer runways to achieve correspondingly greater speed for takeoff.

55. Bernoulli's Principle. For the moving car the pressure will be less on the side of the car where the air is moving fastest—the side nearest the truck, resulting in the car's being pushed by the atmosphere towards the truck. Inside the convertible, atmospheric pressure is greater than outside, and the canvas rooftop is pushed upward toward the region of lesser pressure. Similarly for the train windows, where the interior air is at rest relative to the window and the air outside is in motion. Air pressure against the inner surface of the window is greater than the atmospheric pressure outside. When the difference in pressures is significant enough, the window is blown out.

57. The troughs are partially shielded from the wind, so the air moves faster over the crests than in the troughs. Pressure is therefore lower at the top of the crests than down below in the troughs. The greater pressure in the troughs pushes the water into even higher crests.

59. According to Bernoulli's principle, when a fluid gains speed in flowing through a narrow region, the pressure of the fluid is reduced. The gain in speed, the cause, produces reduced pressure, the effect. But one can argue that a reduced pressure in a fluid, the cause, will produce a flow in the direction of the reduced pressure, the effect. For example, if you decrease the air pressure in a pipe by a pump or by any means, neighboring air will rush into the region of reduced pressure. In this case the increase in air speed is the result, not the cause of, reduced pressure. Cause and effect are open to interpretation. Bernoulli's principle is a controversial topic with many physics types!

SOLUTIONS TO CHAPTER 14 PROBLEMS

1. According to Boyle's law, the pressure will increase to **three times** its original pressure.

3. To decrease the pressure ten-fold, back to its original value, in a fixed volume, 90% of the molecules must escape, leaving **one-tenth** of the original number.

5. If the atmosphere were composed of pure water vapor, the atmosphere would condense to a depth of 10.3 m. Since the atmosphere is composed of gases that have less density in the liquid state, their liquid depths would be more than 10.3 m, about **12 m**. (A nice reminder of how thin and fragile our atmosphere really is.)

7. (a) The weight of the displaced air must be the same as the weight supported, since the total force (gravity plus buoyancy) is zero. The displaced air weighs **20,000 N**.

(b) Since weight = mg, the mass of the displaced air is $m = W/g = (20,000 \text{ N})/(10 \text{ m/s}^2) = 2,000$ kg. Since density is mass/volume, the volume of the displaced air is volume = mass/density = $(2,000 \text{ kg})/(1.2 \text{ kg/m}^3) = $ **1,700 m^3** (same answer to two figures if $g = 9.8 \text{ m/s}^2$ is used).

ANSWERS TO CHAPTER 15 EXERCISES (Temperature, Heat, and Expansion)

1. Inanimate things such as tables, chairs, furniture, and so on, have the same temperature as the surrounding air (assuming they are in thermal equilibrium with the air—i.e., no sudden gush of different-temperature air or such). People and other mammals, however, generate their own heat and have body temperatures that are normally higher than air temperature.

3. Yes, the same average speed, but not the same instantaneous speed. At any moment molecules with the same average speed can have enormously different instantaneous speeds.

5. You cannot establish by your own touch whether or not you are running a fever because there would be no temperature difference between your hand and forehead. If your forehead is a couple of degrees higher in temperature than normal, your hand is also a couple of degrees higher.

7. The hot coffee has a higher temperature, but not a greater internal energy. Although the iceberg has less internal energy per mass, its enormously greater mass gives it a greater total energy than that in the small cup of coffee. (For a smaller volume of ice, the fewer number of more energetic molecules in the hot cup of coffee may constitute a greater total amount of internal energy—but not compared to an iceberg.)

9. Calorie, which is 1000 calories.

11. The average speed of molecules in both containers is the same. There is greater internal energy in the full glass (twice the matter at the same temperature). More heat will be required to increase the temperature of the full glass, twice as much, in fact.

13. Gaseous pressure changes with changes in temperature.

15. Different substances have different thermal properties due to differences in the way energy is stored internally in the substances. When the same amount of heat produces different changes in temperatures in two substances of the same mass, we say they have different specific heat capacities. Each substance has its own characteristic specific heat capacity. Temperature measures the average kinetic energy of random motion, but not other kinds of energy.

17. The slowly cooling object has the greater specific heat.

19. A high specific heat. The more ways a molecule can move internally, the more energy it can absorb to excite these internal motions. This greater capacity for absorbing energy makes a higher specific heat.

21. Alcohol, for less specific heat means less thermal inertia and a greater change in temperature.

23. The climate of Bermuda, like that of all islands, is moderated by the high specific heat of water. What moderates the climates are the large amounts of energy given off and absorbed by water for small changes in temperature. When the air is cooler than the water, the water warms the air; when the air is warmer than the water, the water cools the air.

25. In winter months when the water is warmer than the air, the air is warmed by the water to produce a seacoast climate warmer than inland. In summer months when the air is warmer than the water, the air is cooled by the water to produce a seacoast climate cooler than inland. This is why seacoast communities and especially islands do not experience the high and low temperature extremes that characterize inland locations.

27. The brick will cool off too fast and you'll be cold in the middle of the night. Bring a jug of hot water with its higher specific heat to bed and you'll make it through the night.

29. Water is an exception.

31. When the rivets cool they contract. This tightens the plates being attached.

33. The tires heat up, which heats the air within. The molecules in the heated air move faster, which increases air pressure in the tires.

35. Cool the inner glass and heat the outer glass. If it's done the other way around, the glasses will stick even tighter (if not break).

37. If both expanded differently, as for different materials, the key and lock wouldn't match.

39. The photo was likely taken on a warm day. If it were taken on a cold day there would be more space between the segments.

41. Overflow is the result of liquid gasoline expanding more than the solid tank.

43. The heated balls would have the same diameter.

45. The gap in the ring will become wider when the ring is heated. Try this: draw a couple of lines on a ring where you pretend a gap to be. When you heat the ring, the lines will be farther apart—the same amount as if a real gap were there. Every part of the ring expands proportionally when heated uniformly—thickness, length, gap and all.

47. The U shape takes up the slack of expansion or contraction, without changing the positions at end points.

49. In the construction of a light bulb, it is important that the metal leads and the glass have the same rate of heat expansion. If the metal leads expand more than glass, the glass may crack. If the metal expands less than glass upon being heated, air will leak in through the resulting gaps.

51. 4°C.

53. The atoms and molecules of most substances are more closely packed in solids than in liquids. So most substances are denser in the solid phase than in the liquid phase. Such is the case for iron and aluminum and most all other metals. But water is different. In the solid phase the structure is open-spaced and ice is less dense than water. Hence ice floats in water.

55. The curve for density versus temperature is:

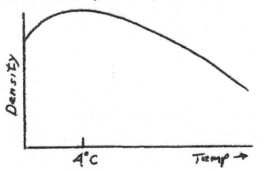

57. At 0°C it will contract when warmed a little; at 4°C it will expand, and at 6°C it will expand.

59. If cooling occurred at the bottom of a pond instead of at the surface, ice would still form at the surface, but it would take much longer for ponds to freeze. This is because all the water in the pond would have to be reduced to a temperature of 0°C rather than 4°C before the first ice would form. Ice that forms at the bottom where the cooling process is occurring would be less dense and would float to the surface (except for ice that may form about and cling to material anchored to the bottom of the pond).

SOLUTIONS TO CHAPTER 15 PROBLEMS

1. Heat gained by the cooler water = heat lost by the warmer water. Since the masses of water are the same, the final temperature is midway, 30°C. So you'll end up with 100 g of **30°C** water.

3. Raising the temperature of 10 gm of copper by one degree takes 10 × 0.092 = 0.92 calories, and raising it through 100 degrees takes 100 times as much, or 92 calories.

   By formula, $Q = cm\Delta T = (0.092 \text{ cal/g°C})(10 \text{ g})(100°C) =$ **92 cal.**
   Heating 10 grams of water through the same temperature difference takes 1,000 calories, **more than ten times** the amount for the copper—another reminder that water has a large specific heat capacity.

5. Heat gained by water = heat lost by nails
   $(cm\,\Delta T)_{\text{water}} = (cm\,\Delta T)_{\text{nails}}$
   $(1)(100)\,(T - 20) = (0.12)(100)(40 - T)$, giving $T =$ **22.1°C.**

7. By formula: $\Delta L = L_o a \Delta T = (1300 \text{ m})(11 \times 10^{-6}/°C)(15°C) =$ **0.21 m.**

9. **Aluminum expands more** as evidenced by its greater coefficient of linear expansion. The ratio of the increases is equal to the ratios of the coefficients of expansion, i.e., $24 \times 10^{-6}/11 \times 10^{-6} = 2.2$. So the same increase in temperature, the change in length of aluminum will be **2.2 times greater** than the change in length of steel.

ANSWERS TO CHAPTER 16 EXERCISES (Heat Transfer)

1. The metal doorknob conducts heat better than wood.

3. No, the coat is not a source of heat, but merely keeps the thermal energy of the wearer from leaving rapidly.

5. When the temperatures of the blocks are the same as the temperature of your hand, then no heat transfer occurs. Heat will flow between your hand and something being touched only if there is a temperature difference between them.

7. Copper and aluminum are better conductors than stainless steel, and therefore more quickly transfer heat to the cookware's interior.

9. In touching the tongue to very cold metal, enough heat can be quickly conducted away from the tongue to bring the saliva to sub-zero temperature where it freezes, locking the tongue to the metal. In the case of relatively nonconducting wood, much less heat is conducted from the tongue and freezing does not take place fast enough for sudden sticking to occur.

11. Heat from the relatively warm ground is conducted by the gravestone to melt the snow in contact with the gravestone. Likewise for trees or any materials that are better conductors of heat than snow, and that extend into the ground.

13. The snow and ice of the igloo is a better insulator than wood. You would be warmer in the igloo than the wooden shack.

15. The high conductivity of metal means a lot of heat transfer, hence the ouch. But the low conductivity of air results in less heat transfer and less pain.

17. The conductivity of wood is relatively low whatever the temperature—even in the stage of red hot coals. You can safely walk barefoot across red hot wooden coals if you step quickly (like removing the wooden-handled pan with bare hands quickly from the hot oven in Exercise 16) because very little heat is conducted to your feet. Because of the poor conductivity of the coals, energy from within the coals does not readily replace the energy that transfers to your feet. This is evident in the diminished redness of the coal after your foot has left it. Stepping on red-hot *iron* coals, however, is a different story. Because of the excellent conductivity of iron, very damaging amounts of heat would transfer to your feet. More than simply ouch!

19. The temperature will be midway because one decreases in temperature and the other increases in temperature.

21. It is correct to say that the increase in *thermal energy* of one object equals the decrease in *thermal energy* of the other—not temperature. The statement is correct when the hot and warm objects are the same material and same mass.

23. Disagree, for although the mixture has the same temperature, which is to say, the same KE per molecule, the lighter hydrogen molecules have more speed than heavier nitrogen for the same KE.

25. Hydrogen molecules will be the faster moving when mixed with oxygen molecules. They will have the same temperature, which means they will have the same average kinetic energy. Recall that KE = $1/2$ mv^2. Since the mass of hydrogen is considerably less than oxygen, the speed must correspondingly be greater.

27. Molecules of gas with greater mass have a smaller average speed. So molecules containing heavier U-238 are slower on the average. This favors the diffusion of the faster gas containing U-235 through a porous membrane (which is how U-235 was separated from U-238 by scientists in the 1940s).

29. More molecules are in the cooler room. The greater number of slower-moving molecules there produce air pressure at the door equal to the fewer number of faster-moving molecules in the warmer room.

31. The smoke, like hot air, is less dense than the surroundings and is buoyed upward. It cools with contact with the surrounding air and becomes more dense. When its density matches that of the surrounding air, its buoyancy and weight balance and rising ceases.

33. If ice cubes were at the bottom they wouldn't be in contact with the warmest part of the tea at the surface, so cooling would be less. Ice cubes are preferable at the surface to decrease the temperature of the warmer part of the tea.

35. Both the molecule and the baseball are under the influence of gravity, and both will accelerate downward at g. When other molecules impede downward fall, then the free-fall acceleration g isn't maintained.

37. Because of the high specific heat of water, sunshine warms water much less than it warms land. As a result, air is warmed over the land and rises. Cooler air from above the cool water takes its place and convection currents are formed. If land and water were heated equally by the Sun, such convection currents (and the winds they produce) wouldn't be.

39.

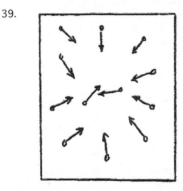

41. Black is the most efficient color for steam radiators. Much of the heat a steam radiator produces, however, is a result of the convection it produces, which has to do with its temperature rather than its radiating ability.

43. The heat you received was from radiation.

45. If good absorbers were not also good emitters, then thermal equilibrium would not be possible. If a good absorber only absorbed, then its temperature would climb above that of poorer absorbers in the vicinity. And if poor absorbers were good emitters, their temperatures would fall below that of better absorbers.

47. Human eyes are insensitive to the infrared radiated by objects at average temperatures.

49. Put the cream in right away for at least three reasons. Since black coffee radiates more heat than white coffee, make it whiter right away so it won't radiate and cool so quickly while you are waiting. Also, by Newton's law of cooling, the higher the temperature of the coffee above the surroundings, the greater will be the rate of cooling—so again add cream right away and lower the temperature to that of a reduced cooling rate, rather than allowing it to cool fast and then bring the temperature down still further by adding the cream later. Also—by adding the cream, you increase the total amount of liquid, which for the same surface area, cools more slowly.

51. Under open skies, the ground radiates upward but the sky radiates almost nothing back down. Under the benches, downward radiation of the benches decreases the net radiation from the ground, resulting in warmer ground and, likely, no frost.

53. For maximum warmth, wear the plastic coat on the outside and utilize the greenhouse effect.

55. Kelvins and Celsius degrees are the same size, and although ratios of these two scales will produce very different results, *differences* in kelvins and *differences* in Celsius degrees will be

236

the same. Since Newton's law of cooling involves temperature differences, either scale may be used.

57. Turn the air conditioner off altogether to keep ΔT small, as in the answer to Exercise 56. Heat leaks at a greater rate into a cold house than into a not-so-cold house. The greater the rate at which heat leaks into kthe house, the greater the amount of fuel consumed by the air conditioner.

59. If the Earth's temperature increases, its rate of radiating will increase. And if much of this extra terrestrial radiation is blocked, and the temperature of the Earth increases more, then its rate of radiating simply increases further. A new and higher equilibrium temperature is established.

SOLUTIONS TO CHAPTER 16 PROBLEMS

1. (a) The amount of heat absorbed by the water is $Q = cm\Delta T = (1.0 \text{ cal/g C°})(50.0 \text{ g})(50°C - 22°C) =$ 1400 cal. At 40% efficiency only 0.4 of the energy from the peanut raises the water temperature, so the calorie content of the peanut is 1400/0.4 = **3500 cal**.
   (b) The food value of a peanut is 3500 cal/0.6 g = **5.8 kilocalories per gram**.

3. Work the hammer does on the nail is given by $F \times d$, and the temperature change of the nail can be found from using $Q = cm\Delta T$. First, we get everything into more convenient units for calculating: 5 grams = 0.005 kg; 6 cm = 0.06 m. Then $F \times d = 500 \text{ N} \times 0.06 \text{ m} = 30 \text{ J}$, and 30 J = $(0.005 \text{ kg})(450 \text{ J/kg°C})(\Delta T)$ which we can solve to get $\Delta T = 30/(0.005 \times 450) = $ **13.3°C**. (You will notice a similar effect when you remove a nail from a piece of wood. The nail that you pull out is noticeably warm.)

5. According to Newton's law of cooling, its rate of cooling is proportional to the temperature difference, so when the temperature difference is half as great, the rate of cooling will be half as great. After another eight hours, the coffee will lose 12.5 degrees, half as much as in the first eight hours, cooling from 50°C to **37.5°C**. (Newton's law of cooling leads to exponential behavior, in which the fractional change is the same in each equal increment of time.)

ANSWERS TO CHAPTER 17 EXERCISES (Change of Phase)

1. Alcohol produces more cooling because of its higher rate of evaporation.

3. The water evaporates rapidly in the dry air, gaining its energy from your skin, which is cooled.

5. When you blow over the top of a bowl of hot soup, you increase net evaporation and its cooling effect by removing the warm vapor that tends to condense and reduce net evaporation.

7. From our macroscopic point of view, it appears that nothing is happening in a covered glass of water, but at the atomic level there is chaotic motion as molecules are continually bumbling about. Molecules are leaving the water surface to the air above while vapor molecules in the air are leaving the air and plunging into the liquid. Evaporation and condensation are taking place continually, even though the net evaporation or net condensation is zero. Here we distinguish between the processes and the net effect of the processes.

9. In this hypothetical case evaporation would not cool the remaining liquid because the energy of exiting molecules would be no different than the energy of molecules left behind. Although internal energy of the liquid would decrease with evaporation, energy per molecule would not change. No temperature change of the liquid would occur. (The surrounding air, on the other hand, would be cooled in this hypothetical case. Molecules flying away from the liquid surface would be slowed by the attractive force of the liquid acting on them.)

11. A fan does not cool the room, but instead promotes evaporation of perspiration, which cools the body.

13. Water leaks through the porous canvas bag, evaporating from its outer surface and cooling the bag. The motion of the car increases the rate of evaporation and therefore the rate of cooling, just as blowing over a hot bowl of soup increases the rate at which soup cools (see Exercise 5).

15. The body keeps its temperature a normal 37°C by the process of evaporation. When the body tends to overheat, perspiration occurs, which cools the body if the perspiration is allowed to evaporate. (Interestingly enough, if you're immersed in hot water, perspiration occurs profusely, but evaporation and cooling do not follow—that's why it is inadvisable to stay too long in a hot bath.)

17. Air above the freezing temperature is chilled in the vicinity of an iceberg and condensation of the water vapor in the air results in fog.

19. On a day where the outside of the windows is warmer than the inside, condensation will occur on the outside of the windows. You can also see this on the windshield of your car when you direct the air conditioner against the inside of the glass.

21. Air swept upward expands in regions of less atmospheric pressure. The expansion is accompanied by cooling, which means molecules are moving at speeds low enough for coalescing upon collisions; hence the moisture that is the cloud.

23. Enormous thermal energy is released as molecular potential energy is transformed to molecular kinetic energy in condensation. (Freezing of the droplets to form ice adds even more thermal energy.)

25. You can withdraw heat without changing temperature when the substance is undergoing a change of phase.

27. As the bubbles rise, less pressure is exerted on them.

29. Decreased pressure lessens the squeezing of molecules, which favors their tendency to separate and form vapor.

31. The hot water is below the boiling point for the very high pressure there, somewhat like the higher boiling point of water in a pressure cooker.

33. You could not cook food in low-temperature water that is boiling by virtue of reduced pressure. Food is cooked by the high temperature it is subjected to, not by the bubbling of the surrounding water. For example, put room-temperature water in a vacuum and it will boil. But this doesn't mean the water will transfer more internal energy to an egg than before boiling—an egg in this boiling water won't cook at all!

35. The ice is indeed cold. Why cold? Because rapid evaporation of the water cooled the water to the freezing point.

37. The air in the flask is very low in pressure, so that the heat from your hand will produce boiling at this reduced pressure. (Your instructor will want to be sure that the flask is strong enough to resist implosion before handing it to you!)

39. The lid on the pot traps heat which quickens boiling; the lid also slightly increases pressure on the boiling water which raises its boiling temperature. The hotter water correspondingly cooks food in a shorter time, although the effect is not significant unless the lid is held down as on a pressure cooker.

41. After a geyser has erupted, it must refill and then undergo the same heating cycle. If the rates of filling and heating don't change, then the time to boil to the eruption stage will be the same.

43. Yes, ice can be much colder than $0°C$, which is the temperature at which ice will melt when it absorbs energy. The temperature of an ice-water mixture in equilibrium is $0°C$. Iced tea, for example, is $0°C$.

45. Regelation would not occur if ice crystals weren't open structured. The pressure of the wire on the open network of crystals caves them in and the wire follows. With the pressure immediately above the wire relieved, the molecules again settle to their low energy crystalline state. Interestingly, the energy score balances for these changes of state: The energy given up by the water that refreezes above the wire is conducted through the wire thickness to melt the ice being crushed beneath. The more conductive the wire, the faster regelation occurs. For an insulator like string, regelation won't occur at all. Try it and see!

47. The wood, because its greater specific heat capacity means it will release more energy in cooling.

49. This is an example that illustrates Figure 17.7. Water vapor in the warm air condenses on the relatively low-temperature surface of the can. When the can is at room temperature, the speeds of the molecules encountering it are unaffected, and condensation doesn't occur.

51. Sugar doesn't freeze with the water in the punch, so half-frozen punch has the sugar of the original mixture—twice the original concentration.

53. Condensation occurs on the cold coils, which is why the coils drip water.

55. The temperature of nearby air increases due to energy released by the melting ice.

57. The answer is similar to the answer of Exercise 56, and also the fact that the coating of ice acts as an insulating blanket. Every gram of water that freezes releases 80 calories, much of it to the fruit; the thin layer of ice then acts as an insulating blanket against further loss of heat.

59. Yes, for the device is a heat pump, with the characteristic of being able to operate both ways—heater when the change of phase is from gas to liquid, and cooler when the change of phase is from liquid to gas.

SOLUTIONS TO CHAPTER 17 PROBLEMS

1. (a) 1 kg 0°C ice to 0°C water requires 80 kilocalories.

   (b) 1 kg 0°C water to 100°C water requires 100 kilocalories.

   (c) 1 kg 100°C water to 100°C steam requires 540 kilocalories.

   (d) 1 kg 0°C ice to 100°C steam requires (80 + 100 + 540) = **720 kilocalories** or 720,000 calories.

3. First, find the number of calories that 10 g of 100°C steam will give in changing to 10 g of 0°C water.
   10 g of steam changing to 10 g of boiling water at 100°C releases 5400 calories.
   10 g of 100°C water cooling to 0°C releases 1000 calories.
   So 6400 calories are available for melting ice.

   $$\frac{6400 \text{ cal}}{80 \text{ cal/g}} = \textbf{80 grams} \text{ of ice.}$$

5. The quantity of heat lost by the iron is $Q = cm\Delta T = (0.11 \text{ cal/g°C})(50 \text{ g})(80°C) = 440$ cal. The iron will lose a quantity of heat to the ice $Q = mL$. The mass of ice melted will therefore be $m = Q/L = (440 \text{ cal})/(80 \text{ cal/g}) = \textbf{5.5 grams}$. (The lower specific of heat of iron shows itself compared with the result of Problem 4.)

7. $0.5mgh = cm\Delta T$
   $\Delta T = 0.5mgh/cm = 0.5gh/c = (0.5)(9.8 \text{ m/s}^2)(100 \text{ m})/450 \text{ J/kg°C} = \textbf{1.1°C}$.

   Again, note that the mass cancels, so the same temperature would hold for any mass ball, assuming half the heat generated goes into warming the ball. As in Problem 6, the units check because 1 J/kg = 1 m²/s².

ANSWERS TO CHAPTER 18 EXERCISES   (Thermodynamics)

1. In the case of the 500-degree oven it makes a lot of difference. 500 kelvins is 227°C, quite a bit different than 500°C. But in the case of the 50,000-degree star, the 273 increments either way makes practically no difference. Give or take 273, the star is still 50,000 K or 50,000°C when rounded off.

3. Not ordinarily. They undergo the same change in *internal energy*, which translates to the same temperature change when both objects are the same mass and composed of the same material.

5. Its absolute temperature is 273 +10 = 283 K. Double this and you have 566 K. Expressed in Celsius; 566 - 273 = 293 °C.

7. You do work in compressing the air, which increases its internal energy. This is evidenced by an increase in temperature.

9. The pump becomes hot for two reasons: First, the work done in compressing the air increases its internal energy which is conducted to and shared with the pump. The second reason for the increase in temperature involves friction, for the piston rubs against the inner wall of the pump cylinder.

11. A given amount of mechanical energy can be easily and commonly converted to thermal energy; any body moving with kinetic energy that is brought to rest by friction transforms all its kinetic energy into thermal energy (for example, a car skidding to rest on a horizontal road). The converse is not true, however. In accord with the 2nd law of thermodynamics, only a fraction of a given amount of thermal energy can be converted to mechanical energy. For example, even under ideal conditions, less than half of the heat energy provided by burning fuel in a power plant can go into mechanical energy of electric generators.

13. When a blob of air rises in the atmosphere it does work on the surrounding lower-pressure air as it expands. This work output is at the expense of its internal energy, which is diminished, which in turn is evidenced by a lower temperature. Hence the temperature of air at the elevation of mountain tops is usually less than down below.

15. Solar energy.

17. The term pollution refers to an undesirable by-product of some process. The desirability or undesirability of a particular by-product is relative, and depends on the circumstances. For example, using waste heat from a power plant to heat a swimming pool could be desirable whereas using the same heat to warm a trout stream could be undesirable.

19. It is advantageous to use steam as hot as possible in a steam-driven turbine because the efficiency is higher if there is a greater difference in temperature between the source and the sink (see Sadi Carnot's equation in the chapter).

21. As in Exercise 20, efficiency is higher with greater difference in temperature between the heat source (combustion chamber in the engine) and sink (air surrounding the exhaust). All other things being equal, and strictly speaking, a car is more efficient on a cold day.

23. When the temperature is lowered in the reservoir into which thermal energy is rejected, efficiency increases; substitution of a smaller value of T_{cold} into $(T_{hot} - T_{cold})/T_{hot}$ will confirm this. (Re-express the equation as $1 - T_{cold}/T_{hot}$ to better see this.)

25. Only when the sink is at absolute zero (0 K) will a heat engine have an ideal efficiency of 100%.

27. Most certainly! Unlike the cooling wished for in Exercise 26, the energy given to the room by the open oven raises room temperature.

29. Work must be done to establish a temperature difference between the inside of the refrigerator and the surrounding air. The greater the temperature difference to be established, the more

241

work and hence more energy is consumed. So the refrigerator uses more energy when the room is warm rather than cold.

31. The gas is more compact—density increases.

33. Most people know that electric lights are inefficient when it comes to converting electrical energy into light energy, so they are surprised to learn there is a 100% conversion of electrical energy to thermal energy. If the building is being heated electrically, the lights do a fine job of heating, and it is not at all wasteful to keep them on when heating is needed. It is a wasteful practice if the air conditioners are on and cooling is desired, for the energy input to the air conditioners must be increased to remove the extra thermal energy given off by the lights.

35. Some of the electric energy that goes into lighting a lamp is transferred by conduction and convection to the air, some is radiated at invisible wavelengths ("heat radiation") and converted to internal energy when it is absorbed, and some appears as light. In an incandescent lamp, only about 5% goes into light, and in a fluorescent lamp, about 20% goes to light. But all of the energy that takes the form of light is converted to internal energy when the light is absorbed by materials upon which it is incident. So by the 1st law, all the electrical energy is ultimately converted to internal energy. By the second law, organized electrical energy degenerates to the more disorganized form, internal energy.

37. Energy in the universe is tending toward unavailability with time. Hotter things are cooling as cooler things are warming. If this is true, the universe is tending toward a common temperature, the so-called "heat death," when energy can no longer do work. (But we don't know for sure that the laws of thermodynamics apply to the universe as a whole, since we don't understand the ultimate source of the vast churning energy that is now apparent throughout the universe. Nature may have some surprises for us!)

39. It is fundamental because it governs the general tendency throughout nature to move from order to disorder, yet it is inexact in the sense that it is based on probability, not certainty.

41. There are more ways for molecules in the liquid phase to move, resulting in more chaotic motion.

43. No, the freezing of water is not an exception to the entropy principle because work has been put into the refrigeration system to prompt this change of state. There is actually a greater net disorder when the environment surrounding the freezer is considered.

45. Such machines violate at least the second law of thermodynamics, and perhaps the first law as well. These laws are so richly supported by so many experiments over so long a time that the Patent Office wisely assumes that there is a flaw in the claimed invention.

47. Remind your friend that perpetual motion is the normal state of the universe, that all substances are composed of perpetually-moving particles. What is impossible is not perpetual motion, but a perpetual motion machine that multiplies energy input.

49. As in Exercise 48, the smaller the number of random particles, the more the likelihood of them becoming "spontaneously" ordered. But the number of molecules in even the smallest room? Sleep comfortably!

SOLUTIONS TO CHAPTER 18 PROBLEMS

1. Heat added to system = change in system's internal energy + work done by the system, $Q = \Delta E + W$ so $W = Q - \Delta E = 0J - (-3000 \text{ J}) = \textbf{3000 J}$.

3. Converting to kelvins; 25°C = 298 K; 4°C = 277 K. So Carnot efficiency $= \dfrac{T_h - T_c}{T_h} = \dfrac{298 - 277}{298} = 0.07$, or **7%.** This is very low, which means that large volumes of water (which there are) must be processed for sufficient power generation.

5. Adiabatic compression would heat the confined air by about 10°C for each kilometer decrease in elevation. The -35°C air would be heated 100°C and have a ground temperature of about (-35 + 100) = **65°C.** (This is 149°F, roasting hot!)

7. (a) For the room, W = **0.044 J.**

(b) For the freezer, W = **0.69 J.**

(c) For the helium refrigerator, W = **74 J.** The bigger the temperature "hill" relative to the lower temperature, the more work is needed to move the energy.

ANSWERS TO CHAPTER 19 EXERCISES (Vibrations and Waves)

1. The period of a pendulum does not depend on the mass of the bob, but does depend on the length of the string.

3. The period of a pendulum depends on the acceleration due to gravity. Just as in a stronger gravitational field a ball will fall faster, a pendulum will swing to-and-fro faster. (The exact relationship, $T = 2\pi\sqrt{l/g}$, is shown in Footnote 1 in the chapter). So at mountain altitudes where the gravitational field of the Earth is slightly less, a pendulum will oscillate with a slightly longer period, and a clock will run just a bit slower and will "lose" time.

5. Assuming the center of gravity of the suitcase doesn't change when loaded with books, the pendulum rate of the empty case and loaded case will be the same. This is because the period of a pendulum is independent of mass. Since the length of the pendulum doesn't change, the frequency and hence the period is unchanged.

7. The frequency of a pendulum depends on the restoring force, which is gravity. Double the mass and you double the gravitational force that contributes to the torque acting on the pendulum. More mass means more torque, but also more inertia—so has no net effect. Similarly, mass doesn't affect free fall acceleration (see Figure 19.1).

9. Lower frequency produces waves farther apart, so wavelength increases. Wavelength and frequency are inverse to each other.

11. Letting $v = f\lambda$ guide thinking, twice the speed means twice the frequency.

13. The periods are equal. Interestingly, an edge-on view of a body moving in uniform circular motion is seen to vibrate in a straight line. How? Exactly in simple harmonic motion. So the up and down motion of pistons in a car engine are simple harmonic, and have the same period as the circularly rotating shaft that they drive.

15. Shake the garden hose to-and-fro in a direction perpendicular to the hose to produce a sine-like curve.

17. (a) Transverse. (b) Longitudinal. (c) Transverse.

19. Frequency and period are reciprocals of one another; $f = 1/T$. and $T = 1/f$. Double one and the other is half as much. So doubling the frequency of a vibrating object halves the period.

21. Violet light has the greater frequency.

23. The frequency of the second hand of a clock is one cycle per minute; the frequency of the minute hand is one cycle per hour; for the hour hand the frequency is one cycle per 12 hours. To express these values in hertz, we need to convert the times to seconds. Then we find for the second hand the frequency = $1/60$ hertz: for the minute hand the frequency = $1/3600$ hertz; for the hour hand the frequency = $1/(12 \times 3600) = 1/(43,200)$ hertz.

25. As you dip your fingers more frequently into still water, the waves you produce will be of a higher frequency (we see the relationship between "how frequently" and "frequency"). The crests of the higher-frequency waves will be closer together—their wavelengths will be shorter.

27. Think of a period as one cycle in time, and a wavelength as one cycle in space, and a little though will show that in a time of one period, a wave travels a full wavelength. Formally, we can see this as follows:
distance = speed × time
where speed = frequency × wavelength, which when substituted for speed above, gives
distance = frequency × wavelength × time
distance = 1/period × wavelength × period = wavelength.

29. The energy of a water wave spreads along the increasing circumference of the wave until its magnitude diminishes to a value that cannot be distinguished from thermal motions in the water. The energy of the waves adds to the internal energy of the water.

31. The speed of light is 300,000 km/s, about a million times faster than sound. Because of this difference in speeds, lightning is seen a million times sooner than it is heard.

33. The frequency is doubled.

35. The Doppler effect is a change in frequency as a result of the motion of source, receiver, or both. So if you move toward a stationary sound source, yes, you encounter wave crests more frequently and the frequency of the received sound is higher. Or if you move away from the source, the wave crests encounter you less frequently, and you hear sound of a lower frequency.

37. No, the effects of shortened waves and stretched waves would cancel one another.

39. Police use radar waves which are reflected from moving cars. From the shift in the returned frequencies, the speed of the reflectors (car bodies) is determined.

41. Oops, careful. The Doppler effect is about changes in *frequency*, not speed.

43. A boat that makes a bow wave is traveling faster than the waves of water it generates.

45. The fact that you hear an airplane in a direction that differs from where you see it simply means the airplane is moving, and not necessarily faster than sound (a sonic boom would be evidence of supersonic flight). If the speed of sound and the speed of light were the same, then you'd hear a plane where it appears in the sky. But because the two speeds are so different, the plane you see appears ahead of the plane you hear.

47. The speed of the sound source rather than the loudness of the sound is crucial to the production of a shock wave. At subsonic speeds, no overlapping of the waves will occur to produce a shock wave. Hence no sonic boom is produced.

49. Open-ended.

SOLUTIONS TO CHAPTER 19 PROBLEMS

1. (a) $f = 1/T = 1/0.10$ s = **10 Hz**;

   (b) $f = 1/5 =$ **0.2 Hz**;

   (c) $f = 1/(1/60)$ s = **60 Hz**.

3. The skipper notes that 15 meters of wave pass each 5 seconds, or equivalently, that 3 meters pass each 1 second, so the speed of the wave must be

   $$\text{Speed} = \frac{\text{distance}}{\text{time}} = \frac{15 \text{ m}}{5 \text{ s}} = \textbf{3 m/s}.$$

   Or in wave terminology:
   Speed = frequency × wavelength = (1/5 Hz)(15 m) = **3 m/s**.

5. To say that the frequency of radio waves is 100 MHz and that they travel at 300,000 km/s, is to say that there are 100 million wavelengths packed into 300,000 kilometers of space. Or expressed in meters, 300 million m of space. Now 300 million m divided by 100 million waves gives a wavelength of 3 meters per wave. Or

   $$\text{Wavelength} = \frac{\text{speed}}{\text{frequency}} = \frac{(300 \text{ megameters/s})}{(100 \text{ megahertz})} = \textbf{3 m}.$$

7. (a) Period = 1/frequency = 1/(256 Hz) = **0.00391 s**, or 3.91 ms.
   (b) Speed = wavelength × frequency, so wavelength = speed/frequency = (340 m/s)/(256 Hz) = **1.33 m.**

9. Below. Speed = frequency × wavelength, so frequency = speed/wavelength = $(3 \times 10^8 \text{ m/s})/(3.42 \text{ m}) = 8.77 \times 10^7$ Hz = **87.7 MHz**, just below the FM band.

ANSWERS TO CHAPTER 20 EXERCISES (Sound)

1. Light travels about a million times faster than sound, hence the delay between what you see and what you hear.

3. Between us and other planets is a vacuum. Sound does not travel in a vacuum.

5. Bees buzz when in flight because they flap their wings at audio frequencies.

7. The carrier frequency of electromagnetic waves emitted by the radio station is 101.1 MHz.

9. The wavelength of the electromagnetic wave will be much longer because of its greater speed. You can see this from the equation speed = wavelength × frequency, so for the same frequency greater speed means greater wavelength. Or you can think of the fact that in the time of one period—the same for both waves—each wave moves a distance equal to one wavelength, which will be greater for the faster wave.

11. Light travels about a million times faster than sound in air, so you see a distant event a million times sooner than you hear it.

13. When sound passes a particular point in the air, the air is first compressed and then rarefied as the sound passes. So its density is increased and then decreased as the wave passes.

15. Because snow is a good absorber of sound, it reflects little sound—hence quietness.

17. The Moon is described as a silent planet because it has no atmosphere to transmit sounds.

19. If the speed of sound were different for different frequencies, say, faster for higher frequencies, then the farther a listener is from the music source, the more jumbled the sound would be. In that case, higher-frequency notes would reach the ear of the listener first. The fact that this jumbling doesn't occur is evidence that sound of all frequencies travel at the same speed. (Be glad this is so, particularly if you sit far from the stage, or if you like outdoor concerts.)

21. Sound travels faster in warm air because the air molecules that compose warm air themselves travel faster and therefore don't take as long before they bump into each other. This lesser time for molecules to bump against one another results in faster sound.

23. Refraction is the result of changing wave speeds, where part of a wave travels at a different speed than other parts. This occurs in nonuniform winds and nonuniform temperatures. Interestingly, if winds, temperatures, or other factors could not change the speed of sound, then refraction would not occur. (The fact that refraction does indeed occur is evidence for the changing speeds of sound.)

25. Sound is more easily heard when the wind traveling toward the listener at elevations above ground level travels faster than wind near the ground. Then the waves are bent downward as is the case of the refraction of sound shown in Figure 20.8.

27. An echo is weaker than the original sound because sound spreads and is therefore less intense with distance. If you are at the source, the echo will sound as if it originated on the other side of the wall from which it reflects (just as your image in a mirror appears to come from behind the glass). Also, the wall is likely not a perfect reflector.

29. First, in outer space there is no air or other material to carry sound. Second, if there were, the faster-moving light would reach you before the sound.

31. If a single disturbance at some unknown distance sends longitudinal waves at one known speed, and transverse waves at a lesser known speed, and you measure the difference in time of the waves as they arrive, you can calculate the distance. The wider the gap in time, the greater the distance—which could be in any direction. If you use this distance as the radius of a circle on a map, you know the disturbance occurred somewhere on that circle. If you telephone two friends who have made similar measurements of the same event from different locations, you can

transfer their circles to your map, and the point where the three circles intersect is the location of the disturbance.

33. Soldiers break step when crossing a bridge so they will not set the bridge into forced vibration or resonance.

35. There are two principal reasons why bass notes are more distinctly heard through walls than higher-frequency notes. One is that waves that vibrate more often per second transfer sound energy into heat more rapidly than waves of lower frequency. The higher-frequency waves are thermally "eaten up" by the material in the walls, while the lower-frequency vibrations pass with less loss through the material. Another reason is that the natural frequency of large walls, floors, and ceilings, is lower than the natural frequency of smaller surfaces. The large surfaces are more easily set into forced vibrations and resonance.

37. The lower strings are resonating with the upper strings.

39. When you are equally distant from the speakers, their tones interfere constructively. When you step to one side, the distance to one speaker is greater than the distance to the other speaker and the two waves are no longer in phase. They interfere destructively. (If you step far enough to one side, they will interfere constructively again.)

41. Long waves are most canceled, which makes the resulting sound so tinny. For example, when the speaker cones are, say, 4 centimeters apart, waves more than a meter long are nearly 180° out of phase, whereas 2-centimeter waves will be in phase. The higher frequencies are least canceled by this procedure. This must be tried to be appreciated.

43. Think of pushing a child on a swing: If you pushed twice as often as the child's period, you would push against the child's motion with every other push, and similarly with increased multiples of frequency. Pushing more often than once each period disrupts the motion. On the other hand, if you pushed the child every other swing, your pushes would match the child's motion and amplitude would increase. So sub-multiple pushes will not disrupt motion. Similarly with sound.

45. No, for the same word refers to different aspects of music. The beat of music involves rhythm, and the beats of sound involve throbbing due to interference.

47. The "beat frequency" is 2 per minute, so you and your friend will be in step twice per minute, or every 30 seconds. You can see this also from the fact that your friend's stride length is a little shorter than yours, 24/25 as long to be exact, so when you have taken exactly 24 strides—which is after half a minute—your friend will have taken exactly 25 and you will be back in step.

49. The possible frequencies are 264 + 4 = 268 Hz, or 264 − 4 = 260 Hz.

SOLUTIONS TO CHAPTER 20 PROBLEMS

1. Wavelength = speed/frequency = $\dfrac{340 \text{ m/s}}{340 \text{ Hz}}$ = **1 m.**

   Similarly for a 34,000 hertz wave; wavelength = $\dfrac{340 \text{ m/s}}{34\ 000 \text{ Hz}}$ = 0.01 m = **1 cm.**

3. The ocean floor is 4590 meters down. The 6-second time delay means that the sound reached the bottom in 3 seconds. Distance = speed × time = 1530 m/s × 3 s = **4590 m.**

5. The woman is about **340 meters** away. The clue is the single blow you hear after you see her stop hammering. That blow originated with the next-to-last blow you saw. The very first blow would have appeared as silent, and succeeding blows synchronous with successive strikes. In one second sound travels 340 meters in air.

7. (a) **Constructively.**

   (b) **Constructively.** (Even though each wave travels 1.5 wavelengths, they travel the *same* distance and are therefore in phase and interfere constructively.)

   (c) **Destructively.** The crest of one coincides with the trough of the other.

9. Wavelength = speed/frequency = (1,500 m/s)/(57 Hz) = **26 m.**
   Alternate method: For sounds of the same frequency in different media, wavelengths are proportional to wave speed. So (wavelength in water)/(wavelength in air) = (speed in water)/(speed in air) = (1,500 m/s)/(340 m/s) = 4.4. Multiply 6 m by 4.4 to get 26 m.

ANSWERS TO CHAPTER 21 EXERCISES (Musical Sounds)

1. Agree, for pitch is the subjective form of frequency.

3. The sound of commercials is concentrated at frequencies to which the ear is most sensitive. Whereas the overall sound meets regulations, our ears perceive the sound as distinctly louder.

5. A low pitch will be produced when a guitar string is (a) lengthened, (b) loosened so that tension is reduced, and (c) made more massive, usually by windings of wire around the string. That's why bass strings are thick—more inertia.

7. Amplitude.

9. The length of a flute is crucial to the notes it plays. Expansion or contraction of the flute with temperature can change its pitch, and therefore change the tuning between the instruments.

11. Less tension means less frequency and lower-pitched sound.

13. If the wavelength of a vibrating string is reduced, such as by pressing it with your finger against the neck of a guitar, the frequency of the vibration increases. This is heard as an increased pitch.

15. The longer tines have greater rotational inertia, which means they'll be more resistant to vibrating, and will do so at lower frequency. Similarly, a long pendulum has greater rotational inertia and swings to-and-fro at a slower pace.

17. The thicker string has more mass and more inertia, and therefore a lower frequency.

19. A plucked guitar string would vibrate for a longer time without a sounding board because less air is set into motion per unit of time, which means the energy of the vibrating string decreases more slowly.

21. In addition to pieces of paper at the supporting ends of the string, when a string vibrates in two segments a piece may be placed at the node in its center. For three segments, two pieces can be supported, each one-third the total distance from each end.

23. Period = $1/f$ = 1/264 second (0.004 second or 4 ms).

25. The amplitude in a sound wave corresponds to the overpressure of the compression or equivalently the under pressure of the rarefaction.

27. The pattern on the right has the greater amplitude and is therefore louder.

29. The range of human hearing is so wide that no single mechanical audio speaker can faithfully reproduce all the frequencies we can hear. So hi-fi speakers divide the range into two (and three) parts. A speaker with a relatively large surface has more inertia and is not as responsive to higher frequencies as a speaker with a smaller surface. So the larger speaker pushes the longer wavelengths, or lower frequencies, and the smaller speaker pushes the shorter wavelengths, or higher frequencies. (Ideally, the diameter of the speaker should be $1/2$ the wavelength of a given sound—so a 12-inch speaker corresponds to about 550 hertz—and even larger speakers are best for bass notes).

31. The person with the more acute hearing is the one who can hear the faintest sounds—the one who can hear 5 dB.

33. Sound at 110 dB is a million times more intense than sound at 50 dB. The difference, 60 dB, corresponds to 10^6, a million.

35. Helium molecules and oxygen molecules at the same temperature have the same kinetic energies. Kinetic energy equals $1/2$ mv^2. The smaller mass of helium is compensated for by a greater speed (Chapter 7).

37. The limited range of frequencies transmitted by a telephone can't match the full range in music. Especially, it cuts off the higher-frequency overtones of music that contribute to its quality.

39. The second harmonic has twice the frequency, 524 Hz.

41. The first harmonic is the fundamental, which is the same 440 Hz. The second harmonic is twice this, 880 Hz. The third harmonic is three times the first, 3 × 440 = 1320 Hz.

43. When the piano string is struck it will oscillate not only in its fundamental mode of 220 Hz when tuned, but also in its second harmonic at 440 Hz. If the string is out of tune, this second harmonic will beat against the 440 Hz tuning fork. You tune the string by listening for those beats and then either tightening or loosening the string until the beating disappears.

45. By controlling how hard he blows and how he holds his mouth, the bugler can stimulate different harmonics. The notes you hear from a bugle are actually harmonics; you don't hear the fundamental.

47. Blue light is higher-frequency light, with shorter waves that allow closer spacing of the pits.

49. The likelihood is high that you subject yourself to louder sounds than your grandparents experienced—particularly via earphones.

SOLUTIONS TO CHAPTER 21 PROBLEMS

1. The decibel scale is based upon powers of 10. The ear responds to sound intensity in logarithmic fashion. Each time the intensity of sound is made 10 times larger, the intensity level in decibels increases by 10 units. So a sound of
   (a) 10 dB is **ten** times more intense than the threshold of hearing

   (b) 30 dB is **one thousand** times more intense than the threshold of hearing.

   (c) 60 dB is **one million** times more intense than the threshold of hearing.

3. One octave above 1000 Hz is **2000 Hz**, and two octaves above 1000 Hz is **4000 Hz**. One octave below 1000 Hz is **500 Hz**, and two octaves below 100 Hz is **250 Hz**.

5. The wavelength of the fundamental is twice the length of the string, or 1.5 m. Then the speed of the wave is
   $v = f\lambda = 220$ Hz × 1.5 m = **330 m/s**. (Note that this is for a transverse vibration of the string. A longitudinal sound-wave within the string could have a much greater speed.)

ANSWERS TO CHAPTER 22 EXERCISES   (Electrostatics)

1. There are no positives and negatives in gravitation—the interactions between masses are only attractive, whereas electrical interactions may be attractive as well as repulsive. The mass of one particle cannot "cancel" the mass of another, whereas the charge of one particle can cancel the effect of the opposite charge of another particle.

3. Electrons are loosely bound on the outside of atoms, whereas protons are very tightly bound within the atomic nuclei.

5. Clothes become charged when electrons from a garment of one material are rubbed onto another material. If the materials were good conductors, discharge between materials would soon occur. But the clothes are nonconducting and the charge remains long enough for oppositely charged garments to be electrically attracted and stick to one another.

7. When the wool and plastic rub against each other, electrons are rubbed from the plastic onto the wool. The deficiency of electrons on the plastic bag results in its positive charge.

9. Excess electrons rubbed from your hair leave it with a positive charge; excess electrons on the comb give it a negative charge.

11. More than two decades ago, before truck tires were made electrically conducting, chains or wires were commonly dragged along the road surface from the bodies of trucks. Their purpose was to discharge any charge that would otherwise build up because of friction with the air and the road. Electrically-conducting tires now in use prevent the buildup of static charge that could produce a spark—especially dangerous for trucks carrying flammable cargoes.

13. Cosmic rays produce ions in air, which offer a conducting path for the discharge of charged objects. Cosmic-ray particles streaming downward through the atmosphere are attenuated by radioactive decay and by absorption, so the radiation and the ionization are stronger at high altitude than at low altitude. Charged objects more quickly lose their charge at higher altitudes.

15. When an object acquires a positive charge, it loses electrons and its mass decreases. How much? By an amount equal to the mass of the electrons that have left. When an object acquires a negative charge, it gains electrons, and the mass of the electrons as well. (The masses involved are incredibly tiny compared to the masses of the objects. For a balloon rubbed against your hair, for example, the extra electrons on the balloon comprise less than a billionth of a billionth of a billionth the mass of the balloon.)

17. The crystal as a whole has a zero net charge, so any negative charge in one part is countered with as much positive charge in another part. So the net charge of the negative electrons has the same magnitude as the net charge of the ions. (This balancing of positive and negative charges within the crystal is almost, but not precisely, perfect because the crystal can gain or lose a few extra electrons.)

19. For the outer electrons, the attractive force of the nucleus is largely canceled by the repulsive force of the inner electrons, leaving a force on the outer electrons little different from the force on the single electron in a hydrogen atom. For the inner electrons, on the other hand, all of the electrons farther from the nucleus exert no net force (it is similar to the situation within the Earth, where only the Earth below, not the Earth above, exerts a gravitational force on a deeply buried piece of matter). So the inner electrons feel the full force of the nucleus, and a large amount of energy is required to remove them. Stripping all of the electrons from a heavy atom is especially difficult. Only in recent years have researchers at the University of California, Berkeley succeeded in removing all of the electrons from the atoms of heavy elements like uranium.

21. The law would be written no differently.

23. The electrons don't fly out of the penny because they are attracted to the five thousand billion billion positively charged protons in the atomic nuclei of atoms in the penny.

25. The inverse-square law is at play here. At half the distance the electric force field is four times as strong; at $1/4$ the distance, 16 times stronger. At four times the distance, one-sixteenth as strong.

27. Doubling one charge doubles the force. The magnitude of the force does not depend on the sign of charge.

29. The huge value of the constant k for electrical force indicates a relatively huge force between charges, compared with the small gravitational force between masses and the small value of the gravitational constant G.

31. By convention, the direction goes from positive to negative.

33. As the name implies, a semiconductor both conducts and insulates depending on certain conditions, whereas a conductor always conducts under all normal conditions and an insulator always insulates under all normal conditions.

35. Planet Earth is negatively charged. If it were positive, the field would point outward.

37. The metal spikes penetrating into the ground reduce electrical resistance between the golfer and the ground, providing an effective electrical path from cloud to ground. Not a good idea!

39. A neutral atom in an electric field is electrically distorted (see Figure 22.11). If the field is strong enough, the distortion results in ionization, where the charges are torn from each other. The ions then provide a conducting path for an electric current.

41. The mechanism of sticking is charge induction. If it's a metal door, the charged balloon will induce an opposite charge on the door. It will accomplish this by attracting opposite charges to it and repelling like charges to parts of the door farther away. The balloon and the oppositely-charged part of the door are attracted and the balloon sticks. If the door is an insulator, the balloon induces polarization of the molecules in the door material. Oppositely-charged sides of the molecules in the surface of the door face the balloon and attraction results. So whether you consider the door to be an insulator or a conductor, the balloon sticks by induction.

43. The paint particles in the mist are polarized and are therefore attracted to the charged chassis.

45. The half ring has the greater electric field at its center because the electric field at the center of the whole ring cancels to zero. The electric field at the center of the half ring is due to a multitude of electric vectors, vertical components canceling, with horizontal components adding to produce a resultant field acting horizontally to the right.

47. The electron will have the greater speed on impact. The force on both will be the same, but the electron experiences more acceleration and therefore gains more speed because of its smaller mass.

49. The bits of thread become polarized in the electric field, one end positive and the other negative, and become the electric counterparts of the north and south poles of the magnetic compass. Opposite forces on the end of the fibers (or compass needle) produce torques that orient the fibers along the field direction (look ahead to Figure 24.3 in the next chapter).

51. 10 joules per coulomb is 10 volts. When released, its 10 joules of potential energy will become 10 joules of kinetic energy as it passes its starting point.

53. Voltage = (0.5 J)/0.0001 C = 5000 V.

55. Because charge is taken off one plate and put on the other.

57. It is dangerous because the capacitor may be charged.

59. You would feel no electrical effects inside any statically charged conducting body. The distribution of mutually-repelling charges is such that the electric field inside the body is zero—true for solids as well as hollow conductors. (If the electric field were not zero, then

conduction electrons would move in response to the field until electrical equilibrium was established—which is a zero electric field.)

SOLUTIONS TO CHAPTER 22 PROBLEMS

1. By the inverse-square law, twice as far is $1/4$ the force; **5 N.**
   The solution involves relative distance only, so the magnitude of charges is irrelevant.

3. From Coulomb's law, $F = k\dfrac{q_1 q_2}{d^2}$ $= (9 \times 10^9)\dfrac{(1.0 \times 10^{-6})^2}{(0.03)^2}$ $= \textbf{10 N}$. This is the same as the weight of a 1-kg mass.

5. $F_{(grav)} = Gm_1 m_2/d^2 = (6.67 \times 10^{-11})\dfrac{(9.1 \times 10^{-31})(1.67 \times 10^{-27})}{(1.0 \times 10^{-10})^2}$

   $= \textbf{1.0} \times \textbf{10}^{-47}$ **N.**

   $F_{(elec)} = kq_1 q_2/d^2 = (9 \times 10^9)\dfrac{(1.6 \times 10^{-19})^2}{(1.0 \times 10^{-10})^2}$ $= \textbf{2.3} \times \textbf{10}^{-8}$ **N.**

   The electrical force between an electron and a proton is more than 1,000,000,000,000,000,000,000,000,000,000,000,000,000 times greater than the gravitational force between them! (Note that this ratio of forces is the same for any separation of the particles.)

7. Energy is charge x potential: $PE = qV = (2\ C)(100 \times 10^6\ V) = \textbf{2} \times \textbf{10}^8$ **J.**

9. (a) From $E = \dfrac{F}{q}$ we see that $q = \dfrac{F}{E}$ $= \dfrac{mg}{E}$ $= \dfrac{(1.1 \times 10^{-14})(9.8)}{1.68 \times 10^5}$

   $= \textbf{6.4} \times \textbf{10}^{-19}$ **C.**

   (b) Number of electrons $= \dfrac{6.4 \times 10^{-19}C}{1.6 \times 10^{-19}C/electron}$ $= \textbf{4 electrons.}$

ANSWERS TO CHAPTER 23 EXERCISES (Electric Current)

1. Make the pipe of low-resistant material and wider. Make the conducting wire of low electrical resistance and wider.

3. Six amperes (10 – 4 = 6).

5. Brightness increases when current increases.

7. No, for the number of electrons are normally balanced by an equal number of protons in the nuclei.

9. Only circuit number 5 is complete and will light the bulb. (Circuits 1 and 2 are "short circuits" and will quickly drain the cell of its energy. In circuit 3 both ends of the lamp filament are connected to the same terminal and are therefore at the same potential. Only one end of the lamp filament is connected to the cell in circuit 4.)

11. Agree with the friend who says energy, not current, is consumed.

13. Agree, for then the same appropriate voltage will power the circuit.

15. You have warmed it, and increased its resistance slightly. (Have you ever noticed that when bulbs burn out, it is usually a moment after they have been turned on? If the filament is weak, the initial pulse of higher current resulting from the lower resistance of the still-cool filament causes it to fail.)

17. A lie detector circuit relies on the likelihood that the resistivity of your body changes when you tell a lie. Nervousness promotes perspiration, which lowers the body's electrical resistance, and increases whatever current flows. If a person is able to lie with no emotional change and no change in perspiration, then such a lie detector will not be effective. (Better lying indicators focus on the eyes.)

19. Thick wires have less resistance and will more effectively carry currents without excessive heating.

21. The thick filament has less resistance and will draw (carry) more current than a thin wire connected across the same potential difference. (Important point: It is common to say that a certain resistor "draws" a certain current, but this may be misleading. A resistor doesn't "attract" or "draw" current, just as a pipe in a plumbing circuit doesn't "draw" water; it instead "allows" or "provides for" the passage of current when an electrical pressure is established across it.)

23. If both voltage and resistance are doubled, current remains unchanged. Likewise if both voltage and resistance are halved.

25. Damage generally occurs by excess heating when too much current is driven through an appliance. For an appliance that converts electrical energy directly to thermal energy this happens when excess voltage is applied. So don't connect a 110-volt iron, toaster, or electric stove to a 220-volt circuit. Interestingly enough, if the appliance is an electric motor, then applying too *little* voltage can result in overheating and burn up the motor windings. (This is because the motor will spin at a low speed and the reverse "generator effect" will be small and allow too great a current to flow in the motor.) So don't hook up a 220-volt power saw or any 220-volt motor-driven appliance to 110 volts. To be safe use the recommended voltages with appliances of any kind.

27. Electric power in your home is likely supplied at 60 hertz and 110-120 volts via electrical outlets. This is ac (and delivered to your home via transformers between the power source and your home. We will see in Chapter 25 that transformers require ac power for operation.) Electric power in your car must be able to be supplied by the battery. Since the + and - terminals of the battery do not alternate, the current they produce does not alternate either. It flows in one direction and is dc.

29. There is less resistance in the higher wattage lamp. Since power = current x voltage, more power for the same voltage means more current. And by Ohm's law, more current for the same voltage means less resistance. (Algebraic manipulation of the equations P = IV and I = V/R leads to P = V²/R.)

31. The equivalent resistance of resistors in series is their sum, so connect a pair of resistors in series for more resistance.

33. Current remains the same in all the resistors in a series circuit.

35. The amount of current any device puts through any conductor depends upon the voltage of the device and the resistance of the conductor. Also important is the amount of charge the device can deliver; a relatively large amount of charge at high voltage represents high energy (like that from a power line) while a small amount of charge at high voltage represents low energy (like discharging a balloon rubbed on your hair). The device being warned about is likely highly energized to a high voltage, and should be respected. It possesses no current to be warned about, but because of its high energy and high voltage, may produce a lethal current in anyone offering a conducting path from it to the ground.

37. No cause for concern. The label is intended as humor. It describes electrons, which are in all matter.

39. Zero. Power companies do not sell electrons; they sell energy. Whatever number of electrons flow into a home, the same number flows out.

41. Electric energy is propagated through a circuit by electric fields moving at close to the speed of light, not by electron collisions. Sound, on the other hand, travels by molecular or atomic collisions—a much slower process.

43. Bulbs will glow brighter when connected in parallel, for the voltage of the battery is impressed across each bulb. When two identical bulbs are connected in series, half the voltage of the battery is impressed across each bulb. The battery will run down faster when the bulbs are in parallel.

45. Most of the electric energy in a lamp filament is transformed to heat. For low currents in the bulb, the heat that is produced may be enough to feel but not enough to make the filament glow red or white hot.

47. As more bulbs are connected in series, more resistance is added to the single circuit path and the resulting current produced by the battery is diminished. This is evident in the dimmer light from the bulbs. On the other hand, when more bulbs are connected to the battery in parallel, the brightness of the bulbs is practically unchanged. This is because each bulb in effect is connected directly to the battery with no other bulbs in its electrical path to add to its resistance. Each bulb has its own current path.

49. What affects the other branches is the voltage impressed across them, and their own resistance—period. Opening or closing a branch doesn't alter either of these.

51. Agree, because even for the smallest resistor, current has an alternative path(s), making for an overall smaller resistance.

53. Connect four 40-ohm resistors in parallel.

55. All are the same for identical resistors in parallel. If the resistors are not the same, the one of greater resistance will have less current through it and less power dissipation in it. Regardless of the resistances, the voltage across both will be identical.

57. All three are equivalent parallel circuits. Each branch is individually connected to the battery.

59. More current flows in the 100-watt bulb. We see this from the relationship "power = current x voltage." More current for the same voltage means less resistance. So a 100-watt bulb has less resistance than a 60-watt bulb. Less resistance for the same length of the same material means

a thicker filament. The filaments of high wattage bulbs are thicker than those of lower-wattage bulbs. (It is important to note that both watts and volts are printed on a light bulb. A bulb that is labeled 100 W, 120 V, is 100 W *only* if there are 120 volts across it. If there are only 110 volts across it, and the resistance remains unchanged, then the power output would be only 84 watts!)

SOLUTIONS TO CHAPTER 23 PROBLEMS

1. From "Power = current × voltage," 60 watts = current × 120 volts, current = $\dfrac{60W}{120V}$
   = **0.5 A.**

3. From power = current × voltage, current = $\dfrac{power}{voltage}$ = $\dfrac{1200W}{120V}$ = **10 A.**
   From the formula derived above, resistance = $\dfrac{voltage}{current}$ = $\dfrac{120V}{10A}$ = **12 W.**

5. **$2.52**. First, 100 watts = 0.1 kilowatt. Second, there are 168 hours in one week (7 days × 24 hours/day = 168 hours). So 168 hours × 0.1 kilowatt = 16.8 kilowatt-hours, which at 15 cents per kWh comes to $2.52.

7. The iron's power is $P = IV$ = (110 V)(9 A) = 990 W = 990 J/s. The heat energy generated in 1 minute is E = power × time = (990 J/s)(60 s) = **59,400 J.**

9. It was designed for use in a **120-V circuit**. With an applied voltage of 120 V, the current in the bulb is $I = V/R$ = (120 V)/(95 W) = 1.26 A. The power dissipated by the bulb is then $P = IV$ = (1.26 A)(120 V) = 151 W, close to the rated value. If this bulb is connected to 240 V, it would carry twice as much current and would dissipate four times as much power (twice the current twice the voltage), more than 600 W. It would likely burn out. (This problem can also be solved by first carrying out some algebraic manipulation. Since current = voltage/resistance, we can write the formula for power as $P = IV = (V/R)V = V^2/R$. Solving for V gives $V = \sqrt{PR}$. Substituting for the power and the resistance gives $V = \sqrt{(150)(95)}$ = 119 V.)

ANSWERS TO CHAPTER 24 EXERCISES (Magnetism)

1. Separation is easy with a magnet (try it and see!)

3. How the charge moves dictates the direction of its magnetic field. (A magnetic field is a vector quantity.) Magnetic fields cancel, more in some materials than others.

5. Attraction will occur because the magnet induces opposite polarity in a nearby piece of iron. North will induce south, and south will induce north. This is similar to charge induction, where a balloon will stick to a wall whether the balloon is negative or positive.

7. The poles of the magnet attract each other and will cause the magnet to bend, even enough for the poles to touch if the material is flexible enough.

9. An electron always experiences a force in an electric field because that force depends on nothing more than the field strength and the charge. But the force an electron experiences in a magnetic field depends on an added factor: velocity. If there is no motion of the electron through the magnetic field in which it is located, no magnetic force acts. Furthermore, if motion is along the magnetic field direction, and not at some angle to it, then no magnetic force acts also. Magnetic force, unlike electric force, depends on the velocity of the charge relative to the magnetic field.

11. Apply a small magnet to the door. If it sticks, your friend is wrong because aluminum is not magnetic. If it doesn't stick, your friend might be right (but not necessarily—there are lots of nonmagnetic materials).

13. Domains in the paper clip are induced into alignment in a manner similar to the electrical charge polarization in an insulator when a charged object is brought nearby. Either pole of a magnet will induce alignment of domains in the paper clip: attraction results because the pole of the aligned domains closest to the magnet's pole is always the opposite pole, resulting in attraction.

15. The needle is not pulled toward the north side of the bowl because the south pole of the magnet is equally attracted southward. The net force on the needle is zero. (The net torque, on the other hand, will be zero only when the needle is aligned with the Earth's magnetic field.)

17. Vertically downward.

19. The mechanism of alignment involves two factors: First, each filing is turned into a tiny magnet by the magnetic field of the bar magnet, which induces domain alignment in the filing. Second, a pair of equal torques act on the filing whenever it is not parallel to the magnetic field lines. These torques rotate the filings into alignment with the field lines like little compass needles.

21. Yes, for the compass aligns with the Earth's magnetic field, which extends from the magnetic pole in the Southern Hemisphere to the magnetic pole in the Northern Hemisphere.

23. Rotation is not produced when the loop is everywhere parallel to the field.

25. Yes, it does. Since the magnet exerts a force on the wire, the wire, according to Newton's third law, must exert a force on the magnet.

27. The needle points perpendicular to the wire. (See Figure 24.8.)

29. Less power because of reduced electrical resistance.

31. An electron has to be moving across lines of magnetic field in order to feel a magnetic force. So an electron at rest in a stationary magnetic field will feel no force to set it in motion. In an electric field, however, an electron will be accelerated whether or not it is already moving. (A combination of magnetic and electric fields is used in particle accelerators such as cyclotrons. The electric field accelerates the charged particle in its direction, and the magnetic field accelerates it perpendicular to its direction, causing it to follow a nearly circular path.)

33. The electric field in a cyclotron or any charged particle accelerator forces the particles to higher speeds, while the magnetic field forces the particles into curved paths. A magnetic force can only change the direction (not the speed) of a charged particle because the force is always perpendicular to the particle's instantaneous velocity. [Interestingly enough, in an accelerator called a betatron, the electric field is produced by a changing magnetic field.]

35. Associated with every moving charged particle, electrons, protons, or whatever, is a magnetic field. Since a magnetic field is not unique to moving electrons, there is a magnetic field about moving protons as well. However, it differs in direction. The field lines about the proton beam circle in one way, the field lines about an electron beam in the opposite way. (Physicists use a "right-hand rule." If the right thumb points in the direction of motion of a positive particle, the curved fingers of that hand show the direction of the magnetic field. For negative particles, the left hand can be used.)

37. When we write *work = force × distance*, we really mean the component of force in the direction of motion multiplied by the distance moved (Chapter 7). Since the magnetic force that acts on a beam of electrons is always perpendicular to the beam, there is no component of magnetic force along the instantaneous direction of motion. Therefore a magnetic field can do no work on a charged particle. (Indirectly, however, a *time-varying magnetic field* can induce an electric field that *can* do work on a charged particle.)

39. If the field interacts with a stationary bar magnet it is magnetic; if with a stationary charge, it is electric. If an electric current is generated in a rotating loop of wire, the field is magnetic. If a force acts only on a moving charge, the field is magnetic. So any of the classes of experiments that deal with electric charge at rest and electric charge in motion could be used to determine the nature of the field in the room.

41. Charged particles moving through a magnetic field are deflected most when they move at right angles to the field lines, and least when they move parallel to the field lines. If we consider cosmic rays heading toward the Earth from all directions and from great distance, those descending toward northern Canada will be moving nearly parallel to the magnetic field lines of the Earth. They will not be deflected very much, and secondary particles they create high in the atmosphere will also stream downward with little deflection. Over regions closer to the equator like Mexico, the incoming cosmic rays move more nearly at right angles to the Earth's magnetic field, and many of them are deflected back out into space before they reach the atmosphere. The secondary particles they create are less intense at the Earth's surface. (This "latitude effect" provided the first evidence that cosmic rays from outer space consist of charged particles—mostly protons, as we now know.)

43. Singly-charged ions traveling with the same speed through the same magnetic field will experience the same magnetic force. The extent of their deflections will then depend on their accelerations, which in turn depend on their respective masses. The least massive ions will be deflected the most and the most massive ions will be deflected least. (See Figure 34.14, further in the book, for a diagram of a mass spectrograph.)

45. To determine only by their interactions with each other which of two bars is a magnet, place the end of the bar #1 at the midpoint of bar #2 (like making a "T"). If there is an attraction, then bar #1 is the magnet. If there isn't, then bar #2 is the magnet.

47. Yes, each will experience a force because each is in the magnetic field generated by the other. Interestingly, currents in the same direction attract, and currents in opposite directions repel.

49. Each coil is magnetically attracted to its electromagnetic neighbor.

ANSWERS TO CHAPTER 25 EXERCISES (Electromagnetic Induction)

1. E & M induction requires change, of the intensity of a magnetic field or of motion in a magnetic field.

3. The magnetic domains that become aligned in the iron core contribute to the overall magnetic field of the coil and therefore increase its magnetic induction.

5. Work must be done to move a current-carrying conductor in a magnetic field. This is true whether or not the current is externally produced or produced as a result of the induction that accompanies the motion of the wire in the field. It's also a matter of energy conservation. There has to be more energy input if there is more energy output.

7. A cyclist will coast farther if the lamp is disconnected from the generator. The energy that goes into lighting the lamp is taken from the bike's kinetic energy, so the bike slows down. The work saved by not lighting the lamp will be the extra "force × distance" that lets the bike coast farther.

9. As in answer to Exercise 8, eddy currents induced in the metal change the magnetic field, which in turn changes the ac current in the coils and sets off an alarm.

11. Copper wires were not insulated in Henry's time. A coil of non-insulated wires touching one another would comprise a short circuit. Silk was used to insulate the wires so current would flow along the wires in the coil rather than across the loops touching one another.

13. In both cases the direction of the magnetic force is perpendicular to the magnetic field and the motion of charges—but with different results. In the motor effect, the magnetic force pushes the wire upward. In the generator effect, the wire is pushed downward and the magnetic force pushes electrons in a direction along the wire to produce a current.

15. Agree with your friend. Any coil of wire spinning in a magnetic field that cuts through magnetic field lines is a generator.

17. Two things occur in the windings of the electric motor driving a saw. Current input causes them to turn and you have a motor. But their motion in the magnetic field of the motor make them a generator as well. The net current in the motor is the input current minus the generated output current, which is opposite in direction to the input current. You pay the power company for the net current. When the motor jams, the net current is increased because of the absence of generated current. This can burn the windings of the saw!

19. The changing magnetic field produced when the current starts to flow induces a current in the aluminum ring. This current, in turn, generates a magnetic field that opposes the field produced by the magnet under the table. The aluminum ring becomes, momentarily, a magnet that is repelled by the hidden magnet. Why repelled? Lenz's law. The induced field opposes the change of the inducing field.

21. If the light bulb is connected to a wire loop that intercepts changing magnetic field lines from an electromagnet, voltage will be induced which can illuminate the bulb. Change is the key, so the electromagnet should be powered with ac.

23. Induction occurs only for a *change* in the intercepted magnetic field. The galvanometer will display a pulse when the switch in the first circuit is closed and current in the coil increases from zero. When the current in the first coil is steady, no current is induced in the secondary and the galvanometer reads zero. The galvanometer needle will swing in the opposite direction when the switch is opened and current falls to zero.

25. A transformer requires alternating voltage because the magnetic field in the primary winding must change if it is to induce voltage in the secondary. No change, no induction.

27. A transformer is analogous to a mechanical lever in that work is transferred from one part to another. What is multiplied in a mechanical lever is *force*, and in an electrical lever, *voltage*. In

both cases, energy and power are conserved, so what is not multiplied is energy, a conservation of energy no-no!

29. The hum heard when a transformer is operating on a 60 hertz ac line is a 60 hertz forced vibration of the iron slabs in the transformer core as their magnetic polarities alternate. The hum is greater if any other mechanical parts are set into vibration.

31. High efficiency requires that the maximum number of magnetic field lines produced in the primary are intercepted by the secondary. The core guides the lines from the primary through the secondary. Otherwise some of the magnetic field generated by the primary would go into heating metal parts of the transformer instead of powering the secondary circuit.

33. The voltage impressed across the lamp is 120 V and the current through it is 0.1 A. We see that the first transformer steps the voltage down to 12 V and the second one steps it back up to 120 V. The current in the secondary of the second transformer, which is the same as the current in the bulb, is one-tenth of the current in the primary, or 0.1 A.

35. By symmetry, the voltage and current for both primary and secondary are the same. So 12 V is impressed on the meter, with a current of 1 A ac.

37. In a power line, the high voltage is between one wire and another, not from one end of a given wire to the other end. The voltage difference between one end of the wire and the other is actually small, corresponding to the small current in the wire. The voltage difference *between the wires* multiplied by the current gives the power transmitted to the load. The voltage difference *between one end of a wire and the other* multiplied by the current gives the (much smaller) power dissipated in the wire. So, in applying Ohm's law, it's important that the voltage and current are applied to the same part of the circuit.

39. As the magnet falls, it induces current that circles in the conducting pipe and is accompanied by its own magnetic field. The moving magnet is slowed by interaction with this induced field.

41. Motion of conducting sheets through a magnetic field induces swirling currents (eddy currents) with fields that interact with the magnet and slow motion. Such doesn't occur in non-conducting cardboard.

43. A voltage difference is induced across the wings of a moving airplane. This produces a momentary current and charge builds up on the wing tips to create a voltage difference that counteracts the induced voltage difference. So charge is pulled equally in both directions and doesn't move.

45. Waving it changes the "flux" of the Earth's magnetic field in the coil, which induces voltage and hence current. You can think of the flux as the number of field lines that thread through the coil. This depends on the orientation of the coil, even in a constant field.

47. The incident radio wave causes conduction electrons in the antenna to oscillate. This oscillating charge (an oscillating current) provides the signal that feeds the radio.

49. Agree with your friend, for light is electromagnetic radiation having a frequency that matches the frequency to which our eyes are sensitive.

SOLUTIONS TO CHAPTER 25 PROBLEMS

1. If power losses can be ignored, in accord with energy conservation, the power provided by the secondary is also **100 W**.

3. From the transformer relationship,

$$\frac{\text{primary voltage}}{\text{primary turns}} = \frac{\text{secondary voltage}}{\text{secondary turns}} \quad ,$$

$$\frac{120V}{240 \text{ turns}} = \frac{6V}{x \text{ turns}}$$

Solve for x: x = (6 V)(240 turns)/(120 V) = **12 turns.**

5. (a) Since power is voltage × current, the current supplied to the users is

$$\text{current} = \frac{\text{power}}{\text{voltage}} = \frac{100000 \text{ W}}{12000 \text{ V}} = \textbf{8.3 A}.$$

(b) Voltage in each wire = current × resistance of the wire = (8.3 A)(10 W) = **83 V**.

(c) In each line, power = current × voltage = (8.3 A)(83 V) = 689 W. The total power wasted as heat is twice this, **1.38 kW.**
This is a small and tolerable loss. If the transmission voltage were ten times less, the losses to heat in the wires would be 100 times more! Then more energy would go into heat in the wires than into useful applications for the customers. That would not be tolerable. That's why high-voltage transmission is so important.

ANSWERS TO CHAPTER 26 EXERCISES   (Properties   of Light)

1. Your friend is correct. Also in a profound voice, your friend could say that sound is the only thing we hear!

3. The fundamental source of electromagnetic radiation is oscillating electric charges, which emit oscillating electric and magnetic fields.

5. Ultraviolet has shorter wavelengths than infrared. Correspondingly, ultraviolet also has the higher frequencies.

7. What waves in a light wave are the electric and magnetic fields. Their oscillation frequency is the frequency of the wave.

9. We can see the Sun and stars.

11. Speed is c, the speed of light.

13. Agree.

15. Agree.

17. The slower wave has the longer wavelength—sound.

19. Radio waves most certainly travel at the speed of every other electromagnetic wave—the speed of light.

21. Radio waves and light are both electromagnetic, transverse, move at the speed of light, and are created and absorbed by oscillating charge. They differ in their frequency and wavelength and in the type of oscillating charge that creates and absorbs them.

23. The average speed of light will be less where it interacts with absorbing and re-emitting particles of matter, such as in the atmosphere. The greater the number of interactions along the light's path, the less the average speed.

25. The person walking across the room and pausing to greet others is analogous to the transmission-of-light model in that there is a pause with each interaction. However, the same person that begins the walk ends the walk, whereas in light transmission there is a "death-birth" sequence of events as light is absorbed and "new light" is emitted in its place. The light to first strike the glass is not the same light that finally emerges. (Another analogy is a relay race, where the runner to begin the race is not the runner to cross the finish line.)

27. The greater number of interactions per distance tends to slow the light and result is a smaller average speed.

29. Clouds are transparent to ultraviolet light, which is why clouds offer no protection from sunburn. Glass, however, is opaque to ultraviolet light, and will therefore shield you from sunburn.

31. Any shadow cast by a faraway object such as a high-flying plane is filled in mainly by light tapering in from the Sun, which is not a point source. This tapering is responsible for the umbra and penumbra of solar eclipses (Figure 26.12). If the plane is low to the ground, however, the tapering of light around the airplane may be insufficient to fill in the shadow, part of which can be seen. This idea is shown in Figure 26.10.

33. A lunar eclipse occurs when the Earth, Sun, and Moon all fall on a straight line, with the Earth between the Sun and the Moon. During perfect alignment the Earth's shadow falls on the Moon. Not-quite-perfect alignment gives Earth observers a full view of the Moon. Moonlight is brightest and the Moon is always fullest when the alignment is closest to perfect—on the night of a lunar eclipse. At the time of a half moon, however, lines from Earth to Moon and from Earth to Sun are at right angles to each other. This is as non-aligned as the Earth, Moon, and Sun can

be, with the Moon nowhere near the Earth's shadow—no eclipse is possible. Similarly for the non-aligned times of a crescent Moon.

EARTH OBSERVERS SEE FULL MOON HERE

EARTH OBSERVERS SEE HALF MOON HERE

35. No eclipse occurred because no shadow was cast on any other body.

37. Rods, not cones, will respond to weak light, so you want to focus low-intensity light on a part of the retina that is composed of rods. That would be off to the side of the fovea. If you're looking at a weak star, look a bit off to the side of where you expect to see it. Then its image will fall on a part of your eye where rods may pick it up.

39. We see no color at the periphery of our vision simply because there are no cones located on the outermost regions of the retina.

41. Unless light reaching her eyes has increased in intensity, her contracting pupils imply that she is displeased with what she sees, hears, tastes, smells, or how she feels. In short, she may be displeased with you!

43. Energy is spread out and diluted, but not "lost." We distinguish between something being diluted and something being annihilated. In accord with the inverse-square law, light intensity gets weaker with distance, but the total amount of light over a spherical surface is the same at all distances from the source.

45. Some airliners bounce electromagnetic waves from the ground below, measuring the round trip time in order to find the distance to the ground, much as a ship bounces sonic waves from the ocean floor to measure water depth. Far above the ground an altimeter is fine for determining the airplane's height above sea level, but close to the ground the pilot wants to know the airplane's distance from local ground.

47. No, for the brightest star may simply be the closest star.

49. You see your hand in the past! How much? To find out, simply divide the distance between your hands and your eyes by the speed of light. (At 30 cm, this is about a billionth of a second.)

SOLUTIONS TO CHAPTER 26 PROBLEMS

1. In seconds, this time is 16.5 min × 60 s = 990 s.

$$\text{Speed} = \frac{\text{distance}}{\text{time}} = \frac{300,000,000 \text{ km}}{990 \text{ s}} = \textbf{303,030 km/s.}$$

3. From $v = \frac{d}{t}$, $t = \frac{d}{v} = \frac{d}{c} = \frac{1.5 \times 10^{11} \text{m}}{3 \times 10^8 \text{m/s}} = 500$ s (which equals 8.3 min).

The time to cross the diameter of the Earth's orbit is twice this, or **1000 s**, slightly more than 990 s in Problem 1.

5. As in Problem 4, $t = \frac{d}{v} = \frac{4.2 \times 10^{16} \text{ m}}{3 \times 10^8 \text{ m/s}} = \textbf{1.4} \times \textbf{10}^{\textbf{8}}$ **s.**

Converting to years by dimensional analysis,

$$1.4 \times 10^8 \text{ s} \times \frac{1 \text{ h}}{3600 \text{ s}} \times \frac{1 \text{ day}}{24 \text{ h}} \times \frac{1 \text{ yr}}{365 \text{ day}} = \textbf{4.4 yr.}$$

7. From $c = f\lambda$, $\lambda = \frac{c}{f} = \frac{3 \times 10^8 \text{m/s}}{6 \times 10^{14} \text{Hz}} = 5 \times 10^{-7}$ **m**, or 500 nanometers. This is 5000 times larger than the size of an atom, which is 0.1 nanometer. (The nanometer is a common unit of length in atomic and optical physics.)

9. (a) Frequency = speed/wavelength = $(3 \times 10^8 \text{ m/s})/(0.03 \text{ m}) = 1.0 \times 10^{10}$ Hz = **10 GHz.**

(b) Distance = speed × time, so time = distance/speed = $(10,000 \text{ m})/(3 \times 10^8 \text{ m/s}) = \textbf{3.3} \times \textbf{10}^{\textbf{-5}}$ **s**. (Note the importance of consistent SI units to get the right numerical answers.)

ANSWERS TO CHAPTER 27 EXERCISES (Color)

1. Red has the longest wavelength; violet has the shortest wavelength.

3. The customer is being reasonable in requesting to see the colors in the daylight. Under fluorescent lighting, with its predominant higher frequencies, the bluer colors rather than the redder colors will be accented. Colors will appear quite different in sunlight.

5. Either a white or green garment will reflect incident green light and be cooler. The complementary color, magenta, will absorb green light and be the best garment color to wear when the absorption of energy is desired.

7. The interior coating absorbs rather than reflects light, and therefore appears black. A black interior in an optical instrument will absorb any stray light rather than reflecting it and passing it around the interior of the instrument to interfere with the optical image.

9. Tennis balls are yellow green so that they match the color to which we are most sensitive.

11. Red cloth appears red in sunlight, and red by the illumination of the red light from a neon tube. But because the red cloth absorbs cyan light, it appears black when illuminated by cyan light.

13. The color that will emerge from a lamp coated to absorb yellow is blue, the complementary color. (White - yellow = blue.)

15. The overlapping blue and yellow beams will produce white light. When the two panes of glass are overlapped and placed in front of a single flashlight, however, little or no light will be transmitted.

17. Red and green produce yellow; red and blue produce magenta; red, blue, and green produce white.

19. The red shirt in the photo is seen as cyan in the negative, and the green shirt appears magenta—the complementary colors. When white light shines through the negative, red is transmitted where cyan is absorbed. Likewise, green is transmitted where magenta is absorbed.

21. The orange-yellow is complementary to blue, which combine to black. Cars would be difficult to see under such light.

23. Deep in water red is no longer present in light, so blood looks black. But there is plenty of red in a camera flash, so the blood looks red when so illuminated.

25. White; Magenta; White.

27. Agree, for the "light mathematics" is correct.

29. The reflected color is white minus red, or cyan.

31. We cannot see stars in the daytime because their dim light is overwhelmed by the brighter skylight, which is sunlight scattered by the atmosphere.

33. The daytime sky is black, as it is on the nighttime sky there.

35. The color of the Sun is yellow-white at all times on the Moon.

37. Such glasses eliminate the distraction provided by the more strongly scattered blue and violet light yet let the pilot see in a frequency range where the eye is sensitive. (Glasses that transmit predominantly red would also get rid of the scattered blue and violet light but would provide light to which the eye is not very sensitive.)

39. Particles in the smoke scatter predominantly blue light, so against a dark background you see the smoke as blue. What you see is predominantly light scattered by the smoke. But against the

bright sky what you see is predominantly the sky minus the light that the smoke scatters from it. You see yellow.

41. The statement is true. A more positive tone would omit the word "just," for the sunset is not *just* the leftover colors, but *is* those colors that weren't scattered in other directions.

43. Through the volcanic emissions, the Moon appears cyan, the complementary color of red.

45. The foam is composed of tiny bits of liquid that scatter light as a cloud does.

47. If the atmosphere were several times thicker, the sunlight reaching the Earth would be predominantly low frequencies because most of the blue light would be scattered away. Snow would likely appear orange at noon, and a deep red when the Sun is not directly overhead.

49. Sunset follows the activities of humans and other life that put dust and other particles in the air. So the composition of the sky is more varied at sunset.

ANSWERS TO CHAPTER 28 EXERCISES (Reflection and Refraction)

1. Fermat's principle for refraction is of least time, but for reflection it could be of least distance as well. This is because light does not go from one medium to another for reflection, so no change in speed occurs and least-time paths and least-distance paths are equivalent. But for refraction, light goes from a medium where it has a certain speed to another medium where its speed is different. When this happens the least-distance straight-line paths take a longer time to travel than the nonstraight-line least-time paths. See, for example, the difference in the least-distance and least-time paths in Figure 28.13.

3. Only light from card number 2 reaches her eye.

5. Light that takes a path from point A to point B will take the same reverse path in going from point B to point A, even if reflection or refraction is involved. So if you can't see the driver, the driver can't see you. (This independence of direction along light's path is the "principle of reciprocity.")

7. When you wave your right hand, image of the waving hand is still on your right, just as your head is still up and your feet still down. Neither left and right nor up and down are inverted by the mirror—but *front and back* are, as the author's sister Marjorie illustrates in Figure 28.8. (Consider three axes at right angles to each other, the standard coordinate system; horizontal x, vertical y, and perpendicular-to-the-mirror z. The only axis to be inverted is z, where the image is $-z$.)

9. When the source of glare is somewhat above the horizon, a vertical window will reflect it to people in front of the window. By tipping the window inward at the bottom, glare is reflected downward rather than into the eyes of passersby. (Note the similarity of this exercise and the previous one.)

11. Rough pages provide diffuse reflection, which can be viewed from any angle. If the page were smooth it could only be viewed well at certain angles.

13. There are two mirrors facing each other.

15. The half-height mirror works at any distance, as shown in the sketch above. This is because if you move closer, your image moves closer as well. If you move farther away, your image does the same. Many people must actually try this before they believe it. The confusion arises because people know that they can see whole distant buildings or even mountain ranges in a hand-held pocket mirror. Even then, the distance the object is from the mirror is the same as the distance of the virtual image on the other side of the mirror. You can see all of a distant person in your mirror, but the distant person cannot see all of herself in your mirror.

17. The wiped area will be half as tall as your face.

19. Farsighted.

21. If the water were perfectly smooth, you would see a mirror image of the round Sun or Moon, an ellipse on the surface of the water. If the water were slightly rough, the image would be wavy. If the water were a bit more rough, little glimmers of portions of the Sun or Moon would be seen above and below the main image. This is because the water waves act like tiny parallel mirrors. For small waves only light near the main image reaches you. But as the water becomes choppier, there is a greater variety of mirror facets that are oriented to reflect sunlight or moonlight into your eye. The facets do not radically depart from an average flatness with the otherwise smooth water surface, so the reflected Sun or Moon is smeared into a long vertical streak. For still rougher water there are facets off to the side of the vertical streak that are tilted enough for Sun or moonlight to be reflected to you, and the vertical streak is wider.

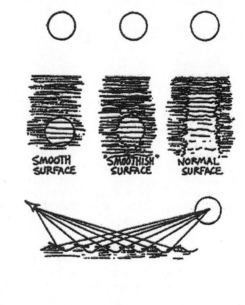

23.

25. Red light travels faster through glass and will exit first.

27. The speeds in both glass and soybean oil are the same, so there is no refraction between the glass and oil.

29. You would throw the spear below the apparent position of the fish because the effect of refraction is to make the fish appear closer to the surface than it really is. But in zapping a fish with a laser, make no corrections and simply aim directly at the fish. This is because the light from the fish you see has been refracted in getting to you, and the laser light will refract along the same path in getting to the fish. A slight correction may be necessary, depending on the colors of the laser beam and the fish—see the next exercise.

31. A fish sees the sky (as well as some reflection from the bottom) when it looks upward at 45°, for the critical angle is 48° for water. If it looks at and beyond 48° it sees only a reflection of the bottom.

33. In sending a laser beam to a space station, make no corrections and simply aim at the station you see. This is like zapping the fish in Exercise 29. The path of refraction is the same in either direction.

35. The "nonwettable" leg of the water strider depresses and curves the surface of the water. This effectively produces a lens that directs light away from its course to form the extended shadow region. (Close observation will show a bright ring around the darker region. Interestingly, the overall brightness of the shadow and bright ring averaged together is the same whether or not the water is depressed—"conservation of light.")

37. The fact that two observers standing apart from one another do not see the same rainbow can be understood by exaggerating the circumstance: Suppose the two observers are several kilometers apart. Obviously they are looking at different drops in the sky. Although they may both see a rainbow, they are looking at different rainbows. Likewise if they are closer together. Only if their eyes are at the very same location will they see exactly the same rainbow.

39. Moon halos and rainbows are similar in that both are produced by light refracting from water. Ice crystals can disperse moonlight into two halos, much as water droplets disperse light into two rainbows. For both, the outer bow is much fainter than the inner one. Halos and rainbows are different in that a halo and Moon are seen in the same part of the sky, with the Moon in the middle of the halo—whereas a rainbow is seen in the part of the sky opposite to the Sun (your shadow, if it can be seen, is in the middle of the rainbow). Another difference is that for rainbows reflection as well as refraction is important, whereas for halos only refraction is important. Yet another difference is that whereas a rainbow involves liquid water droplets, a halo involves frozen water crystals.

41. The average intensity of sunlight at the bottom is the same whether the water is moving or is still. Light that misses one part of the bottom of the pool reaches another part. Every dark region is balanced by a bright region—"conservation of light."

43. Normal sight depends on the amount of refraction that occurs for light traveling from air to the eye. The speed change ensures normal vision. But if the speed change is from water to eye, then light will be refracted less and an unclear image will result. A swimmer uses goggles to make sure that the light travels from air to eye, even if underwater.

45. The diamond sparkles less because there are smaller angles of refraction between the water and the diamond. Light is already slowed when it meets the diamond so the amount of further slowing, and refraction, is reduced.

47. The image will be dimmer, but otherwise unaffected.

49. If light had the same average speed in glass lenses that it has in air, no refraction of light would occur in lenses, and no magnification would occur. Magnification depends on refraction, which in turn depends on speed changes.

51. Sharpness.

53. The image produced by a pinhole is sharp, but very dim—a serious liability for a spy camera. A spy camera needs all the light it can get, particularly for dimly lit areas, which is why a large aperture is advantageous.

55. For very distant objects, effectively at "infinity," light comes to focus at the focal plane of the lens. So your film is one focal length in back of the lens for very distant shots. For shorter distances, the film is farther from the lens.

57. Yes, the images are indeed upside down! The brain re-inverts them.

59. Moon maps are upside-down views of the Moon to coincide with the upside-down image that Moon watchers see in a telescope.

SOLUTIONS TO CHAPTER 28 PROBLEMS

1. When a mirror is rotated, its normal rotates also. Since the angle that the incident ray makes with the normal is the same angle that the reflected ray makes, the total deviation is twice. In the sample diagram, if the mirror is rotated by 10°, then the normal is rotated by 10° also, which results in a 20° total deviation of the reflected ray. This is one reason that mirrors are used to detect delicate movements in instruments such as galvanometers. The more important reason is the amplification of displacement by having the beam arrive at a scale some distance away.

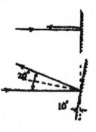

3. Set your focus for **4 m**, for your image will be as far in back of the mirror as you are in front.

5. If 96% is transmitted through the first face, and 96% of 96% is transmitted through the second face, **92%** is transmitted through both faces of the glass.

7. Use ratios: (1440 min)/(360 deg) = (unknown time)/(0.53 deg). So the unknown time is 0.53 × 1440/360 = 2.1 minutes. So the Sun moves a solar diameter across the sky every 2.1 minutes. At sunset, time is somewhat extended, depending on the extent of refraction. Then the disk of the setting Sun disappears over the horizon in a little longer than **2.1 minutes**.

ANSWERS TO CHAPTER 29 EXERCISES (Light Waves)

1. The Earth intercepts such a tiny fraction of the expanding spherical wave from the Sun that it can be approximated as a plane wave (just as a small portion of the spherical surface of the Earth can be approximated as flat). The spherical waves from a nearby lamp have noticeable curvature. (See Figures 29.3 and 29.4).

3. The wavelengths of AM radio waves are hundreds of meters, much larger than the size of buildings, so they are easily diffracted around buildings. FM wavelengths are a few meters, borderline for diffraction around buildings. Light, with wavelengths a tiny fraction of a centimeter, show no appreciable diffraction around buildings.

5. The signals of lower channel numbers are broadcast at lower frequencies and longer wavelengths, which are more diffracted into regions of poor reception than are higher-frequency signals.

7. The alternation of sound from loud to soft is evidence of interference. Where the sound is loud, the waves from each loudspeaker are interfering constructively; where it is soft, destructive interference from the speakers is taking place.

9. Both interference fringes of light and the varying intensities of sound are the result of the superposition of waves that interfere constructively and destructively.

11. The fringes will be spaced farther apart if the pattern is made of longer-wavelength yellow light. The shorter wavelength green light will produce closer fringes. (Investigation of Figure 29.19 should make this clear—note that if the wavelength were longer, the light and dark regions on the screen would be farther apart.)

13. Larger wavelengths diffract more (since the ratio of wavelength to slit size is greater), so red diffracts the most and blue the least.

15. Wider fringes in air, for in water the wavelengths would be compressed (see Figure 28.24), with closer-together fringes.

17. Longer wavelength red light.

19. Destructive interference.

21. Multiple slits of identical spacings produce an interference pattern in which the light is concentrated in fewer, brighter, narrower lines. Such an arrangement makes up a diffraction grating (Figure 29.21), which is a popular alternative to a prism for studying the spectral composition of light.

23. Fringes become closer together as the slits are moved farther apart. (Note this in the photos of Figure 29.15.)

25. Rainbow. Flower petals. Soap bubbles.

27. Interference colors result from double reflections from the upper and lower surfaces of the thin transparent coating on the butterfly wings. Some other butterfly wings produce colors by diffraction, where ridges in the surface act as diffraction gratings.

29. Interference of light from the upper and lower surfaces of the soap or detergent film is taking place.

31. Light from a pair of stars will not produce an interference pattern because the waves of light from the two separate sources are incoherent; when combined they smudge. Interference occurs when light from a single source divides and recombines.

33. Blue, the complementary color. The blue is white minus the yellow light that is seen above. (Note this exercise goes back to information in Chapter 27.)

271

35. Polarization is a property of transverse waves. Unlike light, sound is a longitudinal wave and can't be polarized. Whether a wave can be polarized or not, in fact, is one of the tests to distinguish transverse waves from longitudinal waves.

37. To say that a Polaroid is ideal is to say that it will transmit 100% of the components of light that are parallel to its polarization axis, and absorb 100% of all components perpendicular to its polarization axis. Nonpolarized light has as many components along the polarization axis as it has perpendicular to that axis. That's 50% along the axis, and 50% perpendicular to the axis. A perfect Polaroid transmits the 50% that is parallel to its polarization axis.

39. With polarization axes aligned, a pair of Polaroids will transmit all components of light along the axes. That's 50%, as explained in the answer to Exercise 38. Half of the light gets through the first Polaroid, and all of that gets through the second. With axes at right angles, no light will be transmitted.

41. Glare is composed largely of polarized light in the plane of the reflecting surface. Most glaring surfaces are horizontal (roadways, water, etc.), so sunglasses with vertical polarization axes filter the glare of horizontally polarized light. Conventional nonpolarizing sunglasses simply cut down on overall light transmission either by reflecting or absorbing incident light.

43. Since most glare is due to reflection from horizontal surfaces, the polarization axes of common Polaroid sunglasses are vertical.

45. Call the three Polaroids 1, 2, and 3. The first one acts as a polarizer of the unpolarized light, ideally letting half of it through with a specific polarization direction that is perpendicular to the axis of Number 3. So when only 1 and 3 are present, no light gets through. But Number 2, when placed between 1 and 3, is illuminated by light aligned at 45° to its axis, so it lets half of the light through. The light striking Number 3 is now aligned at 45° to the axis of Number 3. So Number 3 transmits half of the light that strikes it. (The amount that gets through is one-eighth of the original intensity.)

47. Making holograms requires coherent light, exactly what a laser provides. Hence practical holography followed the advent of the laser. (Interestingly enough, the first holograms were made before the advent of the laser, and were crude by today's standards. They were made with monochromatic light from a sodium vapor lamp, through a tiny pinhole to provide a close approximation of coherent light, and required very long exposures.)

49. Interference is central to holography.

ANSWERS TO CHAPTER 30 EXERCISES   (Light   Emission)

1. In accord with $E = hf$, a gamma ray photon has a higher energy because it has a higher frequency.

3. Higher-frequency higher-energy blue light corresponds to a greater change of energy in the atom.

5. Doubling the wavelength of light halves its frequency. Light of half frequency has half the energy per photon. Think in terms of the equation $c = f\lambda$ Since the speed of light c is constant, λ is inversely proportional to f.

7. Spectral lines are images of the slit in a spectroscope. If the slit were crescent shaped, the "lines" would also be crescent shaped.

9. Diffracted light from a neon tube produces a band of colors, most of which are various shades of red. Light from a helium-neon laser is of one color—monochromatic—from only one of the "spectral lines" of neon.

11. By comparing the absorption spectra of various nonsolar sources through the Earth's atmosphere, the lines due to the Earth's atmosphere can be established. Then when viewing solar spectra, extra lines and extra line intensities can be attributed to the atmosphere of the Sun.

13. The moving star will show a Doppler shift. Since the star is receding, it will be a red shift (to lower frequency and longer wavelength).

15. In accord with $E \sim f$, the higher frequency ultraviolet photon has more energy than a photon in the visible part of the spectrum, which in turn has more energy than a photon in the infrared part of the spectrum.

17. Atoms excited in high-pressure gas interfere with one another in a way similar to the way closely-packed atoms in a solid do, resulting in overlapping waves and smearing of light.

19 The many spectral lines from the element hydrogen are the result of the many energy states the single electron can occupy when excited.

21. The "missing" energy may appear as light of other colors or as invisible infrared light. If the atoms are closely packed, as in a solid, some of the "missing" energy may appear as heat. In that case, the illuminated substance warms.

23. Fluorescence is the process in which high-frequency (high energy) ultraviolet radiation converts to low-frequency (lower energy) visible radiation with some energy left over, possibly appearing as heat. If your friend is suggesting that low-energy infrared radiation can be converted to higher-energy visible light, that is clearly a violation of the conservation of energy—a no-no! Now if your friend is suggesting that infrared radiation can cause the fluorescence of still lower-frequency infrared radiation, which is not seen as light, then your friend's reasoning is well founded.

25. Fabrics and other fluorescent materials produce bright colors in sunlight because they both reflect visible light and transform some of the Sun's ultraviolet light into visible light. They literally glow when exposed to the combined visible and ultraviolet light of the Sun. (Certain fluorescent dyes added to inks are sometimes called "Day-Glo" colors.)

27. Just as a time delay occurs with the opening and closing of a spring door, a similar time delay occurs between excitation and de-excitation in a phosphorescent material.

29. The acronym says it: microwave *a*mplification by *s*timulated *e*mission of *r*adiation.

31. Its energy is very concentrated in comparison with that of a lamp.

33. If it weren't relatively long-lived, there wouldn't be enough accumulation of atoms in this excited state to produce the "population inversion" that is necessary for laser action.

35. Your friend's assertion violates the law of energy conservation. A laser or any device cannot put out more energy than is put into it. Power, on the other hand, is another story, as is treated in the following exercise.

37. f bar is the peak frequency of incandescent radiation—that is, the frequency at which the radiation is most intense. T is the temperature of the emitter. (Scientists also describe the radiation as having a temperature. Incandescent radiation emitted by a body at a certain temperature is said to have that same temperature. Thus we can use radiation to measure temperature, whether it be the radiation emitted by a blast furnace or by the Sun or by frigid outer space.)

39. Both radiate energy in accord with $f \sim T$ (peak frequency proportional to absolute temperature). Since the Sun's temperature is so much greater than the Earth's, the frequency of radiation emitted by the Sun is correspondingly greater than the frequency of radiation emitted by the Earth. Earth's radiation is called terrestrial radiation, treated back in Chapter 16. The amount of energy radiated by the Sun is also much greater than the amount radiated by the Earth. (The *amount* varies in proportion to the fourth power of the absolute temperature, so the Sun with surface temperature 20 times the Earth's surface temperature radiates $(20)^4$, or 160,000 times as much energy as the Earth.)

41. The metal is glowing at all temperatures, whether we can see the glow or not. As its temperature is increased, the glow reaches the visible part of the spectrum and is visible to human eyes. Light of the lowest energy per photon is red. So the heated metal passes from infra-red (which we can't see) to visible red. It is red hot.

43. Star's relative temperatures—lowish for reddish; midish for whitish; and hotish for bluish.

45. An incandescent source that peaks in the green part of the visible spectrum will also emit reds and blues, which would overlap to appear white. Our Sun is a good example. For green light and only green light to be emitted, we would have some other kind of a source, such as a laser, not an incandescent source. So "green-hot" stars are white.

47. Six transitions are possible, as shown. The highest-frequency transition is from quantum level 4 to level 1. The lowest-frequency transition is from quantum level 4 to level 3.

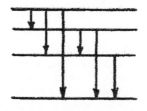

49. Yes, there is a relationship among the wavelengths, but it is not as simple as the relationship among frequencies. Because energies are additive, so are the frequencies. But since wavelength is inversely proportional to frequency, it is the inverses of the wavelengths that are additive.

Thus, $\dfrac{1}{\lambda(4 \to 3)} + \dfrac{1}{\lambda(3 \to 1)} = \dfrac{1}{\lambda(4 \to 1)}$

(a) The B-to-A transition has twice the energy and twice the frequency of the C-to-B transition. Therefore it will have half the wavelength, or **300 nm**. Reasoning: Since $c = f\lambda$, $\lambda = c/f$. Wavelength is inversely proportional to frequency. Twice the frequency means half the wavelength.

(b) The C-to-A transition has three times the energy and three times the frequency of the C-to-B transition. Therefore it will have one-third the wavelength, or **200 nm**.

ANSWERS TO CHAPTER 31 EXERCISES (Light Quanta)

1. Classical physics is primarily the physics known before 1900 that includes the study of motion in accord with Newton's laws and the study of electromagnetism in accord with the laws of Maxwell. Classical mechanics, often called Newtonian mechanics, is characterized by absolute predictability. After 1900 scientists discovered that Newtonian rules simply don't apply in the domain of the very small—the submicroscopic. This is the domain of quantum physics, where things are "grainy" and where values of energy and momentum (as well as mass and charge) occur in lumps, or quanta. In this domain, particles and waves merge and the basic rules are rules of probability, not certainty. Quantum physics is different and not easy to visualize like classical physics. We nevertheless tend to impress our classical wave and particle models on our findings in an effort to visualize this subatomic world.

3. $E \sim f$ is a proportion. When E is divided by f we have the constant h. With h the proportion becomes the exact equation $E = hf$. So we see h is the proportionality constant for the energy and frequency of a photon of light.

5. Higher-frequency ultraviolet light has more energy per photon.

7. Higher-frequency green light has more energy per photon.

9. Finding materials that would respond photoelectrically to red light was difficult because photons of red light have less energy than photons of green or blue light.

11. The energy of red light is too low per photon to trigger the chemical reaction in the photographic crystals. Very bright light simply means more photons that are unable to trigger a reaction. Blue light, on the other hand, has sufficient energy per photon to trigger a reaction. Very dim blue light triggers fewer reactions only because there are fewer photons involved. It is safer to have bright red light than dim blue light.

13. The kinetic energy of ejected electrons depends on the frequency of the illuminating light. With sufficiently high frequency, the number of electrons ejected in the photoelectric effect is determined by the number of photons incident upon the metal. So whether or not ejection occurs depends on frequency, and how many electrons are ejected depends on the brightness of the sufficiently high-frequency light.

15. Ultraviolet photons are more energetic.

17. Particle nature.

19. *Electric eye*: A beam of light is directed to a photosensitive surface that completes the path of an electric circuit. When the beam is interrupted, the circuit is broken. The entire photoelectric circuit may be used as a switch for another circuit.
    Light meter: The variation of photoelectric current with variations in light intensity activates a galvanometer, or its equivalent, that is calibrated to show light intensity.
    Sound track: An optical sound track on motion picture film is a strip of emulsion of variable density that transmits light of variable intensity onto a photosensitive surface, which in turn produces an electric current of the desired variations. This current is amplified and then activates the loudspeaker.

21. There will be colors toward the red end of the spectrum where the meter will show no reading, since no electrons are ejected. As the color is changed toward the blue and violet, a point will be reached where the meter starts to give a reading. If a color for which the meter reads zero is made more intense, the meter will continue to read zero. If a color for which the meter shows a reading is made more intense, the current recorded by the meter will increase as more electrons are ejected.

23. Young's explanation of the double-slit experiment is based on the wave model of light; Einstein's explanation of the photoelectric effect uses a model in which light is composed of particles. The effectiveness of one model or another doesn't invalidate the other model, particularly in this instance where the models are used to describe completely different phenomena. Models are not to be judged as being "true" or "false" but as being useful or not

useful. The particle model of light is useful in making sense of the details of the photoelectric effect, whereas the wave model of light is not useful in understanding these details. On the other hand, the wave model of light is useful for understanding the details of interference, whereas the particle model is not. The effectiveness of one model over another means simply that: One model is more effective than another. This effectiveness doesn't mean that one model is correct and the other invalid. As we gather more data and gain new insights, we refine our models. The fact that two quite different models are needed to describe light lead to what is called the "wave-particle duality," a central part of quantum physics.

25. Diffraction, polarization, and interference are evidence of the wave nature of light; the photoelectric effect is evidence of the particle nature of light.

27. No. Complementarity isn't a compromise, but suggests that what you see depends on your point of view. What you see when you look at a box, for example, depends on whether you see it from one side, the top, and so on. All measurements of energy and matter show quanta in some experiments and waves in others. For light, we see particle behavior in emission and absorption, and wave behavior in propagation between emission and absorption.

29. By absorbing energy from the impact of a particle or photon.

31. Uranium possesses more momentum. Hydrogen has the longer wavelength, which is inversely-proportional to momentum.

33. The more massive proton has more momentum, while the electron with its smaller momentum has the longer wavelength.

35. By de Broglie's formula, as velocity increases, momentum increases, so wavelength decreases.

37. The principal advantage of an electron microscope over an optical microscope is its ability to see things that are too small for viewing with an optical microscope. This is because an object cannot be discerned if it is smaller than the wavelength of the illuminating beam. An electron beam has a wavelength that is typically a thousand times shorter than the wavelength of visible light, which means it can discern particles a thousand times smaller than those barely seen with an optical microscope.

39. Planck's constant would be zero.

41. In the best spirit of science, from our observations we develop a theory that gives meaning to those observations. However, it is often the case that belief in a theory precedes observations and influences our perception of those observations and the meaning we give them. We should be aware of this "human factor." Sometimes it is very beneficial and sometimes it is not.

43. If somebody looks at an electron on the tip of your nose with an electron beam or a light beam, then its motion as well as that of surrounding electrons will be altered. We take the view here that passively looking at light after it has reflected from an object does not alter the electrons in the object. We distinguish between passive observation and probing. The uncertainty principle applies to probing, not to passive observation. (This view, however, is not held by some physicists who assert any measure, passive or probing, alters that being measured at the quantum level. These physicists argue that passive observation provides knowledge, and that without this knowledge, the electron might be doing something else or might be doing a mixture, a superposition, of other things.)

45. Heisenberg's uncertainty principle applies *only* to quantum phenomena. However, it serves as a popular metaphor for the macro domain. Just as the way we measure affects what's being measured, the way we phrase a question often influences the answer we get. So to various extents we alter that which we wish to measure in a public opinion survey. Although there are countless examples of altering circumstances by measuring them, the uncertainty principle has meaning only in the sub-microscopic world.

47. The uncertainty principle refers only to the quantum realm, and not the macroworld. Air escaping from a tire is a macro-world event.

49. Unless the term is meant to leap into a completely different realm, no, for a quantum leap is the *smallest* transition something can undergo.

SOLUTIONS TO CHAPTER 31 PROBLEMS

1. Frequency is speed/wavelength: $f = (3 \times 10^8 \text{ m/s})/(2.5 \times 10^{-5} \text{ m}) = 1.2 \times 10^{13}$ Hz. Photon energy is Planck's constant × frequency: $E = hf = (6.6 \times 10^{-34} \text{ J s})(1.2 \times 10^{13} \text{ Hz}) = \mathbf{7.9 \times 10^{-21}}$ **J.** (In the electron-volt unit common in atomic and optical physics, this is 0.05 eV, about one-twentieth the energy acquired by an electron in being accelerated through a potential difference of 1 V. 1 eV is equal to 1.6×10^{-19} J.)

3. The ball's momentum is $mv = (0.1 \text{ kg}) (0.001 \text{ m/s}) = 1 \times 10^{-4}$ kg m/s, so its de Broglie wavelength is $h/p = (6.6 \times 10^{-34} \text{ J s})/(1 \times 10^{-4} \text{ kg m/s}) = \mathbf{6.6 \times 10^{-30}}$ **m**, incredibly small relative even to the tiny wavelength of the electron. There is no hope of rolling a ball slowly enough to make its wavelength appreciable.

ANSWERS TO CHAPTER 32 EXERCISES (The Atom and the Quantum)

1. Photons from the ultraviolet lamp have greater frequency, energy, and momentum. Only wavelength is greater for photons emitted by the TV transmitter.

3. The vast majority of alpha particles passed through the foil undeflected.

5. Rutherford's experiments showed that the positive charge must be concentrated in a small core, the atomic nucleus.

7. The answer is given in the legend to Figure 32.4, namely that an electron accelerating around its orbit should emit radiation. This loss of energy should be accompanied by a spiraling of the electron into the atomic nucleus (akin to the fate of satellites that encounter the atmosphere in low Earth orbit).

9. Spectral lines are as characteristic of the elements as fingerprints are of people. Both aid identification.

11. If the energy spacings of the levels were equal, there would be only two spectral lines. Note that a transition between the 3rd and 2nd level would have the same difference in energy as a transition between the 2nd and first level. So both transitions would produce the same frequency of light and produce one line. The other line would be due to the transition from the 3rd to the first level.

13. The smallest orbit would be one with a circumference equal to one wavelength.

15. If we think of electrons as orbiting the nucleus in standing waves, then the circumference of these wave patterns must be a whole number of wavelengths. In this way the circumferences are discrete. This means that the radii of orbits are therefore discrete. Since energy depends upon this radial distance, the energy values are also discrete. (In a more refined wave model, there are standing waves in the radial as well as the orbital direction.)

17. The electron shells are pulled in more tightly because of the greater number of protons in the nucleus. Hence atoms get smaller from left to right along a row in the periodic table.

19. Atoms with many electrons reside with nuclei with greater numbers of protons, and subsequently, greater attraction to the nucleus.

21. The frequency of every photon is related to its energy by $E = hf$, so if two frequencies add up to equal a third frequency, two energies add up to equal a third energy. In a leapfrog transition such as from the third to the first energy level in Figure 32.10, energy conservation requires that the emitted energy be the same as the sum of the emitted energies for the cascade of two transitions. Therefore the frequency for the leapfrog transition will be the sum of the frequencies for the two transitions in the cascade.

23. Constructive interference to form a standing wave requires an integral number of wavelengths around one circumference. Any number of de Broglie wavelengths not a whole number would lead to destructive interference, preventing the formation of a standing wave.

25. The answer to both questions is yes. Since a particle has wave properties and a wavelength related to its momentum, it can exhibit the same properties as other waves, including diffraction and interference.

27. Atoms would be larger if Planck's constant were larger. We can see this from de Broglie's equation (wavelength = h/momentum), where for a given momentum if h were larger, the wavelengths of the standing waves that comprise electron shells would be larger, and hence atoms would be larger.

29. The laws of probability applied to one or a few atoms give poor predictability, but for hordes of atoms, the situation is entirely different. Although it is impossible to predict which electron will absorb a photon in the photoelectric effect, it is possible to predict accurately the current produced by a beam of light on photosensitive material. We can't say where a given photon will

hit a screen in double-slit diffraction, but we can predict with great accuracy the relative intensities of a wave-interference pattern for a bright beam of light. Predicting the kinetic energy of a particular atom as it bumbles about in an atomic lattice is highly inaccurate, but predicting the average kinetic energy of hordes of atoms in the same atomic lattice, which measures the temperature of the substance, is possible with high precision. The indeterminacy at the quantum level can be discounted when large aggregates of atoms so well lend themselves to extremely accurate macroscopic prediction.

31. Electrons have a definite mass and a definite charge, and can sometimes be detected at specific points—so we say they have particle properties; electrons also produce diffraction and interference effects, so we say they have wave properties. There is a contradiction only if we insist the electron may have only particle OR only wave properties. Investigators find that electrons display both particle and wave properties.

33. Both are consistent. The correspondence principle requires agreement of quantum and classical results when the "graininess" of the quantum world is not important, but permits disagreement when the graininess is dominant.

35. Bohr's correspondence principle says that quantum mechanics must overlap and agree with classical mechanics in the domain where classical mechanics has been shown to be valid.

37. The philosopher was speaking of classical physics, the physics of the macroscopic world, where to a high degree of accuracy the same physical conditions do produce the same results. Feynman must have been speaking of the quantum domain where for small numbers of particles and events, the same conditions are not expected to produce the same results.

39. The speed of light is large compared with the ordinary speeds with which we deal in everyday life. Planck's constant is small in that it gives wavelengths of ordinary matter far too small to detect and energies of individual photons too small to detect singly with our eyes.

SOLUTION TO CHAPTER 32 PROBLEM

1. When n = 50, the atom is $(50)^2$, or 2500, times larger than when n = 1, so its radius is $(2500)(1 \times 10^{-10}$ m$) = $ **2.5 $\times 10^{-7}$ m**. The volume of this enlarged atom is $(2500)^3$, or 1.6×10^{10}, times larger than the volume of the atom in its lowest state. **Sixteen billion unexcited atoms** would fit within this one excited atom! (Atoms this large and larger have been made in recent years by trapping single atoms in an evacuated region. These giant atoms with their barely tethered distant electrons are known as Rydberg atoms.)

ANSWERS TO CHAPTER 33 EXERCISES (The Atomic Nucleus and Radioactivity)

1. Kelvin was not aware of radioactive decay, a source of energy to keep Earth warm for billions of years.

3. Gamma radiation is in the form of electromagnetic waves, while alpha and beta are particles.

5. It is impossible for a hydrogen atom to eject an alpha particle, for an alpha particle is composed of four nucleons—two protons and two neutrons. It is equally impossible for a 1-kg melon to disintegrate into four 1-kg melons.

7. The alpha particle has twice the charge, but almost 8000 times the inertia (since each of the four nucleons has nearly 2000 times the mass of an electron). Even though the alpha particle is slower than the electron, it has more momentum due to its great mass, and hence deflects less than an electron in a given magnetic field.

9. Alpha radiation decreases the atomic number of the emitting element by 2 and the atomic mass number by 4. Beta radiation increases the atomic number of an element by 1 and does not affect the atomic mass number. Gamma radiation does not affect the atomic number or the atomic mass number. So alpha radiation results in the greatest change in both atomic number and mass number.

11. Gamma predominates inside the enclosed elevator because the structure of the elevator shields against alpha and beta particles better than against gamma-ray photons.

13. An alpha particle undergoes an acceleration due to mutual electric repulsion as soon as it is out of the nucleus and away from the attracting nuclear force. This is because it has the same sign of charge as the nucleus. Like charges repel.

15. Because it has twice as much charge as a beta particle, an alpha particle interacts more strongly with atomic electrons and loses energy more rapidly by ionizing the atoms. (The slower speed of the alpha particle also contributes to its ability to ionize atoms more effectively.)

17. Within the atomic nucleus, it is the strong nuclear force that holds the nucleons together, and the electric force that mutually repels protons and pushes them apart.

19. Yes, indeed!

21. Chemical properties have to do with electron structure, which is determined by the number of protons in the nucleus, not the number of neutrons.

23. In accord with the inverse-square law, at 2 meters, double the distance, the count rate will be one-fourth of 360 or 90 counts/minute; at 3 meters, the count rate will be one-ninth of 360, or 40 counts/minute.

25. Number of nucleons and electric charge.

27. The mass of the element is 157 + 104 = 261. Its atomic number is 104, a transuranic element recently named rutherfordium.

29. After the polonium nucleus emits a beta particle, the atomic number increases by 1 to become 85, and the atomic mass is unchanged at 218.

31. Both have 92 protons, but U-238 has more neutrons than U-235.

33. An element can decay to an element of greater atomic number by emitting electrons (beta rays). When this happens, a neutron in the nucleus becomes a proton and the atomic number increases by one.

35. When a phosphorus nucleus (atomic number 15) emits a positron (a "positively-charged electron") the charge of the atomic nucleus decreases by 1, converting it to the nucleus of the element silicon (atomic number 14).

37. If nuclei were composed of equal numbers of protons and electrons, nuclei would have no net charge. They wouldn't hold electrons in orbit. The fact that atoms do have a positive nucleus and orbiting electrons contradicts your friend's assertion.

39. The elements below uranium in atomic number with short half-lives exist as the product of the radioactive decay of uranium or another very long-lived element, thorium. For the billions of years that the uranium and thorium last, the lighter elements will be steadily replenished.

41. Your friend will encounter more radioactivity from the granite outcroppings than he or she will living near a nuclear power plant. Furthermore, at high altitude your friend will be treated to increased cosmic radiation. But the radiations encountered in the vicinity of the plant, on the granite outcropping, or at high altitude are not appreciably different than the radiation one encounters in the "safest" of situations. Advise your friend to enjoy life anyway!

43. Although there is significantly more radioactivity in a nuclear power plant than in a coal-fired power plant, almost none of it escapes from the nuclear plant, whereas most of what radioactivity there is in a coal-fired plant does escape, through the stacks. As a result, a typical coal plant injects more radioactivity into the environment than does a typical nuclear plant. (Unfortunately, if you mention this to people you meet at a normal social gathering, you'll be seen as some sort of ally of Darth Vader!)

45. The irradiated food does not become radioactive as a result of being zapped with gamma rays. This is because the gamma rays lack the energy to initiate the nuclear reactions in atoms in the food that could make them radioactive.

47. Dinosaur bones are simply much too old for carbon dating.

49. Stone tablets cannot be dated by the carbon dating technique. Nonliving stone does not ingest carbon and transform that carbon by radioactive decay. Carbon dating works for organic materials.

SOLUTIONS TO CHAPTER 33 PROBLEMS

1. At the end of the second year $1/4$ of the original sample will be left; at the end of the third year, $1/8$ will be left; and at the end of the fourth year, $1/16$ will be left.

3. $1/16$ will remain after 4 half-lives, so $4 \times 30 =$ **120 years**.

5. The intensity is down by a factor of 16.7 (from 100% to 6%). How many factors of two is this? About 4, since $2^4 = 16$. So the age of the artifact is about 4×5730 years or **about 23,000 years**.

ANSWERS TO CHAPTER 34 EXERCISES (Nuclear Fission and Fusion)

1. Unenriched uranium—which contains more than 99% of the non-fissionable isotope U-238—undergoes a chain reaction only if it is mixed with a moderator to slow down the neutrons. Uranium in ore is mixed with other substances that impede the reaction and has no moderator to slow down the neutrons, so no chain reaction occurs. (There is evidence, however, that several billion years ago, when the percentage of U-235 in uranium ore was greater, a natural reactor existed in Gabon, West Africa.)

3. The electric repulsion between protons reaches across the whole nucleus, affecting all protons, whereas the attractive nuclear force reaches only from one nucleon to its immediate neighbors, so the more protons in a nucleus, the more likely is it that their mutual repulsion will overcome the attractive forces and lead to fission.

5. A neutron makes a better "bullet" for penetrating atomic nuclei because it has no electric charge and is therefore not repelled by an atomic nucleus.

7. Critical mass is the amount of fissionable mass that will just sustain a chain reaction without exploding. This occurs when the production of neutrons in the material is balanced by neutrons escaping through the surface. The greater the escape of neutrons, the greater the critical mass. We know that a spherical shape has the least surface area for any given volume, so for a given volume, a cube shape would have more area, and therefore more "leakage" of the neutron flux. So a critical-mass cube is more massive than a critical-mass sphere. (Look at it this way: A sphere of fissionable material that is critical will be subcritical if flattened into a pancake shape—or molded into any other shape—because of increased neutron leakage.)

9. The average distance increases. (It's easier to see the opposite process where big pieces broken up into little pieces decreases the distance a neutron can travel and still be within the material. Proportional surface area increases with decreasing size, which is why you break a sugar cube into little pieces to increase the surface area exposed to tea for quick dissolving.) In the case of uranium fuel, the process of assembling small pieces into a single big piece increases average traveling distance, decreases surface area, reduces neutron leakage, and increases the probability of a chain reaction and an explosion.

11. Only trace amounts of plutonium can occur naturally in U-238 concentrations. When U-238 captures a stray neutron it becomes U-239 and after beta emission becomes Np-239, which further transforms by beta emission to Pu-239. Because of its short half-life (24,360 years) it doesn't last long. Any plutonium initially in Earth's crust has long since decayed. (There are elements in the Earth's crust with half-lives even shorter than plutonium's, but these are the products of uranium decay; between uranium and lead in the periodic table of elements.)

13. The resulting nucleus is $_{92}U^{233}$. The mass number is increased by 1 and the atomic number by 2. U-233, like U-235, is fissionable with slow neutrons. (Notice the similarity to the production of $_{94}Pu^{239}$ from $_{92}U^{238}$.)

15. When a neutron bounces from a carbon nucleus, the nucleus rebounds, taking some energy away from the neutron and slowing it down so it will be more effective in stimulating fission events. A lead nucleus is so massive that it scarcely rebounds at all. The neutron bounces with practically no loss of energy and practically no change of speed (like a marble from a bowling ball).

17. If the difference in mass for changes in the atomic nucleus increased tenfold (from 0.1% to 1.0%), the energy release from such reactions would increase tenfold as well.

19. Both chemical burning and nuclear fusion require a minimum ignition temperature to start and in both the reaction is spread by heat from one region to neighboring regions. There is no critical mass. Any amount of thermonuclear fuel or of combustible fuel can be stored.

21. Each fragment would contain 46 protons (half of 92) and 72 neutrons (half of 144), making it the nucleus of Pd-118, an isotope of palladium, element number 46.

23. No. U-235 (with its shorter half-life) undergoes radioactive decay six times faster than U-238 (half-life 4.5 billion years), so natural uranium in an older Earth would contain a much smaller percentage of U-235, not enough for a critical reaction without enrichment. (Conversely, in a younger Earth, natural uranium would contain a greater percentage of U-235 and would more easily sustain a chain reaction.)

25. In 1 billion years U-235 would be in short supply, and fission power a thing of history.

27. Splitting light nuclei (which happens in particle accelerators) costs energy. As the curve in Figure 34.16 shows, the total mass of the products is greater than the total mass of the initial nucleus.

29. If uranium were split into three parts, the segments would be nuclei of smaller atomic numbers, more toward iron on the graph of Figure 34.16. The resulting mass per nucleon would be less, and there would be more mass converted to energy in such a fissioning.

31. The fusion of 2 hydrogens with an oxygen would produce neon, atomic number 10.

33. If the masses of nucleons varied in accord with the shape of the curve of Figure 34.15 instead of the curve of Figure 34.16, then the fissioning of all elements would liberate energy and all fusion processes would absorb rather than liberate energy. This is because all fission reactions (decreasing atomic number) would result in nuclei with less mass per nucleon, and all fusion reactions (increasing atomic number) would result in the opposite; nuclei of more mass per nucleon.

35. The initial uranium has more mass than the fission products.

37. Although more energy is released in the fissioning of a single uranium nucleus than in the fusing of a pair of deuterium nuclei, the much greater number of lighter deuterium atoms in a gram of matter compared to the fewer heavier uranium atoms in a gram of matter, results in more energy liberated per gram for the fusion of deuterium.

39. A hydrogen bomb produces a lot of fission energy as well as fusion energy. Some of the fission is in the fission bomb "trigger" used to ignite the thermonuclear reaction and some is in fissionable material that surrounds the thermonuclear fuel. Neutrons produced in fusion cause more fission in this blanket. Fallout results mainly from the fission.

41. Energy from the Sun is our chief source of energy, which itself is the energy of fusion. Harnessing that energy on Earth has proven to be a formidable challenge.

43. Minerals which are now being mined can be recycled over and over again with the advent of a fusion-torch operation. This recycling would tend to reduce (but not eliminate) the role of mining in providing raw materials.

45. The lists can be very large. Foremost considerations are these: Conventional fossil-fuel power plants consume our natural resources and convert them into greenhouse gases and poisonous contaminants that are discharged into the atmosphere, producing among other things, global climate change and acid rain. A lesser environmental problem exists with nuclear power plants, which do not pollute the atmosphere. Pollution from nukes is concentrated in the radioactive waste products from the reactor core. Any rational discussion about the drawbacks of either of these power sources must acknowledge that *both* are polluters—so the argument is about which form of pollution we are more willing to accept in return for electrical power. (Before you say "No Nukes!," rational thinking suggests that you first be able to say that you "Know Nukes!.")

47. The nuclei will be positively charged and will move toward the negative plate (and away from the positive one). The negative electrons will move in the opposite direction, toward the positive plate (and away from the negative one.)

49. The lighter nuclei with less mass deflect the most, while the more massive one are less deflected due to greater inertia. The mass spectrometer deflects ions in the same way, with

less massive ions sweeping into circular paths of small radii and more massive ions sweeping in wider circular paths. In this way ions are separated according to their mass.

SOLUTIONS TO CHAPTER 34 PROBLEMS

1. The energy released by the explosion in kilocalories is (20 kilotons)(4.2 × 10¹² J/kiloton)/(4,184 J/kilocalorie) = 2.0 × 10¹⁰ kilocalories. This is enough energy to heat 2.0 × 10¹⁰ kg of water by 1 °C. Dividing by 50, we conclude that this energy could heat **4.0 × 10⁸ kilograms of water** by 50 °C. This is nearly half a million tons.

3. The neutron and the alpha particle fly apart with equal and opposite momentum. But since the neutron has one-fourth the mass of the alpha particle, it has four times the speed. Then consider the kinetic-energy equation, $KE = (1/2)\, mv^2$. For the neutron, $KE = (1/2)\, m(4v)^2 = 8\, mv^2$, and for the alpha particle, $KE = (1/2)\,(4m)v^2 = 2\, mv^2$. The KEs are in the ratio of 8/2, or 80/20. So we see that the neutron gets **80% of the energy, and the alpha particle 20%**. (Alternative method: The formulas for momentum and KE can be combined to give $KE = p^2/2m$. This equation tells us that for particles with the same momentum, KE is inversely proportional to mass.)

ANSWERS TO CHAPTER 35 EXERCISES (Special Theory of Relativity)

1. The effects of relativity become pronounced only at speeds near the speed of light or when energies change by amounts comparable to mc^2. In our "non-relativistic" world, we don't directly perceive such things, whereas we do perceive events governed by classical mechanics. So the mechanics of Newton is consistent with our common sense, based on everyday experience, but the relativity of Einstein is not consistent with common sense. Its effects are outside our everyday experience.

3. (a) The bullet is moving faster relative to the ground when the train is moving (forward).
   (b) The bullet moves at the same speed relative to the freight car whether the train is moving or not.

5. Michelson and Morley considered their experiment a failure in the sense that it did not confirm the result that was expected. What was expected, that differences in the velocity of light would be encountered and measured, turned out not to be true. The experiment was successful in that it widened the doors to new insights in physics.

7. The *average* speed of light in a transparent medium is less than c, but in the model of light discussed in Chapter 26, the photons that make up the beam travel at c in the void that lies between the atoms of the material. Hence the speed of individual photons is always c. In any event, Einstein's postulate is that the speed of light in *free* space is invariant.

9. Yes, for example, a distant part of a beam sweeping the sky. What it doesn't allow is energy or particles to exceed c.

11. No energy or information is carried perpendicular to the swept beam.

13. As explained in the answer to Exercise 12, the moving points are not material things. No mass or no information can travel faster than c, and the points so described are neither mass nor information. Hence, their faster motion doesn't contradict special relativity.

15. It's all a matter of relative velocity. If two frames of reference are in relative motion, events can occur in the order AB in one frame and in the order BA in the other frame. (See Exercise 16.)

17. Experimental evidence has again and again shown that more and more energy must be put into an object that is accelerated to higher and higher speeds. This energy is evidenced by increased momentum. As the speed of light is approached, the momentum of the object approaches infinity. In this view there is infinite resistance to any further increase in momentum, and hence speed. Hence c is the speed limit for material particles. (Kinetic energy likewise approaches infinity as the speed of light is approached.)

19. When we say that light travels a certain distance in 20,000 years we are talking about distance in our frame of reference. From the frame of reference of a traveling astronaut, this distance may well be far shorter, perhaps even short enough that she could cover it in 20 years of her time (traveling, to be sure, at a speed close to the speed of light). Someday, astronauts may travel to destinations many light years away in a matter of months in their frame of reference.

21. A twin who makes a long trip at relativistic speeds returns younger than his stay-at-home twin sister, but both of them are older than when they separated. If they could watch each other during the trip, there would be no time where either would see a reversal of aging, only a slowing or speeding of aging. A hypothetical reversal would result only for speeds greater than the speed of light.

23. If you were in a high-speed (or no speed!) rocket ship, you would note no changes in your pulse or in your volume. This is because the velocity between the observer, that is, yourself, and the observed is zero. No relativistic effect occurs for the observer and the observed when both are in the same reference frame.

25. Narrower as well.

27. Yes, although only high speeds are significant. Changes at low speeds, although there, are imperceptible.

29. The density of a moving body is measured to increase because of a decrease in volume for the same mass.

31. For the speed of light equation, v is c. Before relativity, c might have one value in one frame of reference and a different value in another frame. It depended on the motion of the observer. According to relativity, c is a constant, the same for all observers.

33. The stick must be oriented in a direction perpendicular to its motion, unlike that of a properly-thrown spear. This is because it is traveling at relativistic speed (actually $0.87c$) as evidenced by its increase in momentum. The fact that its length is unaltered means that its long direction is not in the direction of motion. The thickness of the stick, not the length of the stick, will appear shrunken to half size.

35. As with the stick in the preceding exercise, the momentum of the rocket ship will be twice the classical value if its measured length is half its normal length.

37. For the moving electron, length contraction reduces the apparent length of the 2-mile long tube. Because its speed is nearly the speed of light, the contraction is great.

39. The acid bath that dissolved the latched pin will be a little warmer, and a little more massive (in principle). The extra potential energy of the latched pin is transformed into a bit more mass.

41. To make the electrons hit the screen with a certain speed, they have to be given more momentum and more energy than if they were nonrelativistic particles. The extra energy is supplied by your power utility. You pay the bill!

43. The correspondence principle just makes good sense. If a new idea is valid, then it ought to be in harmony with the areas it overlaps. If it doesn't, then either the areas themselves are suspect, or the new idea is suspect. If a new theory is valid, it must account for the verified results of the older theory, whether the theory is or isn't in the field of science.

45. Both the feathers and the iron have the same mass, and hence, the same energy.

47. Just as time is required for knowledge of distant events to reach our eyes, a lesser yet finite time is required for information on nearby things to reach our eyes. So the answer is yes, there is always a finite interval between an event and our perception of that event. If the back of your hand is 30 cm from your eyes, you are seeing it as it was one-billionth of a second ago.

49. Kierkegaard's statement, "Life can only be understood backwards; but it must be lived forwards," is consistent with special relativity. No matter how much time might be dilated as a result of high speeds, a space traveler can only effectively slow the passage of time relative to various frames of reference, but can never reverse it—the theory does not provide for traveling backward in time. Time, at whatever rate, flows only forward.

SOLUTIONS TO CHAPTER 35 PROBLEMS

1. Frequency and period are reciprocals of one another (Chapter 19). If the frequency is doubled, the period is halved. For uniform motion, one senses only half as much time between flashes that are doubled in frequency. For accelerated motion, the situation is different. If the source gains speed in approaching, then each successive flash has even less distance to travel and the frequency increases more, and the period decreases more as well with time.

3. $V = \dfrac{c + c}{1 + \dfrac{c^2}{c^2}} = \dfrac{2c}{1 + 1} = c$

5. In Problem 4 we see that for $v = 0.99\ c$, g is 7.1. The momentum of the bus is more than seven times greater than would be calculated if classical mechanics were valid. The same is true of electrons, or anything traveling at this speed.

7. Gamma at $v = 0.10\ c$ is $1/\sqrt{[1 - (v^2/c^2)]} = 1/\sqrt{[1 - (0.10)^2]} = 1/\sqrt{[1 - 0.01]} = 1/\sqrt{0.99} =$ 1.005. You would measure the passenger's catnap to last 1.005 (5 m) = **5.03 min**.

9. Gamma at $v = 0.5\ c$ is $1/[\sqrt{1 + (v^2/c^2)}] = 1/[\sqrt{1 - 0.5^2}] = 1/[\sqrt{1 - 0.25}] = 1/\sqrt{0.75} = 1.15$. Multiplying 1 h of taxi time by g gives 1.15 h of Earth time. The drivers' new pay will be (10 hours)(1.15) = **11.5 stellars** for this trip.

ANSWERS TO CHAPTER 36 EXERCISES (General Relativity)

1. The reference frames of special relativity are of uniform motion—constant velocity. The reference frames of general relativity include accelerated frames.

3. The train could have stopped on a banked section of track, or worse, derailed and ended up leaning against an embankment. Or perhaps some now fashionable aliens with a chunk of superdense matter have landed next to the train, attracting its occupants to one side. By the principle of equivalence, gravity can duplicate the effects of acceleration.

5. For the linear acceleration of a spaceship, a net force must be provided, which requires the use of fuel. But if the spaceship is set into rotation, it will spin of its own rotational inertia like a top, once it is set spinning. An astronaut in the spaceship experiences a centrifugal force that provides a simulated "gravity." No fuel is consumed to sustain this effect because the centrifugal (or centripetal) force is perpendicular to rotational motion and does no work on the astronaut.

7. Ole Jules called his shot wrong on this one. In a spaceship that drifts through space, whether under the influence of Moon, Earth, or whatever gravitational field, the ship and its occupants are in a state of free fall—hence there is no sensation of up or down. Occupants of a spaceship would feel weight, or sense an up or down, only if the spaceship were made to accelerate—say, against their feet. Then they could stand and sense that down is toward their feet, and up away from their feet.

9. We don't notice the bending of light by gravity in our everyday environment because the gravity we experience is too weak for a noticeable effect. If there were stellar black holes in our vicinity, the bending of light near them would be quite noticeable.

11. We say that a tightened chalk line forms a straight line. It doesn't. We say the surface of a still lake is flat and that a line laid across it is straight. It isn't. But these approximate the straight lines in our practical world. A much better approximation, however, is a beam of light. For distances used by surveyors, a beam of light is the best approximation of a straight line known. Yet we know that a laser beam is ever-so-slightly deflected by gravity. In actual practice, however, we say that a laser beam of light *defines* a straight line.

13. Mercury's mass is much too small for observation of this effect.

15. The change in energy for light is not evidenced by a change in speed, but by a change in frequency. If the energy of light is lowered, as in traveling against a strong gravitational field, its frequency is lowered, and the light is said to be gravitationally red shifted. If the energy of the light is increased, as when falling in a gravitational field, for example, then the frequency is increased and the light is blue shifted.

17. Events on the Moon, as monitored from the Earth, run a bit faster and are slightly blue shifted. And even though signals escaping the Moon are red shifted in ascending the Moon's gravitational field, they are blue shifted even more in descending to the Earth's stronger g field, resulting in a net blue shift.

19. The gravitational field intensity will increase on the surface of a shrinking star because the matter that produces the field is becoming more compact and more localized. This is easiest to see by considering the force on a body of mass m at the surface of the star of mass M via Newton's equation, $F = GmM/d^2$, where the only term that changes is d, which diminishes and therefore results in an increasing F.

21. At the top of the mountain you age slower (See Figure 36.10).

23. Yes, but due to the time dilation of special relativity, which is consistent with the same slowing of general relativity.

25. The photons of light are climbing against the gravitational field and losing energy. Less energy means less frequency. Your friend sees the light red shifted. The frequency she receives is less than the frequency you sent.

27. We would need a telescope sensitive to very long wavelength radiation such as radio waves. The light from the astronauts would be red shifted to very long wavelength, eventually infinitely long wavelength.

29. There are various ways to "see" black holes. If it is the partner of a visible star, we can see its gravitational effect on the visible star's orbit. We could see its effect on light that passes close enough to be deflected but not close enough to be captured. We can see radiation emitted by matter as it is being sucked into a black hole (before it crosses the horizon to oblivion). In the future, perhaps, we will detect gravitational radiation emitted by black holes as they are being formed.

31. Mercury follows an elliptical path in its orbit about the Sun, with its perihelion in a stronger part of the Sun's gravitational field than its aphelion. If Mercury followed a circular orbit, then there would be no variation of the Sun's gravitational field in its orbit.

33. Yes. For example, place the Sun just outside one of the legs in Figure 36.14.

35. Gravitational waves are difficult to detect because of their long waves.

37. Yes, for Einstein's theory of gravitation predicts the same results as Newton's theory of gravitation in weak gravitational fields such as those of the solar system. In weak fields, Einstein's theory overlaps, corresponds, and gives the same results as Newton's theory, and therefore obeys the correspondence principle.

39. Open-ended.

ANSWERS TO APPENDIX E (Exponential Growth and Doubling Time)

1. A dollar loses half its value in one doubling time of the inflationary economy; this is 70/7% = 10 years.

3. For a 5% growth rate, 42 years is three doubling times (70/5% = 14 years; 42/14 = 3). Three doubling times is an eightfold increase. So in 42 years the city would have to have 8 sewage treatment plants to remain as presently overloaded; more than 8 if overloading is to be reduced while serving 8 times as many people.

5. Doubling one penny for 30 days yields a total of $10,737,418.23.

7. It is generally acknowledged that if the human race is to survive, even from an overheating of the world standpoint, while alleviating even part of the misery that afflicts so much of humankind, the present rates of energy consumption and population growth must be reduced. The chances of achieving reduced growth rates are better in a climate of scarce energy than in a climate of abundant energy. We must hope that by the time we have fusion under control, we will have learned to optimize our numbers and to use energy more wisely.